ANDREW

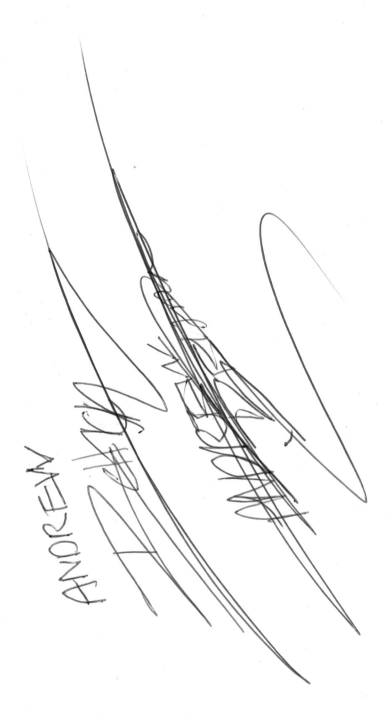

Contents

Cover Art: The cover photograph is a scanning electron microscope image of the underside of a hazelnut leaf magnified 250 ×. Shown are various types of leaf hairs. The ones with bulbous tips contain substances which give the leaf its fragrance.

Photo Credits

Alberta Archives, 356 (bottom)

Canapress, 118, 169, 303 (solar panels, solar vehicles), 307, 309, 333, 364, 391, 401, 403, 405, 408

Jack Chin, 229

Dow Chemical Canada Inc., 93, 107, 115

Sandra Hannah, 56, 63, 68, 77

Robert Hartley, 128

Bill Ivy, 17, 24, 50, 53 (lynx), 57, 62, 65, 71, 102, 114, 152, 189, 203, 235, 239, 244, 249, 271, 272, 288, 292, 312, 313, 347, 348, 349 (limestone), 395 (cars)

Joan Jolliffe, 278

Jeremy Jones, 9, 13, 47, 83, 84, 85, 87, 98, 101, 103, 111, 131, 144, 148, 156, 236, 243, 247, 248 (except truck), 250, 252, 257, 260, 277, 349 (right), 353

Rose Jones, 26, 30, 42, 49, 54, 55, 59, 64, 66 (lichens), 67, 70, 72, 74, 182, 183, 373

Masterfile, 8 (Tony Stone/Worldwide), 15 (Gabe Palmer), 92 (slag) (John de Visser), 135 (SP) (CNRI), 149 (Barrett and MacKay), 206 (SS) (Danny Brass), 211 (Freeman Patterson), 212 (John de Visser), 228 (SS) (Alexander Tsiaras), 251 (Ron Watts), 259 (SS) (Dick Luria), 303 (Satellite) (Telegraph Colour Library), 346 (Freeman Patterson), 355 (Hans Blohm), 362 (SP) (Robin Scagell), 395 (stars) (SP) (Phil Jude), 409, (Hans Blohm)

Miller Comstock, 45 (J. Merrithew), 53 (hare) (K. Sommerer), 66 (mountains), (J. Taylor), 75 (Heilman), 82 (Comstock/Marvin Koner), 88 (M. Gluss), 91 (J. Jacquemain), 92 (aerial) (K. Sommerer), 99 (Roberts/R. Lamb), 104 (garbage collectors) (F. Prazak), 121 (B. Hoferichter), 146 (George Hunter), 150 (Roberts/J. Barstys), 163 (M. Beedell), 172 (Roberts), 186 (P. St Jacques), 187 (Comstock/Tom Grill), 188 (E. Otto), 197 (P. St Jacques), 205 (Comstock/Jack Elness), 207 (Roberts), 276 (E. Otto), 337 (George Hunter), 338 (George Hunter), 339 (K. Wright), 341 (George Hunter), 344 (George Hunter), 345 (Heilman), 350 (K. Sommerer), 356 (skyscrapers) (W. Greibeling), 357 (panning, gold bricks) (Kroll, B. Hoferichter), 358 (W. Greibeling), 359 (O. Bierwagen)

National Archives of Canada, 356 (top), 357 (drawings)

Noranda Minerals Inc., 336

Ontario Hydro, 264, 290, 305

Ontario Ministry of Energy, 296, 297, 308

Ontario Ministry of the Environment, 78, 79, 105, 108, 109, 112, 240, 331

Ontario Science Centre, 234

Recycling Advisory Committee, 104 (landfill), 106, 323

Royal Ontario Museum (McLaughlin Planetarium), 21, 363, 374, 379, 382, 383, 384, 402

SEEDS, 96

Toronto *Star*, 231

Safety in the Science Lab

Every effort has been made to ensure that the rooms you do science in are as safe as possible. However, anything can be dangerous if you don't think about safety, if you act foolishly, or if you don't follow instructions.

Read the following pages carefully. They present some possible dangers in a science lab. They also tell you how you can avoid hurting yourself, and others.

I. Kinds of Hazards

In a science lab, your body can be harmed in three ways:

A. *Poisoning*
   1. through the skin (absorption)
   2. by breathing or smelling (inhalation)
   3. by swallowing (ingestion)

B. *Contact*
   1. burns from hot objects, flames, and chemicals
   2. cuts from glassware, metal edges, and other sharp objects
   3. explosions

C. *Electrical Shock*
   1. from faulty wires or plugs
   2. from defective electrical equipment

II. Sources of Hazards — Preventative Actions

A. *Chemicals* can cause poisoning, burns, or explosions

1. Follow all written and verbal instructions *carefully*.
2. Read the labels on chemicals for safety warnings.
3. Never smell or taste a substance in the lab unless told to do so by your teacher.
4. Clean up any spills immediately.
5. Wear safety goggles if chemicals are being poured or mixed.
6. Absolutely no ''horseplay'' in the laboratory!

B. Glassware
can cause cuts
or burns

1. Place hot glassware on a heat-proof pad.
2. Always remember that hot glass and cold glass look the same.
3. Fire-polish cut ends of glass tubing.
4. Never force a glass tube into a rubber stopper.
5. Dispose of broken glass properly.
6. Never heat a liquid in a closed container.

C. Heat Sources
can cause burns
or explosions

1. Learn the proper use of a heat source, such as a Bunsen burner.
2. Tie back or tuck in loose hair and clothing if you are working near a flame.
3. Keep your work area clear of non-essential papers, books, and other objects.
4. Never store or use flammable or explosive chemicals near a flame.
5. When heating liquids, make sure that the open end of the container does not point towards anyone.

D. Electrical Shock

1. Do not touch any wire, outlet, or equipment that appears damaged. Report the possible danger immediately.
2. Do not splash or spill liquids near electrical equipment.
3. Be aware of possible dangers of anything electrical.

III. In Case of an Emergency

1. Inform your teacher immediately.
2. Be able to locate quickly and use correctly:
   - fire alarm
   - fire extinguisher
   - fire blanket
   - eyewash fountain
   - emergency shower
3. Have your plan-of-action ready in case:
   a) clothing catches on fire.
      (Use fire blanket, emergency shower, fire extinguisher, or water from tap.)
   b) hazardous chemical contacts skin or clothing.
      (Rinse with lots of water.)
   c) any chemical splashes in eye.
      (Use eyewash fountain to rinse eye with lots of water for at least ten minutes.)

ALWAYS INFORM THE TEACHER OF ANY ACCIDENT OR INJURY.

    d) chemical is swallowed or sniffed.
      (Inform teacher of the kind of chemical involved.)
    e) cut occurs.
      (Apply pressure directly on the cut with a clean cloth.)
    f) burn from a hot object occurs.
      (Apply ice or cold water.)

Symbols for Chemical Hazards

In this text, any source of danger from a chemical is identified by a symbol. The meaning of each symbol is explained below. Learn the meaning of these symbols. You will see the same ones on products that you buy.

Type of Hazard	Symbol	Description
Toxic or Poisonous		A substance that could be harmful to human health, could cause cancer or birth defects, or could contaminate, harm, or kill fish and wildlife.
Corrosive		An acidic or basic substance that could corrode storage containers or damage human tissue if touched.
Reactive or Explosive		A substance that could change rapidly (or even explode) if exposed to heat, shock, air, or water.
Flammable		A substance that could explode, catch on fire, or give off poisonous fumes or gases.

Symbolic Code for Degree of Hazardousness

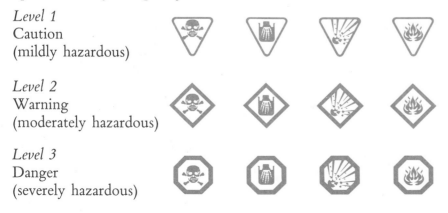

Level 1
Caution
(mildly hazardous)

Level 2
Warning
(moderately hazardous)

Level 3
Danger
(severely hazardous)

Contents

Chapter One

All Systems Go

1.1 Systems: Things Work Together

Science includes many different topics as you discovered during last year's science program. Sometimes the topics can become rather complicated. In order to study them, scientists try to organize complex topics into systems. A **system** is simply a group of separate parts, or components, that are connected and work together to achieve a common purpose. Each component has a separate function, but they all contribute to the same common purpose.

Consider a system that many people already know — a SOUND SYSTEM. A typical sound system may include the following components:

- speakers
- amplifier
- tape deck
- compact disk player (CD player)
- record turntable
- tuner

Each of these components has a specific function:

- The tuner receives radio waves from radio stations and converts the waves into electrical impulses.
- The turntable converts irregular grooves on a record into electrical impulses.
- The CD player converts digital signals on a compact disk into electrical impulses.

Fig. 2 A sound system is probably a necessary part of many of your activities.

Fig. 1 *On the opposite page, human systems and a series of mechanical and electronic systems interact to fly a complex modern aircraft.*

- The tape deck converts magnetic signals on a tape into electrical impulses.
- The amplifier changes the tiny electrical impulses from the previous components into larger electrical impulses.
- The speakers convert the large electrical impulses into sounds — usually music for people to enjoy.

The components must be connected together so that each component can transfer its function to another component in the system. If one component is of poor quality or doesn't work at all, your enjoyment of the entire system is affected. The illustration shows the connections in a sound system.

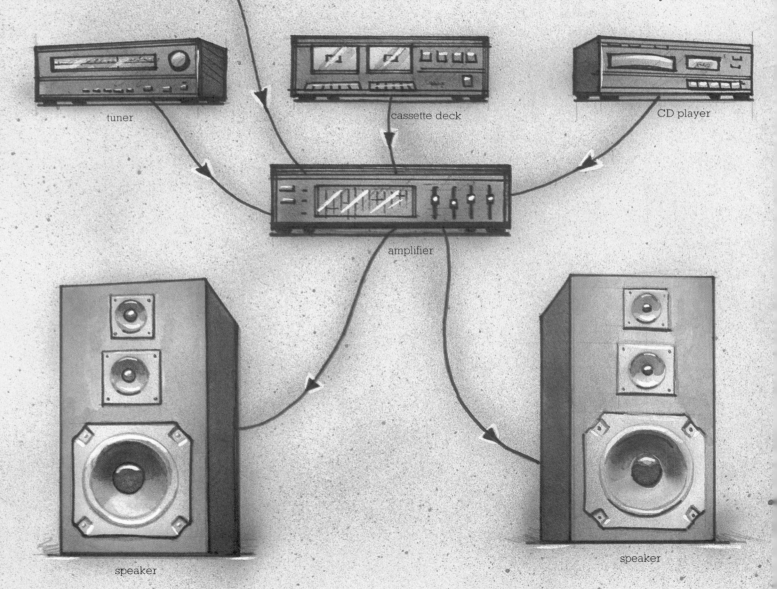

turntable

tuner

cassette deck

CD player

amplifier

speaker

speaker

1.2 **A Pattern for Analysing Systems**

The system may be represented by a simplified **system diagram**. Each component is shown as a circle or square and is labelled with its name. The components are connected by lines. Sometimes arrows may be used to show the transfer of information from one component to another. Occasionally, information may move in both directions between two components.

A system diagram for a sound system is shown in figure 3.

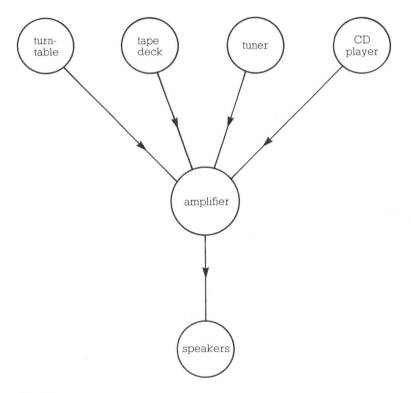

Fig. 3

FEEDBACK

1. What is a system?
2. List the components of a sound system.
3. What is the common purpose of a sound system?

Investigation

1.3 **Investigation: A Ballpoint Pen—A Simple System**

A ballpoint pen is a simple device that you have probably used all your life. It may be considered as a system which is designed with writing as the common purpose of its components.

Find out

FIND OUT states the question that you will try to answer in the investigation. It is the purpose of the experiment.

What are the components of a ballpoint pen? What is the function of each component?

You need

YOU NEED lists the materials to be used in the investigation.

- a ballpoint pen

Try this

TRY THIS states the actions you will carry out to answer the FIND OUT question. This is the procedure for the investigation. TRY THIS also indicates what you should record in your notebook as you carry out the actions.

1. *Write the title of this investigation in your notebook.*
2. Carefully take the ballpoint pen apart.

Fig. 4

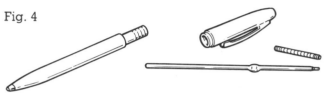

3. *In your notebook, write the name of each part or component.* If you don't know the correct name for the part, invent one. *Beside each name, describe the function of each component.*
4. *Draw a system diagram for a ballpoint pen.*

What happened?

WHAT HAPPENED? helps you think about what you have observed. It includes an answer to the FIND OUT question if the experiment is successful. This answer is a conclusion to the investigation.

1. What is the purpose of the ballpoint pen system?
2. What is the function of the:
   a) pen barrel (or case)?
   b) clip?
   c) retractor?
   d) spring?
   e) refill cartridge?
   f) ink?

The common purpose of a ballpoint pen system is to create some form of visible symbol. This may be done by writing letters or numbers, or by drawing lines or diagrams. The refill cartridge holds the ink which is used to make the visible symbols. The barrel holds the refill cartridge and provides a handle with which to grasp the pen. The retractor contains a button which allows the refill cartridge to be pushed out of the barrel for writing, or returned inside the barrel for storage in a pocket or pen case. The spring provides the push or force to help move the refill cartridge in or out of the barrel. The clip can be used to hold the pen in a shirt or jacket pocket. All these components work together to provide a convenient tool for writing. As in a stereo system, if all components are not working properly, you cannot use the system as intended. As a system, it can be represented by a system diagram.

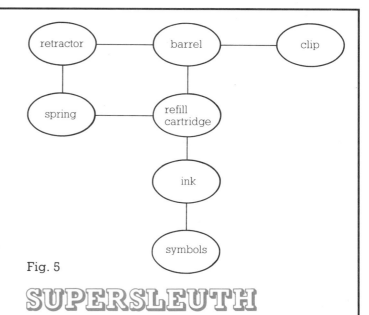

Fig. 5

SUPERSLEUTH

Many technological devices can be represented by system diagrams. A bicycle is one such device and contains about nine components. Prepare a system diagram for a ten-speed racing bicycle or for a trail bike.

Fig. 6

1.4 Systems, Technology, and You

Science has produced libraries full of information. **Technology** is the use of scientific information to develop new processes, products, and systems. Some of these systems have improved our everyday lives. Computer systems are constantly being refined to make them more efficient and easier to use. New fuel systems in cars burn less fuel and emit fewer pollutants into the air. Technology has helped improve farming, harvesting, storage, and transportation processes to make for an efficient food production system that benefits us all.

Technology will continue to be with us and will affect the world we live in. Some kinds of jobs have disappeared, and other jobs will disappear due to such inventions as huge combines, computerized machinery, and electronic bank tellers. Employees must learn new skills to cope with the changes. On the other hand, new and interesting careers often arise from new technology. Recall the stereo system you examined on page 10. How many jobs are created by systems such as that? How many people are involved in the design, construction, sales, and maintenance of the system and in the sales of records, tapes, and CDs that will be played on the system?

Some of the other systems that technology has created or contributed to are not so beneficial. Waste disposal systems were constructed by communities with the belief that the gases and other pollutants they produced would be absorbed harmlessly into the land or the air. Local governments are now grappling with the problem of finding new sites for waste disposal and less damaging ways to dispose of wastes.

An understanding of the body systems of insects and other pests has helped scientists develop pesticides that work within the insect's system to destroy it. Applying this technology didn't fully take into account the limits of the ecosystem and the many ways it would be affected by these insecticides.

Both of these examples deal with living, rather than mechanical, systems. It's not always easy to tell right away when a living system is being damaged, and a living system can't be mended or replaced the way you might fix or replace a damaged mechanical system, such as a stereo.

FEEDBACK

1. What is technology?
2. Name three ways in which technological systems have improved everyday life.
3. Name three systems that you would not want to live without.
4. What is one very basic difference between a system such as a stereo and the system of an insect?

Fig. 7 *Many students enjoy video games. Is this a system you wouldn't want to live without?*

1.5 **Living Systems**

Your body contains many systems. Some, like the breathing system, circulatory system, and nervous system, are well known. Others, such as the endocrine and integumentary systems, are less familiar to most people. Each system has a specific purpose; all the systems are essential to maintain the life of your body.

Your digestive system works to break down food so that the chemicals (nutrients) in the food can be used by other parts of the body. The components of the digestive system are shown in figure 8.

Fig. 8

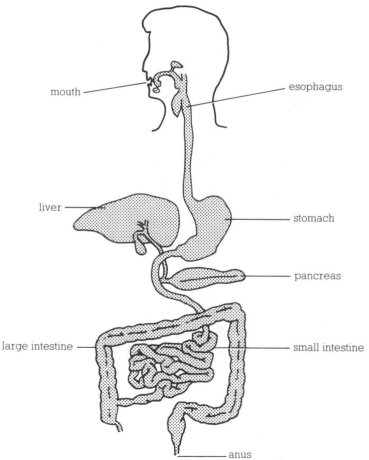

mouth — esophagus — liver — stomach — pancreas — large intestine — small intestine — anus

Each component carries out two or three specific functions. For example, in the small intestine, the large molecules of food are changed into smaller chemicals. These nutrients are then absorbed into the blood, which is part of the circulatory system. The blood carries them to other parts of the body. You can see that each component of each system has its own purpose and that each system has a purpose that helps other systems.

FEEDBACK

1. List seven systems found in your body.
2. Describe the purpose of any three of these systems.
3. Suggest one way that the circulatory system helps the muscular system.

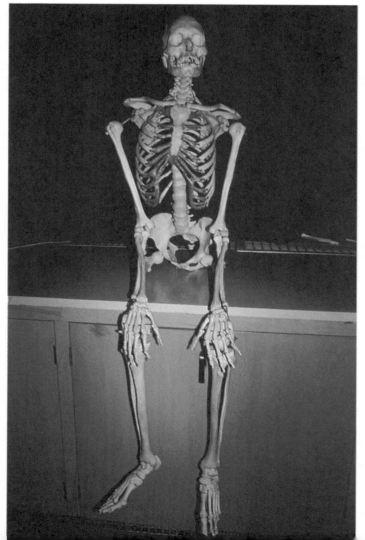

Fig. 9 *You would be in poor shape without the system shown here.*

1.6 Investigation: Beginning in the Mouth

As young children, we were all told to chew our food well. Chewing food is one obvious function of the mouth. But we have also noticed that as we chew our food, saliva from the mouth mixes with the food. As you know, the mouth and the saliva are both parts of the digestive system. What are the functions of saliva? There are several functions, but you can investigate one of these right now. To keep the investigation simple, it is best to examine the effect of saliva on only one kind of food at a time. Consider saliva's effect on STARCH, one of the chemicals found in potatoes, bread, or the bun of a tasty hamburger.

Find out

What is the effect of saliva on starch?

You need

- 2 test tubes
- test tube rack
- labelling materials
- 10 mL graduated cylinder
- soda straw
- starch solution
- 4 pieces Tes-Tape™

Try this

1. After labelling the test tubes 1 and 2, support them in the test tube rack.
2. Use the soda straw to deposit some saliva from your mouth into test tube number 1. Add sufficient saliva so that there is about 2 cm in the test tube.

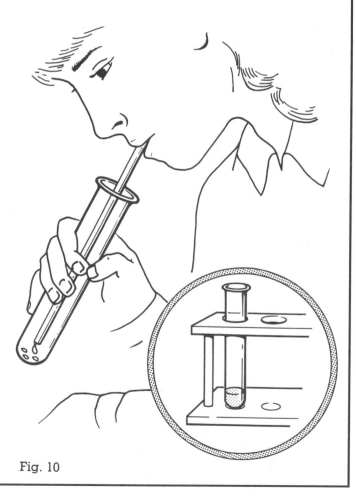

Fig. 10

3. Add an equal amount of tap water to test tube number 2. This test tube will act as a CONTROL.
4. Now place 5 mL of starch solution in the two test tubes. Gently shake the test tubes to mix the contents.
5. Dip a strip of Tes-Tape™ in each test tube. A colour change indicates the presence of sugar. *Was there any sugar in the test tubes?*
6. Now allow 15 min for the saliva to act on the starch. Keep the test tubes warm by holding them in your hands.
7. After 15 min, test the contents of each test tube with the Tes-Tape™ again. *What happened to the Tes-Tape™? Was there any sugar in the test tubes?*

What happened?

1. a) What substance was present in test tube number 1 after 15 min?
   b) How do you know?
   c) How did this substance get into test tube number 1?
2. Test tube number 2 was a CONTROL. What is a control?
3. a) Was there any sugar in test tube number 2?
   b) Explain why.
4. Explain why the test tubes were kept warm, in your hands, close to body temperature.
5. Describe the effect that saliva has on starch.

Now you know

After the starch and saliva had been mixed together for 15 min, a new substance, sugar, was present in the test tube. This was indicated by the colour change of the Tes-Tape™. Since there was no sugar in the test tube initially, the sugar must have been produced from the starch. The control test tube was the test tube in which there was no saliva. The experimental variable, in this case, saliva, was missing. No sugar formed in test tube number 2 because there was no saliva to act on the starch. The test tubes were kept warm in order to duplicate as closely as possible the conditions in a person's mouth. The warm temperature was similar to the warm temperature in the mouth.

Saliva helps to convert starch into sugar. This is only one process that occurs in the digestive system. The other organs, or components, have their functions too. Together, they achieve the common purpose of the digestive system — to digest all types of food and absorb the nutrients into the circulatory system.

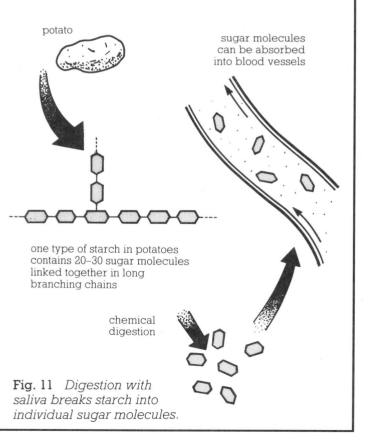

potato

sugar molecules can be absorbed into blood vessels

one type of starch in potatoes contains 20–30 sugar molecules linked together in long branching chains

chemical digestion

Fig. 11 *Digestion with saliva breaks starch into individual sugar molecules.*

1. What effect does saliva have on food such as starch?

2. Food molecules must be changed to smaller molecules so that my body can use them.

3. Why don't I mix some saliva with starch and see what happens?

1.7 A Pattern for Doing Science

There is a pattern that is often followed to solve problems using science. This pattern involves:

1. **asking a question** about a problem that makes you wonder
2. thinking about what you already know about the problem, then **making a guess (hypothesis)** about a possible answer to the question
3. **making up an investigation** that could give an answer to the question
4. **collecting the materials** you need to do the investigation
5. **doing the steps** in the investigation and **recording your observations** while doing these steps
6. thinking about the observations that you recorded and the question that you asked, then **reporting your answer**
7. **using new information to ask a new question**, and the pattern may begin again.

Science is a useful means of answering some questions. Science is something YOU can do!

4. I need two test tubes...

5. ..... add some saliva to mix with starch.

6. Tes-Tape™ can be used to test for sugar. And the answer is.........

7. I wonder if saliva has an effect on protein (or fat)?

1.8 Systems in Science

Most subjects in science, and in many other subjects as well, include topics that can most easily be understood if we think of them as a SYSTEM. By now, you have considered some technological devices as systems: a sound system, a ballpoint pen, and a bicycle. Living things can be examined as systems too: the digestive system, the breathing system, and the circulatory system. You have also heard of weather systems and ecosystems. Certainly you have heard of the solar system.

In every case, the system is composed of several components, each with a specific function, each connected to other components, each contributing to the common purpose of the system.

SUPERSLEUTH

This science textbook consists of several chapters, each dealing with one major subject of science. Their subject areas are listed below.

- Community Ecology
- Environmental Chemistry
- The Functioning Animal
- Continuity
- Electricity and Magnetism
- The Wise Use of Resources
- Minerals and Mining
- The Science of Space

Fig. 12 *The solar system is a fascinating topic that still holds many mysteries.*

For each of these subjects, try to name one system that you might expect to find in the chapter. For one of the systems you name, draw a system diagram to show its components and to illustrate the connections among the components. What is the common purpose of this system? Try to describe the function of each component in the system.

1.9 Chapter Summary

- Using a scientific approach to solve problems involves a pattern:

  1. asking a question
  2. making a hypothesis (guess) about the possible answer
  3. making up an investigation (experiment)
  4. collecting materials to do the investigation
  5. doing the steps in the investigation, and recording observations
  6. stating a conclusion (answer) to the question
  7. using the new information to ask a new question

- Systems are useful aids for simplifying and understanding science topics and technological devices.
- There are various components in a system, all working toward a common purpose.
- Systems each have a purpose that helps other systems.
- System diagrams can be used to represent many topics and devices.

1.10 Are You Ready to Go On?

Do not write in the textbook.

1. Define each of these words: system, ecosystem, technology, component, control, hypothesis.

2. a) The statements below would provide an example of scientific thinking if they were in the correct order. Rewrite them in the correct order.
   - I made the soup and ate it slowly.
   - I collected a pot, spoon, water, and soup mix.
   - The stomach pains went away.
   - One day at 11:30 I had stomach pains.
   - The stomach pains were caused by hunger.
   - I thought that I might be hungry.

   b) Which statement above represents:
   - i) the problem?
   - iv) the procedure?
   - ii) a hypothesis?
   - v) an observation?
   - iii) the materials?
   - vi) a conclusion?

3. Describe the common purpose of the following systems:
   a) the nervous system
   b) a sewer system
   c) a telephone system

4. Your TV set is only one part of a television system. List the components that make up a television system.

5. There are ten systems in the human body. Five of these systems are shown below but their letters have been scrambled. Can you unscramble the letters to discover which systems have been listed?
   a) S N R E O V U
   b) R A L M U S C U
   c) U T O R Y L A C I R C
   d) D C T U O R P E R V I E
   e) L A T E L E K S

6. Write each of the following sentences in your notebook. Fill in the blank with the appropriate word.
   a) A CD player is one _____ of a sound system.
   b) Your body uses its _____ system to obtain oxygen from the air.
   c) This oxygen is carried to all parts of the body by the _____ system.
   d) System diagrams may be used to show the transfer of _____ from one component to another.

7. Choose the correct completion to the following sentences:
   a) Saliva helps to convert starch into
      i) potatoes
      ii) sugar
      iii) bread
      iv) water
   b) The salivary glands which produce saliva are part of the
      i) digestive system
      ii) circulatory system
      iii) muscular system
      iv) breathing system

c) In the human body, the muscular system receives information from the
   i) digestive system
   ii) nervous system
   iii) skeletal system
   iv) breathing system
d) In a sound system, electrical impulses may be converted to musical sounds by the
   i) tape deck
   ii) CD player
   iii) amplifier
   iv) speakers

8. Listed below are five devices that function as systems. Select one of these devices and, in your notebook, prepare a system diagram to show the components and connections for the system:
   a) electric guitar
   b) swimming pool
   c) video game
   d) personal cassette player
   e) flashlight

9. When scientists build a space station, they must design a system that allows people to live there for long periods of time. Draw a system diagram which includes all the components necessary to maintain life on the space station.

Contents

Chapter Two

Balancing Acts

2.1 Oh, To Be Independent!

"I got fired from my job at the campgrounds last night. My boss was counting on me to get there early and I didn't. I was depending on my friend to drive me there. He was depending on his old junk heap he calls a car, and it wouldn't start. It's anything but dependable because he doesn't take care of it. Now everybody's mad, and I'm out of a job and out of money."

We often depend on other people and things around us. In a similar way, we depend on the plants and animals in our environment. We usually realize it's up to us to take care of relationships and the things we depend on to keep them working. We don't always realize that we have to take care of our environment if we expect to keep depending on it.

Plants are the organisms in our environment that capture the sun's energy and combine carbon, oxygen, hydrogen, and nitrogen to make sugars, starches, and proteins. Humans and other animals use these nutrients as food. We couldn't live without plants. We breathe air containing oxygen that they produce through photosynthesis. We also use plants as food and eat some animals that eat plants. Living and non-living components in the environment interact with one another. The study of the relationships among living and non-living components of the environment is called **ecology**.

In this chapter, you will study ecology in order to recognize relationships among various organisms in your environment and the ways they affect one another. Most importantly, you will learn some ways that one type of dominant organism, the human organism, is affecting both living and non-living components and changing the Earth, our home.

Investigation

2.2 A System You Can Live With

Your environment consists of all the living and non-living things around you. The living and non-living things are interrelated, forming a system. In fact, our whole planet can be thought of as a system. You can set up a simple system in the classroom. By observing it for several weeks, you can watch the various kinds of interactions that take place in it.

Fig. 2

Find out

How do the living and non-living components interact in the environment?

You need

- large, wide-necked bottle or jar with a top
- light source
- 2 small plant-eating fish
- 5–7 sprigs of aquatic plants
- 5–10 small pond snails
- clean gravel or sand
- chlorine-free water
- pen or marker to write on glass

Try this

1. Cover the bottom of the jar with clean sand or gravel.
2. Add water to fill the jar to 5 cm from the top. Mark the upper level of the water.
3. Put the plants in the water. Anchor them in the gravel.
4. Carefully add the snails and the fish to the water.
5. Seal the jar tightly.
6. Put the jar near a fairly bright light source.
7. *Draw and label a diagram to show the number of organisms and the position of both the living and the non-living factors in the environment you have created.* (Keep this drawing. You will need it in a later activity.)
8. You will be observing this environmental system from time to time over the next month.

What happened?

1. a) Identify the living parts of the system that you created.
   b) List its non-living parts.
2. a) What are the roles of the plants in this system?
   b) What are the roles of the fish?
3. Of what use is the gravel to the plants?
4. What are some interactions that occur between the water and the living things?

Now you know

The living component of a community is the **biotic component.** The non-living component is the **abiotic component**. The biotic community interacts with its abiotic environment. An interacting system such as this is called an **ecosystem**. An ecosystem is a model invented by people to help them observe and understand what happens in the environment. The environment you created in the jar is a mini-ecosystem.

Your mini-ecosystem is a **closed system**. It is "closed" because organisms and non-living substances can't enter or leave it. The components in the ecosystem can be controlled. Scientists can make use of closed ecosystems to observe the effect of adding and removing various components. In an **open system**, organisms are free to enter and leave the area.

2.3 Communities

As a rule, you probably have little reason to think about the biotic and abiotic components of your environment. However, you certainly take them into account when you choose an area for outdoor recreational use. For example, you'd probably choose a campsite near a lake and wooded area. You might look for a shady spot to pitch your tent. You might want to be close to some nature trails through the woods. If you wanted to fish, you'd make sure the lake at the campsite contained game fish. Many people like to camp, so you'd be aware of your fellow campers' needs and expect to share the available space and facilities with them. Although the needs of plants and animals in the area may not be as evident, it would be important to respect their use of the space and some of the facilities.

Every organism, plant or animal, needs a place to live. The place where an organism lives is called its **habitat**. However, no organism lives and functions completely on its own. Each organism is part of a **population**. A population is a group of individuals of the same species living together in the same area at the same time. Several populations make up a **community**. A community consists of all of the living things in an area. Biotic communities are made up of a lot of different populations which need places to live.

Your campground community may be part of a much larger community, such as a forested area. It may include populations of maple trees, spruce trees, pine trees, oak trees, chipmunks, squirrels, hawks, owls, robins, rabbits, deer, mosses, trilliums, poison ivy, caterpillars, earthworms, bacteria, mosquitoes, and many others.

NATURE TRAIL

Just as a campground provides a temporary habitat for campers and some other organisms, a single maple tree may be a community.

Let's consider some of the possible biotic components of the maple tree. Maple keys can provide food for organisms such as birds and chipmunks. Leaf-eating and juice-sucking insects feed on the leaves. Birds feed on the insects that live in the bark. Birds live among the tree's branches, and small animals may occupy hollows in the trunk. As you can see, the maple tree as a community provides habitats for many organisms.

The maple tree also changes abiotic components to the benefit of the environment. It provides the shade needed for the growth of ferns, mosses, and young saplings. Decayed leaves provide food for earthworms and nutrients for soil. Oxygen, given off by the tree, can be used by humans and other animals. The maple tree itself is dependent on abiotic components of the environment, such as air, sunlight, temperature, and soil minerals.

Fig. 3 A pond community includes many different organisms.

Fig. 4

consumers

producers

scavengers

FEEDBACK

1. How do abiotic components differ from biotic components in an environment?
2. What is ecology?
3. What is a community?
4. How are populations related to biotic communities?
5. Why is the maple tree considered to be a community?
6. How are maple keys used by other organisms?
7. List three ways that other organisms depend on the leaves of the maple tree.

2.4 Who's Who in Which Niche?

In any ecosystem, many different organisms usually share the same habitat. For example, tadpoles, cattails, and ducks may live in a pond. Robins, raccoons, and caterpillars may share a tree as their habitat. How can so many organisms survive in the same habitat? In a human community, if everyone held the job of plumber, there wouldn't be enough work to go around and some plumbers would go out of business. However, people do different kinds of jobs, so a fairly large number of people are able to make a living and meet their housing and food needs. Similarly, each organism in a pond or a tree meets its needs in a slightly different way. The way in which an organism obtains its food requirements or makes its living is called a **niche**. You can think of the niche as an organism's occupation and its habitat as its address.

In a human community, people survive partially because they do different jobs. A person in one job may help other people through the work he or she does and may depend on others in order to do the job successfully. The same is true of an ecosystem. Various organisms have different roles to play in order for the organisms in the ecosystem to survive. You can see examples of this in your mini-ecosystem.

In your mini-ecosystem, the green plants carry out photosynthesis. They use energy from the sun and combine carbon dioxide and water to produce sugar. Oxygen and some water are released as waste products. Green plants, the

30

organisms that can carry out photosynthesis, are **producers**. They occupy the producer niche in a community. Many organisms cannot make their own food because they can't carry out photosynthesis. They have to eat other organisms in order to meet their needs for food. They are called **consumers**.

An organism that eats only plants is called a **herbivore**. The fish in your mini-ecosystem eat the plants it contains. Thus they occupy the herbivore niche. A **scavenger** is an organism that consumes the dead remains of plants and the waste products of fish and algae. Snails occupy the scavenger niche and help to keep the environment clean.

Fig. 5 Caterpillars eat leaves and are in turn eaten by some birds. When living organisms die, decomposers turn them into soil nutrients which help fungi to grow and become food for other organisms.

There are niches in your mini-ecosystem that are not yet occupied. In natural ecosystems, fish have enemies, which catch and eat some of them. These enemies are called **predators**. Predators are organisms that feed on animal meat. Meat-eating organisms are called **carnivores**. The animals they eat are called their **prey**. Organisms that eat both meat and plants are called **omnivores**. Some organisms get their food by living inside, or attached to, other living organisms. Such organisms are known as **parasites**. An organism that a parasite lives in or on is a **host**. Organisms such as bacteria, yeast, moulds, and other kinds of fungi are called **decomposers**. They break down dead organisms and their waste products into simpler substances which can then be used by plants. Some parasites can make their hosts unhealthy. If the fish, plants, or snails in your ecosystem become unhealthy, you probably have some of these parasites in your ecosystem.

FEEDBACK

1. a) Which niches are occupied in your mini-ecosystem?
   b) How do the niches differ from one another?
2. How are prey and predators related?
3. What effects might parasites have on an ecosystem?
4. a) How do carnivores differ from herbivores?
   b) How are they similar?
5. Why is the mini-ecosystem considered to be a closed system?

Activity

2.5 How Does It Work?

You can do an extended observation of your closed ecosystem to see how the various components interact and to observe changes over an extended period of time.

1. *Copy the chart into your notebook.*

Biotic and abiotic components of ecosystem	Niche	Description	Date and changes

2. *On the chart, list the biotic and abiotic components in your ecosystem.*
3. *Identify the niche that each component fills. (Some may occupy more than one niche.)*
4. *Briefly describe the appearance of each component.*
5. *Over a period of one month, record your observations at set intervals, such as every two days.*

Think about it

At the end of the examination period, analyse and summarize the data. What changes did you notice in your ecosystem?

Fig. 6

Activity

2.6 Keeping Track

You are employed by a logging company in Northern Ontario. You have to decide if it is environmentally wise to continue removing lumber from that area. To help you make your decision, you have drawn a map of the area to show the kinds of trees and some of the other organisms that exist there. You have used symbols to show the location of the organisms.

Think about it

1. How did you show where the trees are located?
2. a) What other kinds of organisms live in the area?
   b) Why might you, as a logger, want to be aware of their existence?
3. How would you go about making decisions that would affect this area?

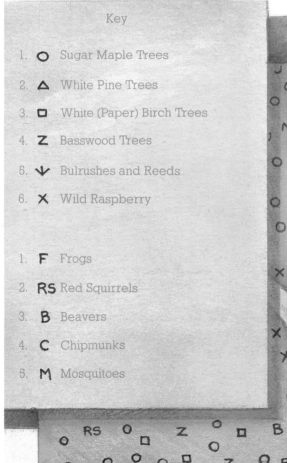

Key

1. O   Sugar Maple Trees
2. △   White Pine Trees
3. ▢   White (Paper) Birch Trees
4. Z   Basswood Trees
5. ↓   Bulrushes and Reeds
6. X   Wild Raspberry

1. F   Frogs
2. RS Red Squirrels
3. B   Beavers
4. C   Chipmunks
5. M   Mosquitoes

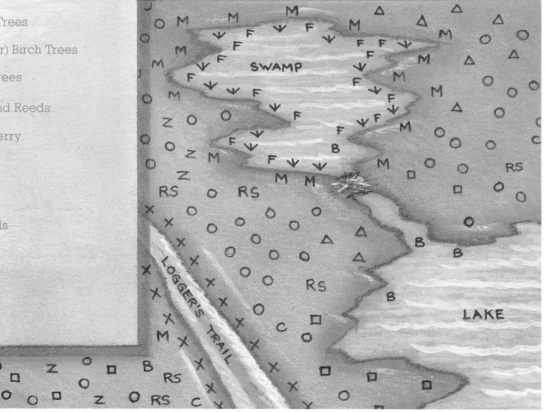

2.7 **A World at Your Doorstep**

You have observed your own mini-ecosystem and a map of an outdoor system in your imaginary logging area. In this investigation, you will go outdoors and study a natural ecosystem by gathering both abiotic and biotic data from a staked-out area. This method is known as **quadrat analysis**.

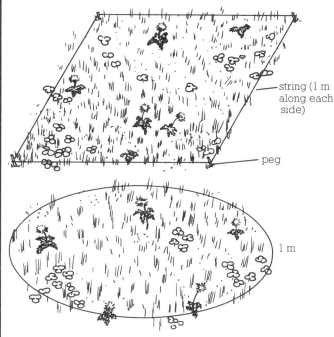

Fig. 7 *A quadrat is an enclosed area—it can be square or circular in shape.*

Find out

A. How do you set up a quadrat?
B. What are the organisms and their niches in the quadrat?

C. What kinds of data can you collect about the abiotic factors operating in the quadrat?
D. How do you prepare an overall map of the area?

You need

- measuring device(s) for the outline of the quadrat
- 4 pegs
- string
- metric ruler
- soil thermometer
- air thermometer
- soil auger
- paper (15 cm × 15 cm)
- marker
- timing device
- light source

Part A:
Setting Up the Quadrat

Try this

1. Select an area on the lawn or field near your school.
2. Measure an area of 1 m². Place a peg at each corner. Use string to enclose the area you have marked off.
3. The area you have enclosed is a quadrat. *In a paragraph, describe the appearance of the plants in the quadrat. Is it covered well or sparsely by plants? Are there many different kinds of plants? Do many animals live in the quadrat?*

continued

Part B:
Biotic Factors in the Quadrat

1. Determine which plant species occurs most often in the quadrat.
2. Select one plant of this dominant species. Without removing the plant from the ground, measure the size of its leaves, stems, flower(s), and how much of the ground each plant covers (its leaf spread). *Record your findings.*
3. *Construct a 15 cm × 15 cm quadrat map, similar to the map on page 34, showing the location of all the plants of the dominant species in the quadrat. Show relative sizes of the plants and the space they occupy. Title this quadrat map "Dominant Plants in a Quadrat," and record the niche of the plant.*
4. Select one or two other plant species. *Repeat step 3 for each species chosen. Prepare a separate 15 cm × 15 cm diagram for each species. Give a title to each diagram, and record the niche of each organism.*

Fig. 8   Plant A   Plant B

5. Study the quadrat carefully for evidence of the presence of animals and insects. *Map your findings in another quadrat diagram. Identify (not necessarily by name) each type of animal and record its niche.*

Part C:
Studying Abiotic Factors

1. *Draw a 15 cm × 15 cm quadrat map to locate rocks, barren soil, holes, water, garbage, and any other abiotic factors present in the quadrat. Identify each type of abiotic factor on your map.*
2. *Record the time of day.*
3. *Measure and record the air temperature.*
4. Using the soil auger, carefully remove as deep a core of soil as you can. Keep this core in the auger so as not to disturb it.

Fig. 9

soil core

5. Set the soil thermometer in the hole made by the auger. Leave it for 7 min. *Record the temperature of the soil.*
6. Examine the soil core and describe its appearance (colour) and texture. Look for evidence of the presence of animals. *Record your findings.*

Part D:
Making a Composite Quadrat Map

1. Create a symbol to represent each of the following: the dominant plant, the other plant species chosen, each animal, and each

abiotic factor. *Make a key similar to the one on page 34 to show what the symbols represent.*

2. *Using a 15 cm × 15 cm quadrat map, use the symbols to show as accurately as possible the locations of the above-mentioned biotic and abiotic components of the quadrat.*
Title this diagram "Composite Quadrat Map."
(A **composite map** is a single map that is formed using information from several different maps.)

3. Take all the other quadrat diagrams. Place one on top of the other. Hold them up to a light source or a window so that you can get an overall view. *Compare it with the Composite Quadrat Map.*

What happened?

1. Describe how to set up a quadrat.
2. How can you determine which plant is the dominant plant in a quadrat?
3. Superimpose the quadrat maps of all the plant species. Where are the other plant species located relative to the dominant plant species?
4. a) Account for the difference in appearance of the Composite Quadrat Map to the superimposed maps.
   b) Decide which overall appearance is more accurate. Give reasons to support your decision.
5. How does the size of the leaf spread appear to affect other plants close to it?
6. What abiotic factors appear to affect the growth of the dominant plant species and of the other plant species that you studied?
7. Select five plants and five animals, and state the niche that each occupies in the area.

8. How are animals that live in the same habitat able to survive?
9. Describe the habitats of five animals that seem to live in the quadrat.
10. Was there any evidence of the presence of humans in your quadrat? If so, does the evidence indicate that the presence of humans in the area is helpful or harmful?

Now you know

A **quadrat** is a staked-out area in an ecosystem. When you first look at the contents of a quadrat, you may see little variety. Many of the different producers may look alike. However, a close study of the organisms in a quadrat reveals much diversity.

A carefully mapped quadrat often shows the interconnections between the biotic and abiotic components of an ecosystem. Careful investigation will reveal the niches and habitats of the biotic components. The type of soil, temperature, and availability of water and light are some of the factors that determine whether an organism's habitat can keep the organism alive.

Biologists use quadrat studies to gather data about the location of plants and animals. They also use them to learn about the conditions under which some plants and animals live, and about the population of a given species in an area. They can use the information when monitoring changing environmental conditions, and in advising how a given area can be maintained or improved.

SUPERSLEUTH

You may wish to send the soil sample away for further analysis. If your school has a soil test kit, you might team up with a senior student and learn how to do soil tests.

2.8 Getting Fed Up With a Food Chain

In any ecosystem, there are many interconnections among the organisms. Organisms of one niche often become the supper for organisms of another niche. This is the way that organisms transfer energy.

Producers, such as green plants, are the only organisms that can make their own food. All other organisms depend on them directly or indirectly. In your mini-ecosystem, the green plants (producers) absorb energy from the sun. Herbivores, such as fish, eat parts of the plants to obtain energy. These fish could provide food for carnivores if carnivores were present. This series of organisms obtaining energy by eating other organisms is called a **food chain**. This transfer of energy follows certain paths. Every food chain begins with the sun. Some energy from the sun is transferred by the producers into food through the process of photosynthesis. Some energy is then transferred from consumer to consumer during the eat-and-be-eaten sequence.

Many food chains are short because humans have eliminated some of the top carnivores. In remote and protected areas, organisms such as bears, moose, hawks, and other carnivores are still to be found.

FEEDBACK

1. What is a food chain?
2. Why are other organisms dependent on producers?
3. Look at your mini-ecosystem or at the notes you made as you observed it.
   a) How do the snails in your mini-ecosystem get their food energy?
   b) What role does the sunlight play in the mini-ecosystem?
   c) Make up a food chain for your ecosystem.
4. Consider this food chain: grass ———⟶ rabbit ———⟶ hawk. What would you expect to happen if all the hawks in an area were killed off?
5. How would the fact that humans have eliminated the top carnivores affect an ecosystem?
8. What materials are transferred throughout an ecosystem?

It's a Fact
A. A porcupine has very few enemies. Most of the animals that might like to eat a porcupine would wind up with a mouth full of quills. The fisher, however, is able to kill the porcupine by attacking its stomach which is not covered with quills.
B. Timber wolves eat insects, rodents, deer, caribou, and moose. They kill and eat animals that are old or diseased.

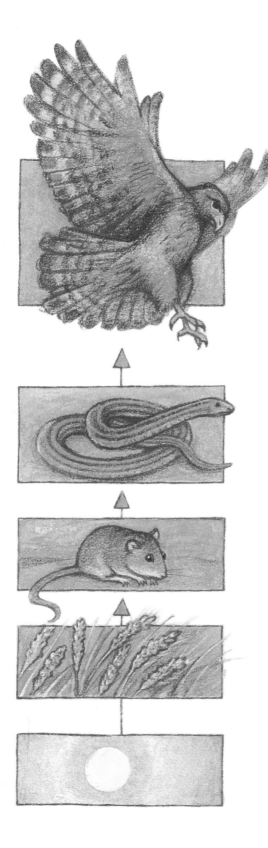

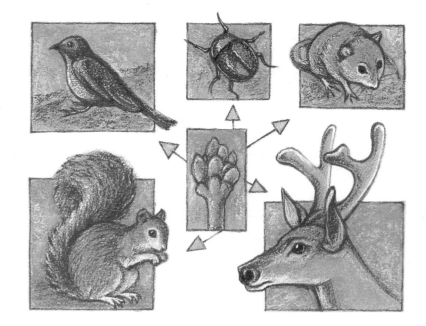

Fig. 10 *On the left is a simple food chain. Above, the producer that feeds several organisms is shown. Below, several foods eaten by one organism are shown.*

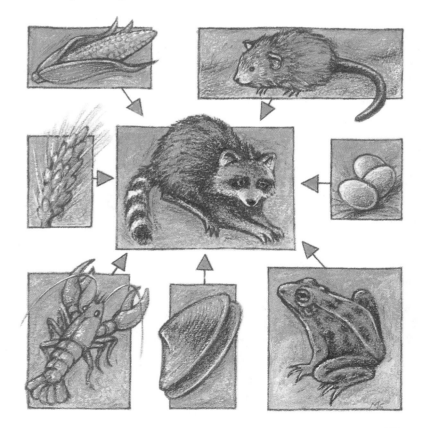

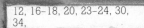

Owl (31)

12, 16–18, 20, 23–24, 30, 34,

2.9 Linking Food Chains

You have looked at examples of simple food chains. In a natural ecosystem, there are so many organisms feeding on other organisms that the various food chains become very complex.

Look at the illustration of forest food chains. The numbers below each organism indicate the organisms it eats.

FEEDBACK

1. Why is the bear an omnivore?
2. How can the owl and the hawk survive in the same area?
3. List the organisms that eat the following:
   - deer
   - rabbit

Twig-feeding bird (17)
4, 16, 21, 25, 30

Squirrel (18)
2, 4–10, 17

Mice (20)
2, 4, 7, 9, 15, 16, 25, 26, 30

Porcupine (11)
1, 2, 6, 7, 9, 10

Rabbit (12)
1, 3, 7, 9, 10

Deer (13)
2–10

Buds, twigs (10)

Nuts (2)

Seeds (4)

Fungi (5)

Beetles, bees (19)

Grass (3)

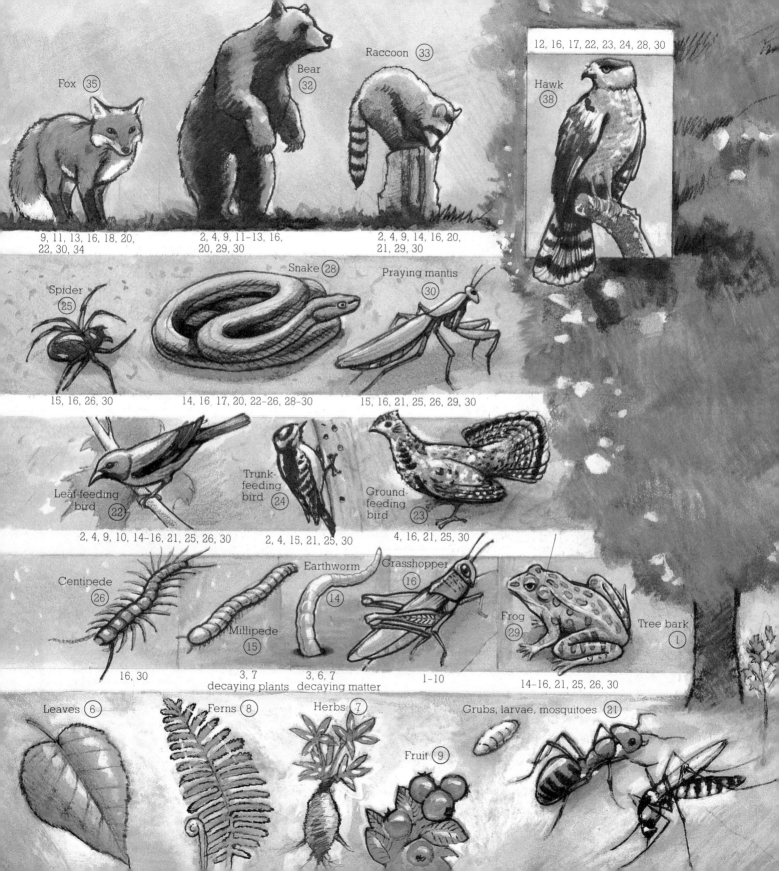

Fox ㉟
9, 11, 13, 16, 18, 20, 22, 30, 34

Bear ㉜
2, 4, 9, 11–13, 16, 20, 29, 30

Raccoon ㉝
2, 4, 9, 14, 16, 20, 21, 29, 30

Hawk ㊳
12, 16, 17, 22, 23, 24, 28, 30

Spider ㉕
15, 16, 26, 30

Snake ㉘
14, 16, 17, 20, 22–26, 28–30

Praying mantis ㉚
15, 16, 21, 25, 26, 29, 30

Leaf-feeding bird ㉒
2, 4, 9, 10, 14–16, 21, 25, 26, 30

Trunk-feeding bird ㉔
2, 4, 15, 21, 25, 30

Ground-feeding bird ㉓
4, 16, 21, 25, 30

Centipede ㉖
16, 30

Millipede ⑮
3, 7
decaying plants

Earthworm ⑭
3, 6, 7
decaying matter

Grasshopper ⑯
1–10

Frog ㉙

Tree bark ①
14–16, 21, 25, 26, 30

Leaves ⑥

Ferns ⑧

Herbs ⑦

Fruit ⑨

Grubs, larvae, mosquitoes ㉑

The chart shows you how some of the producers and consumers interact in an ecosystem such as a forested area. Some organisms appear in more than one list.

Producers	Herbivores	Carnivores		Decomposers	Scavengers
		Secondary consumer	Tertiary consumer		
leaves	caterpillars	robins	owls	bacteria	vultures
clover	bees	snakes	hawks	fungi (moulds, mushrooms, toadstools)	
maple keys	beetles	praying mantises	snakes		crows
bark	mice	owls	herons		
grass	raccoons	hawks			
seeds	grasshoppers	skunks			
fruit	porcupines	woodpeckers			
saplings	rabbits	spiders			
	deer	centipedes			
	squirrels	millipedes			
	skunks	beetles			
	bears	foxes			
	partridges	bears			
	earthworms				
	centipedes				
	millipedes				

Fig. 11 *Great blue heron*

1. a) Make up two food chains using rabbits.
   b) Make up two food chains using bears.

2. Make a food chain using a snake and a hawk. Use one as a second consumer and one as a third consumer.

3. Make a food chain with a bear and a raccoon to show that they are omnivores.

Activity

2.11 Weaving a Food Web

Each time a member (organism) of a food chain eats, it does so to obtain energy to carry on life processes. Most organisms eat more than one food; most "foods" are eaten by more than one organism. Very often several food chains are interconnected. Many herbivores, such as deer, caterpillars, adult insects, and mice, may eat the leaves of the maple tree. Maple keys can be eaten by squirrels, insects, or birds; while some birds eat caterpillars. Birds' eggs may be eaten by snakes, and hawks may eat snakes and mice. The mice may then be eaten by owls. A fox may kill and eat part of a squirrel. A crow may later finish off the squirrel's remains. Most food chains in a community interconnect in this way. The intermingling of food chains is called a **food web**.

Think about it

1. Use the data from the forest food chain to make up a food web with 15 different organisms in it. Include bees, beetles, grass, and clover.
2. List the organisms you used and state the niche of each.
3. a) How many producers did you use?
   b) How many consumers did you use?

Fig. 12 *A food web*

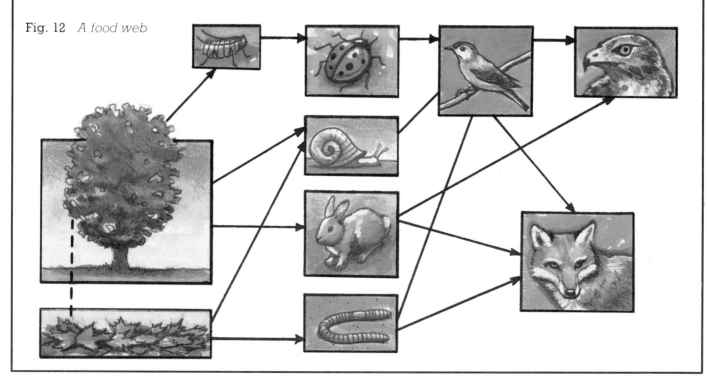

43

2.12 Upsetting the Food Web

Suppose that, in the forested area you have been examining, mosquitoes became a problem for people. The area was sprayed with chemicals which killed the mosquitoes but also killed the bees and some beetles, and prevented the grass and clover from producing seeds.

Think about it

1. What effect would the absence of bees, beetles, and mosquitoes have on the food web?
2. How would a hawk be affected?
3. What would happen to the food web if grass and clover were reduced?
4. Why should humans be cautious about where spraying takes place?

2.13 Upsetting the Balance

From your study of food and food webs, you know that organisms provide food energy for other organisms. However, food webs do not show how many of any one organism are necessary to supply food for others. The food web usually shows one mouse as the food for one hawk. In fact, it takes many mice to feed a hawk and more blades of grass than there

Fig. 13 *A pyramid of numbers.*

are mice to keep the mice alive. A way of showing this relationship is by a **pyramid of numbers**. The organisms at the bottom of the pyramid are larger in number than the organisms at the top. The further up the pyramid an organism is, the more organisms it needs to support life. For example, a lion may not appear to eat as many organisms as the small animal it eats. However, the lion has actually eaten all of the organisms that the small animal had consumed.

Why is this the case? The energy from the sun which is captured by the plants is not completely transferred to the herbivores. Much of the energy is lost as heat during respiration and through activities such as growing, running, and breathing. More and more energy is lost as it is transferred through a food chain, so that the top carnivore gets only a fraction of the energy stored by the plants.

As the Earth's population increases, we need more food and housing. As a result, forests, marshes, and swamps are destroyed so that crops can be planted and houses and roads can be constructed.

As these natural ecosystems are destroyed and not replaced, many organisms die and the balance among them is upset. We are then faced with questions such as:
• How can we both protect nature and feed more people?
• If it isn't possible to do both, what should our priority be?

Fig. 14 Land that is converted for human use no longer performs its original function.

FEEDBACK

1. Define:
   a) food chains
   b) food webs
   c) pyramid of numbers
   d) Describe how the above are similar to each other. How do they differ?
2. Predict what would happen to an ecosystem if all the maple trees were cut down. How would the other organisms in the maple tree community cope with such a change?
3. Suppose that you have been given a parcel of land which has very good soil to grow some grain crops. On this land, there are also many rare plants that support a rare species of animal found nowhere else in the world. What would you do?

2.14 Out for the Count

The activity "Upsetting the Food Web" gave you an idea of how crucial it is to maintain the balance of populations in an ecosystem. How do you know what the balance in a particular area should be? If the area is relatively undisturbed, you will have to assume that its balance is being maintained. An undisturbed area is one that has not been subject to weeding, spraying, hunting, or any other means of changing the numbers of its populations. One way to determine population is to count all of the organisms that exist in a particular area. You can take a population count in the quadrat area that you set up earlier for Investigation 2.7.

Fig. 15

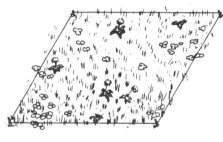

Find out

How many common plants are there in a marked-off area close to the school?

You need

- metre stick
- data recording paper
- pencil
- 4 pegs
- string

Try this

1. Use the metre stick to mark out a square of land 50 cm by 50 cm in an area you have previously observed.
2. Select two types of plants that appear to be the most plentiful in the area.
3. Carefully count every specimen of the two types of plants in your quadrat.
4. *Record the data.*

What happened?

1. How many of each plant were in your quadrat?
2. Imagine counting the numbers of these two types of plants if your area were five times as large or if your area included the entire province. What errors do you think might occur in your count?
3. Why might this method of counting not be very efficient?
4. Why is this method of counting not likely used in industry?

Now you know

Counting each member of a population individually can be tedious, time-consuming, and not necessarily accurate. People who need to learn something about the population of a given area have devised other methods to count efficiently and usually with enough accuracy for their needs.

2.15 Too Many to Count

Have you ever been telephoned by a radio or T.V. station about your listening or viewing habits? If so, you have been chosen randomly in an attempt by those in charge to sample a cross-section of the population, since there probably wasn't time to call everyone in the viewing area. A similar technique can be used to sample a biotic community.

Fig. 16

Find out

How can you best estimate large numbers?

You need

- metre stick or tape measure
- 10 cm × 10 cm wire frame
- pencil
- data page to record observations

Try this

1. Measure out an area that is 5 m × 5 m.
2. Mark the enclosed area with stakes, rocks, or books.
3. Stand at the edge of the marked area and toss your wire frame anywhere in the area.
4. *Record the number of plants inside the frame.*
5. *Repeat nine times, moving to a different spot on the periphery of the enclosed area for each toss of the frame.*
6. *Record your observations in a chart.*

What happened?

1. Total the number of plants found and divide by ten to find the average number of plants that might be found in any one sample area.
2. Your area which is enclosed is 25 m². Your sampler is 0.01 m². Calculate how many times larger the enclosed area is than the sampler.
3. Select three dominant plants in your area. Predict how many of each plant there are in the enclosed area. Compare these results with those of other class members.

Now you know

By throwing your sampler anywhere in the staked-out area, you were taking a **random sample**. Random sampling can be used to estimate the population of organisms in a large area. In a very large area, larger quadrats are used for greater accuracy.

2.16 **Population Changers**

Quadrat studies are used as a sampling method to determine the population of a given species in an area. If you took a further sampling from your quadrat at a later date and another one still later, you might find that some changes had occurred. There might be more or fewer of the dominant plants. There might be more or less evidence of animals. Since the analysis of your quadrat took place over a very short period, there was insufficient time to note any changes in population size. In natural ecosystems, the population size of a species continuously fluctuates. This is because the biotic and abiotic factors that affect the species are not constant, and every change has an effect on some other part of the ecosystem.

For example, members of a human population may move out of an area because there are no jobs. This kind of movement is called **emigration**. They move into an area where jobs do exist. This is called **immigration**.

Another way a population can increase is by having new members born into it. The number of births is called **natality**. As members die, they decrease the population. This decrease due to death is called **mortality**.

Fig. 17 *Population changers*

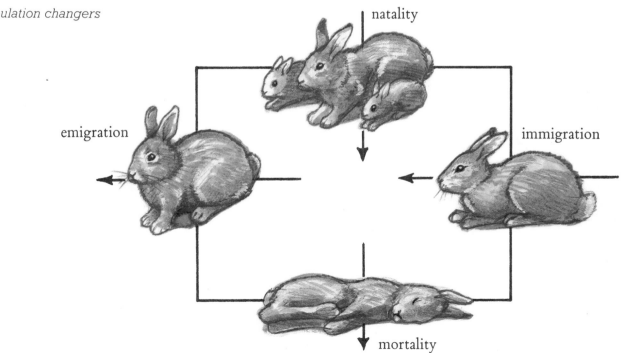

natality

emigration

immigration

mortality

Abiotic factors that affect population size in a community include:

- temperature changes
- total rainfall
- seasons
- soil conditions
- wind
- air quality
- natural disasters such as fire, drought, and flooding

FEEDBACK

1. Define immigration and give an example.
2. How does emigration affect population size?
3. If the natality of a population equals its mortality, what happens to the population size?
4. Speculate about how an excessively dry, hot summer could affect the population of:
   a) mosquito larvae in ponds
   b) earthworms
5. Why would a dry, hot summer have a greater effect on frogs than on owls?

SUPERSLEUTH

A maple tree, standing alone in a field, under IDEAL conditions will produce an average of 15 000 seeds annually.

Under IDEAL conditions, what is the natality rate? If the mortality rate for maple seeds is 95%, how many trees would you expect to grow from those 15 000 seeds?

Fig. 18 This quadrat study will provide information about populations in this area.

Activity

2.17 Population Problems Can Grow on You

See if you can solve the following problems based on information you have just been reading.

Part A:

You need

- paper
- coloured pencils

Prepare a graph to show two separate population curves, one for grey mice and one for brown mice living in a barn. Plot "Time" on the horizontal axis and "Number of Mice" on the vertical axis. Use the same scales for both kinds of mice. Plot one curve first and then the other one, in a different colour. Label each curve.

Month	Number of GREY mice	Number of BROWN mice
January	28	11
February	30	10
March	24	19
April	23	20
May	18	18
June	25	25
July	21	24
August	18	21
September	15	28
October	11	30
November	9	28
December	9	32

Think about it

1. When does the population of brown mice exceed that of the grey mice?
2. a) What population changes occur among the brown mice?
   b) How do they differ from the changes among the grey mice?

Fig. 19

Part B:

You need

- pencil
- paper

Here is some information about a small town population.

Year	Births (natality)	Deaths (mortality)	New-comers (Immigration)	Moved away (Emigration)
1975	This was the year of the Census: Population was 250			
1976	4	1	8	12
1977	3	5	4	9
1978	5	4	6	7
1979	2	6	6	4
1980	4	2	5	3
1981	6	4	5	7
1982	3	8	2	5
1983	0	2	4	2
1984	1	3	2	0
1985	5	3	8	6
1986	3	0	5	0
1987	8	4	2	3
1988	0	2	5	2
1989	2	4	3	8

1. Use these figures to calculate the population of the small town for each year.
2. *Plot the information on a graph. Plot the date in years along the horizontal axis. Plot the population of people on the vertical axis.*

Think about it

1. Was the population of the town increasing or decreasing?
2. With the same information, plot the graph, this time with the population on the horizontal axis and the date on the vertical axis. Which of the two graphs is easier to read and understand? Why?

Part C:

You need

- paper
- coloured pencils

1. a) The following is a graph of changes or fluctuations in the snowshoe rabbit population, as indicated by the number of pelts received by the Hudson's Bay Company. *Copy or trace the graph into your notebook.*

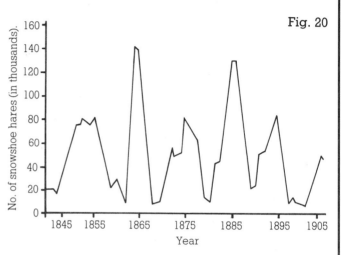

Fig. 20

b) *Plot the following information on the graph from above:*

Year	Number of lynx (in thousands)
1845	30
1847	50
1951	7
1855	35
1860	3
1867	70
1871	4
1874	35
1876	48
1880	11
1881	11
1885	80
1887	45
1891	12

continued

2. Look at this population study of snowshoe
   rabbits and Canada lynx:

Year	Snowshoe rabbit (in thousands)	Canada lynx (in thousands)	Year	Snowshoe rabbit (in thousands)	Canada lynx (in thousands)
1895	95	55	1916	15	25
1897	20	25	1918	10	2
1899	1	5	1920	35	2
1901	1	15	1922	75	13
1903	45	58	1924	60	28
1904	75	62	1925	25	35
1905	65	50	1926	15	30
1906	20	20	1927	10	25
1907	20	5	1928	2	17
1908	21	2	1929	2	10
1909	25	5	1930	3	8
1910	50	10	1931	25	8
1911	55	15	1932	75	10
1912	75	25	1933	95	13
1913	70	45	1934	75	—
1914	55	35	1935	20	—
1915	25	25			

3. Graph the above population counts, in thousands,
   of the snowshoe rabbit and the Canada lynx over a
   40-year period in northern Canada.

Fig. 21

1. Explain why the snowshoe rabbit population fluctuates the way it does.
2. How do the changes in the snowshoe rabbit population compare with the changes in the lynx population?
3. What would you now say caused the decrease in the snowshoe rabbit population?
4. Estimates of the number of rabbits vary greatly. At its peak the number exceeds 1000/km². At its low point, the count drops to less than one. Rabbits, like other animals, are subject to bacterial and parasitic diseases, both internal and external. At times of great abundance, epidemics seem to occur, when large numbers of dead and dying rabbits are observed in their natural habitat. These epidemics seem to have occurred in the years when the population of rabbits was "crashing," that is, declining rapidly (1899, 1901, 1902, 1928, 1929, 1930). Clearly, predators could not be responsible for the deaths of these rabbits.

a) What does the above information suggest to you about the possibility of animal populations rising and falling in cycles?
b) Why should disease be a factor in decreasing the rabbit population at times of great abundance?
c) What happens to the supply of food for the lynx population when the snowshoe rabbit population decreases?
d) What effect might the fluctuation of lynx and rabbit populations have on other organisms in the area?

53

Silent Death

By David Suzuki

Fig. 22 *These trees in the Black Forest in Germany have been damaged by acid rain. Do our maple trees face the same fate?*

As a teenager, I read a short story in Reader's Digest about a farmer who went to New York to visit a friend.

In the heart of the city, the farmer suddenly stopped and exclaimed: "I hear a cricket." His friend scoffed, saying that amid all the din of traffic and people, he couldn't be hearing a cricket.

The farmer responded by taking a coin out of his pocket and flipping it into the air. When it landed on the concrete, several people immediately looked around for the coin. The visiting farmer had made his point — it is what you have been conditioned to notice.

Whenever my father comes to our cottage, he points out things such as diseased shrubs or fallen trees that leave me wondering why I didn't see them before. We blithely go about our life unconscious of much of what is happening around us. It is only when we have become sensitized to something — such as a cricket's call, or trees and shrubs — that we notice things.

Recently, I saw a film that opened my eyes to what was once completely invisible but is now glaringly obvious.

Filmmakers Holly Dressel and Gary Toole live in the rural part of eastern Quebec. A few years ago, they became aware that something was terribly wrong in the woodlot on their farm — the trees seemed to be sick.

Investigating, they discovered to their horror that the deciduous forests in Quebec and much of eastern North America are dying from the effects of the increase in soil acidity from acid rain.

Their story, Trouble in the Forest, is a documentation of the dying stages of Quebec's famous sugar maple trees. All indications are that the terrible blight is spreading across the northeastern part of the continent and affecting more than the maples.

The die-off has been going on for years. Why haven't we noticed? Part of the reason is that we take plants for granted and don't notice them. They aren't cute and cuddly like animals, nor do they move or make sounds. They just stand there, silently storing the energy of sunlight in molecules of sugar, cleansing the air and clinging to water and releasing it into the air. If trees could make sounds, their collective screams around the world would be deafening.

Even though scientists in Scandinavia and West Germany have known for years that forests were being adversely affected by acidity, there has been a great deal of denial in North America. President Ronald Reagan refused to acknowledge the reality of acid rain as an important ecological factor, even suggesting it might be a by-product of the trees themselves.

Meanwhile, once you know the signs of trees dying from acidity, you can see them everywhere. The leaves are often sparse on the branches and discoloured from nutritional imbalances.

In late August or early September, trees may change colour with their leaves falling prematurely. The most obvious sign is bare branches at the top that protrude like naked bones above the leafy part of the tree. Then over the next five or six years, more branches die while the tree rots, so its wood is not suitable even for burning.

The billion-dollar maple sugar industry is an integral part of Quebec's economy and cultural history, yet Ottawa has acknowledged that within a decade, the province's sugarbushes will be gone, and all the deciduous forests could be dead in 20 years!

Driving along the Don Valley Expressway through the heart of Metro Toronto or along Highway 401 on the north end of that metropolitan region in early September, one could no longer avoid the obvious—what has afflicted Quebec is happening in Ontario, too.

The ecological consequences of deciduous die-off are catastrophic. The flora and fauna of the forests are changing completely. It is already happening—birds depending on heavy foliage are being driven from the forest while others, such as the pileated woodpecker, which exploits insects in rotting wood, are having a field day. Many animals that are forced to move don't survive.

Much of the effect of acidity on the trees is due to changes in the soil. But soil isn't just dirt: it has a vast population of micro-organisms too numerous to count. If trees and the soil are being changed, do we dare think that we are not also part of that biosphere and are not being affected as well?

There will be an effort to find more acid-resistant trees and reforest the land with them. And no doubt something will grow where the deciduous trees once flourished. But we will have lost the original tree community forever.

Just as a canary's death once warned coal miners that the air was foul, the Quebec maples are the latest canaries, an urgent warning we can no longer afford to ignore.

Think about it

1. a) What were the people described in the article unaware of? Why were they unaware?
   b) Look around your own environment. What aspects of your environment have you become used to that a newcomer might notice?
2. What are the effects of increased soil acidity in eastern Quebec? What further effects can we expect?
3. Have you ever noticed trees such as the author describes? Make a point of looking at trees in your area to see if they display the symptoms described in the article.

4. Why would governments deny that acid rain is a problem?
5. a) Keep an ecology file during the time you study ecology. Find as much material as you can to include in it. Newspapers, magazines, and ecology-related organizations are good sources. Make your material available to the class.
   b) Based on all the material you have read, choose an action to take on acid rain. Work with one or more of your classmates who wish to take similar action. The action you take might involve designing a poster to alert the community to the effects and the dangers of acid rain. It might involve preparing a petition to be sent to the Prime Minister's office requesting that more effort be made to eliminate acid rain. It might involve making a presentation to a local manufacturer whose company contributes to acid rain.
   c) Share any responses you receive with your class.

Fig. 23 *Are maple trees doomed?*

Conservation Officer?

Fig. 24 *Conservation officers are required to carry out a variety of interesting jobs in the outdoors.*

More and more people are becoming concerned about the effects of human activities on the environment. One group who is particularly concerned are people who enjoy using our wilderness areas for hunting, fishing, and observing wildlife. They hope that the populations of animals such as deer, moose, ducks, gamefish and other wildlife will always be large enough for them to enjoy their sport or hobby. It is the job of a conservation officer to keep track of animal populations, to enforce laws and regulations that protect wildlife, and to inform the public about resource use and conservation. He or she helps to ensure that one valuable natural resource—wildlife—is treated wisely.

Conservation officers are usually employed by a provincial government. Some may work for timber companies, wildlife sanctuaries, or hunting and fishing lodges. Most conservation officers have gained experience through summer or part-time work as junior rangers, as members of a maintenance crew for lands and parks, or in forestry through jobs such as tree planting and timber cruising. Useful experience can also be gained by volunteering for environmental clean-up projects or for clearing portages. Ability to operate and maintain snowmobiles and motorboats is very desirable since a conservation officer will often use these for travelling through wilderness areas. As well, a person who wants to become a conservation officer will have demonstrated an appreciation of the natural environment by pursuing recreational activities such as hunting, fishing, canoeing, camping, hiking, and bird watching. Knowledge and skills for this job must also be learned in one of the community college programs for natural resource technicians. High school graduation is required for entry into these programs. Some of the on-the-job training is given at a police college.

A conservation officer spends much time travelling alone outdoors, sometimes in weather and insect conditions that are unpleasant. This requires good physical conditioning, toughness, and resourcefulness. He or she is usually responsible for doing population samples of wildlife in a certain area so that wise decisions can be made to manage population sizes. Usually limits are placed on how many living creatures such as deer, moose, trout, or ducks can be taken; a conservation officer can lay charges and make arrests when hunting or fishing laws are broken. In this role he or she must display good judgment, tact, and integrity. Another role of conservation officers requires that they provide information and assistance to members of the public, sometimes by visiting schools or sportsman's shows to talk about the importance of wildlife and wilderness for recreation. Good communication skills are thus a definite asset.

Conservation officers help ensure that we will have wildlife and wilderness that can be used for recreation. The tasks they do are varied and interesting. Will this be you?

2.18 Predicting Population Trends

You have been examining data about various populations in the environment. Biologists keep careful records of worldwide population data. They use the data to help them make decisions about the amount of hunting or fishing to allow in a given area. They might use the data to advise government officials about whether or not certain chemicals should be used in an area, given the effect the chemicals will likely have. They might recommend ways of preventing the extinction of an endangered species.

After data have been collected for a period of time, the figures are examined carefully. Those who have collected the data look for trends in the figures. By looking at the cycles that occur in population changes, scientists can predict what will probably happen, given similar conditions, in the future.

Fig. 25 All of these creatures are members of endangered species.

You have seen examples of population fluctuations in the activities you have just completed. How might such population fluctuations occur in the human race and what might be their eventual effect? The following activity will show you.

Activity

2.19 How Many More?

Populations do not stay the same. Consider figure 26 which shows the population of fruit flies in a closed system. The graph shows that fruit flies reproduce very rapidly. Then, as space and food become less available and wastes accumulate, the population decreases very rapidly. It tends to level off for a while and then die out completely.

The Earth's ecosystem is very large, but it IS a closed system. The resources it contains are not unlimited. Look at the graph of human population.

It took more than 16 centuries for the world's population to increase from 200 or 300 million to double this size. In the next 200 years, another 200 or 300 million were added and yet another thousand million in a mere hundred years, with the population reaching two thousand million in about 1930. In less than a half century, 45 years to be more accurate, the population increased to four thousand million.

Think about it

1. How are the two graphs similar?
2. State what will happen to the human graph in the next 15 years.
3. a) Based on the data in the graph, sketch a graph to show how the human population might look from year 0 to year 3000.
   b) If this kind of growth continues, what kinds of problems do you think will result? Can you think of any ways of preventing or resolving these problems?

Fig. 26

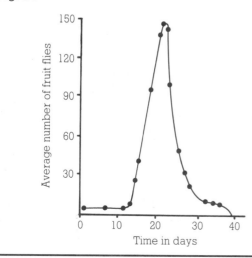

Fig. 27

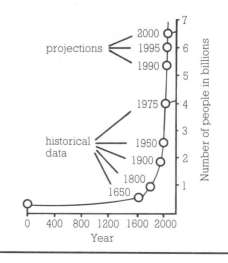

2.20 You Can't Cheat the System

Section 2.1 of this chapter was called "Oh, to Be Independent!" At certain times in our lives, being independent is important to all of us. However, as you have seen in this chapter, becoming truly independent is an impossible goal. You depend on family, friends, possessions, and natural elements to keep your life running smoothly. Every organism and every non-living part of the environment depends on some organism for its continuation. If one link in the vast food web is broken, many organisms may be affected, and some may die. If we humans pollute the Earth, our air, soil, and water may be poisoned; and we, and all other organisms, will suffer.

You do have choices about how you live and how responsibly you depend on your environment. By learning about the operation of ecosystems, you are placing yourself in a position to co-operate with others in making wise choices and solving the urgent problems our world faces. In Earth's huge but limited ecosystem, there's no such thing as independence.

It's a Fact
In 1986, 481 678 people visited Algonquin Park. The park has 765 345 ha and 1385 campsites. Of the people who visited in 1986, 177 614 camped overnight.

Fig. 28 Learning how organisms depend on each other is a step toward helping to solve environmental problems.

2.21 Chapter Summary

- Communities include both living (biotic) and non-living (abiotic) components.
- The place where an organism lives is its habitat.
- The way an organism obtains its food requirements is its niche.
- Populations are groups of individuals of the same species living together at the same time.
- Populations can change by emigration, immigration, natality, or mortality.
- All organisms need food to carry out life's functions.
- Producers can make their own food supply through photosynthesis, by using sunlight, water, and carbon dioxide.
- Consumers must rely on other organisms for their food requirements.
- Decomposers are special consumers who break down other organisms into simpler molecules.
- Food chains show how energy in food is passed on from one organism to another.
- The intermingling of many food chains is a food web.
- Quadrats are enclosed areas used for studying communities.
- Sampling is done to estimate the number of organisms in a given area.
- Graphing population and other kinds of data allows predictions to be made about the environment.

2.22 Are You Ready to Go On?

Do not write in the textbook.

1. Why are both biotic and abiotic components studied in ecology?

2. How does an ecosystem differ from a community?

3. How does a carnivore differ from a herbivore?

4. Why are producers essential in a food web?

5. Why would the number of plants in an ecosystem increase if the herbivores in the area decreased?

6. Insect larvae often eat different food from adult insects. How does this help the species to survive?

7. a) Why are lawns, farm field, and football fields considered to be open ecosystems?
   b) Select one of the above ecosystems and list
      i) 5 biotic components of the area
      ii) 4 abiotic components of the area

8. How does the closed mini-ecosystem set up in the laboratory differ from open ecosystems?

9. How do predators help keep a balance in many ecosystems?

10. List the steps you would take to calculate the population of a dominant plant in an area that is 10 m^2.

11. Analysis of a swamp area indicated the following organisms either live there or frequent the area: cattails, aquatic plants, duckweed, swamp grass, water lilies, snails, mosquito larvae, diving beetles, giant water bugs, frogs, dragonflies, minnows, perch, herons, redwing blackbirds, sparrows, mice, hawks, raccoons, owls, willow trees, pine

trees, and wild flowers such as dandelions and timothy grass.

a) Make up 3 food chains from the given information (Be sure to place the arrows in the right direction).
b) Make up 1 food web for the area (Be sure to place the arrows in the right direction). Explain the transfer of energy in this food web.
c) What would be the effect on the swamp area if there were
  i) no hawks in the area
  ii) no snails in the area
  iii) decreased aquatic plants?

12. This study concerns a population of voles, over a period of ten days. On the horizontal axis, select equal divisions and number them from 0 to 10, so that this scale covers most of the open space. DON'T CROWD THE NUMBERS TOGETHER. On the vertical axis, you will be putting the number of voles. Select a value for the squares on the graph which will allow you to spread out values as much as possible.

Day	Number of voles
0	15
1	15
2	21
3	24
4	23
5	23
6	22
7	14
8	14
9	13
10	9

a) Plot the information on a graph.
b) What has caused the change which is shown on the second day?
c) What has caused the change which is shown on the seventh day?

13. Select the answer for each question which makes the statement correct. Write the correct answer in a complete sentence in your notebook.

a) _____ are a biotic component of a community.
  i) rocks ii) winds iii) lakes iv) plants
b) A quadrat is
  i) the wind factor in an ecosystem.
  ii) a given area in an ecosystem.
  iii) a number of plants in an ecosystem.
  iv) a number of animals in an ecosystem.
c) Producers in a biotic community
  i) make their own food.
  ii) eat plants.
  iii) break down dead animals.
  iv) use oxygen and water to make sugar.
d) Herbivores in a biotic community
  i) make their own food.
  ii) eat plants.
  iii) break down dead animals.
  iv) use oxygen and water to make sugar.
e) Decomposers in a biotic community
  i) make their own food.
  ii) eat plants.
  iii) break down dead animals.
  iv) use oxygen and water to make sugar.
f) An example of an omnivore is
  i) a dandelion.
  ii) fungus.
  iii) a raccoon.
  iv) a flea.
g) An increase in population is caused by
  i) mortality and natality.
  ii) mortality and emigration.
  iii) immigration and emigration.
  iv) immigration and natality.
h) Which of the following is the correct sequence for a food chain?
  i) owl → mouse → grass
  ii) grass → mouse → owl
  iii) mouse → owl → grass
  iv) mouse → grass → owl

Contents

Chapter Three

Beyond the School Yard

3.1 You Can't Live Without It

Everywhere you look, advertisers are trying to convince you
that you can't live without the products they are selling.
However, the things you really can't live without are free.
You need Earth, air, and water in order to live. All three
combine to produce the two main types of ecosystems —
terrestrial (land) and aquatic (water). The more you know
about these, the more able you are to make responsible
decisions concerning the future of specific ecosystems. In this
chapter, you will have the opportunity to investigate both
terrestrial and aquatic ecosystems in your area.

Fig. 2 Aquatic ecosystems offer
some interesting data.

3.2 **Some Terrestrial Ecosystems**

A terrestrial ecosystem is an area that has land (soil or rock) as its main base. It may be as small as a handful of soil or as large as the Sahara Desert. Sometimes terrestrial ecosystems have very little soil to support the growth of vegetation. Barren mountain tops or barren rock areas, such as those found in the Canadian Shield, are examples. Other terrestrial ecosystems have sufficient soil to support the growth of many types of vegetation. Many animals can exist and maintain the food chain in areas with a lot of vegetation.

Fig. 3 *A common Canadian ecosystem*

The photo shows a common sight in Canada. The dominant plant may be wheat, corn, or hay. This type of ecosystem provides the basis for many food chains. Many animals, such as insects, rodents, and humans are part of this ecosystem.

Fig. 4

Forests cover a large portion of Canada. The dominant
producer may be pine, spruce, maple, or oak trees. This type
of ecosystem also forms the basis of food webs for different
kinds of animals than the ploughed field. In these areas, many
birds and larger mammals would be found, as well as many
rodents.

In this ecosystem, there are primary plants, lichens, and moss, which eventually break down the rock to produce soil for other plants. Animals in the food webs that rely on these plants are primarily insects. The insects form part of a much larger food web.

Fig. 5

Fig. 6 In western Canada, mountain ecosystems exist above the tree line. In these areas, plants grow to a limited height. Animals such as mountain goats live on the vegetation in these areas.

FEEDBACK

1. List three similarities in all of the ecosystems pictured.
2. a) Select the ecosystem that you think would have the largest number of organisms in its food web.
   b) Make up a food web of that ecosystem.
   c) Why can this area support more animals in the food web?
3. How can transient animals (those in the area only occasionally) affect the available food in a forested area?

Summer jobs in the outdoors

Camping, hiking and fishing are pleasant recreational activities. Our many national, provincial, and private camps and parks provide us with a variety of sites where we can carry out these activities. But none of these activities would be so enjoyable without the camp and park staff who work together to make our parks and camping areas very suitable for us to enjoy. Most of our parks are staffed by permanent staff but each summer there are positions available for interested high school students to earn money in an enjoyable setting. Each park offers different opportunities to employees. One such opportunity is assistant to the wilderness skills programs. People who work in these areas assist in programs such as canoeing skills, backpacking skills, food planning for extended canoe and hiking trips, as well as alerting people to safety skills that will help them enjoy their holiday. Information attendants may be involved in registering campers, issuing camping permits, or attending the entry gates to many parks.

Maintenance crews are always needed, since areas suitable for outdoor recreation must always be

Fig. 7 *Summer jobs in the outdoors are a good way to find out if a permanent career in the outdoors would appeal to you.*

well maintained. People on maintenance crews, could spend time canoeing into remote areas to campsites to remove litter and provide wood for campfires. Students with clerical and computer skills might find a job in a park office during the peak season.

Junior forest rangers are employed each summer to go to Northern Ontario's forested areas. Students in these jobs work at clearing brush, planting trees, and other activities to help maintain our forests.

Often these summer jobs can lead to permanent employment once students graduate. Think about these chances — Will this be you?

3.3 Who Lives on This Land?

You have already analysed a small terrestrial ecosystem. You gathered data by using your senses of sight, smell, and touch. An analysis that is based on properties that can't be measured is called a **qualitative analysis**. You also gathered data by counting, measuring, and testing to support the data base. An analysis in which you record specific numbers and measurements is a **quantitative analysis**. Both types of analysis are used to gather information about different ecosystems.

You are now ready to do an expanded version of the field work you did near your school. In this investigation, you can gather data from one or more of several different areas such as open fields, shrub areas, marsh lands, wooded areas, and barren rock areas.

Fig. 8

Find out

What relationships exist between plants and animals in a given terrestrial ecosystem?

You need

- data book
- identification books
- string — marked off
- measuring devices
- plastic bags
- soil augers
- thermometers

Try this

Abiotic Data
1. Set up a quadrat in the designated area.
2. *Record these abiotic factors of the ecosystem:*
   - soil depth using a soil auger
   - soil profile — texture of the soil you removed (colour, feel, amount)
   - depth of litter (if applicable).
   - temperature of the soil
   - temperature of the air
   - direction of the sun
   - wind direction
   - percentage of shade in the area (make an estimate)
   - diameter of the five largest trees in the area.
   - height of ten saplings in the area.

Biotic Data

1. *Record these biotic factors of the ecosystem.*
   - Use the quadrat mapping method to record the location and percentage of the major plants.
   - Note which plants seem most likely to grow close together.
   - Estimate the number of organisms in the quadrat. (Be sure to look under leaves, in soil litter, etc.).
   - Use the data gathered to sketch the dominant plant.
   - Record evidence of animals present. What evidence indicated their presence?
   - Place on your quadrat map the location of abiotic factors such as rocks, barren soil, etc.

Keep all these data for future reference.

What happened?

It is difficult to analyse data in a short field trip, but if you have recorded all the information carefully, you can determine relationships that exist amongst organisms in the ecosystem.

1. List the different plants in the area.
2. Select the dominant plant in your area.
   a) Why do you consider this to be the dominant plant?
   b) What is the height of this plant?
   c) What other organisms seem to benefit from the presence of this plant?
   d) Show how this plant relates to other organisms in the immediate area.
   e) State the environmental conditions (at the time of your field trip) that this plant seems to tolerate.
   f) From your data, select the animals that you consider to be dominant in this area.
   g) Why is it more difficult to state the dominant animal rather than the dominant plant?
   h) What type of competition does this animal appear to have?
3. Plants and animals interrelate in all areas.
   a) Make a food web for the area.
   b) What effect did the abiotic factors have on this area?

Now you know

Data gathered by quadrat sampling can be used to determine interrelationships amongst plants and animals in any given area. This is one of the techniques used by our government environmental agencies. They monitor areas over a period of time to see what changes occur. It is important to study interrelationships because one organism in the ecosystem is never affected alone. Effects spread and multiply as you move up through the system. (You saw evidence of this when you constructed your food chains and food webs in Chapter 2.) An environmental study group may note a change in the plant and insect life in the soil under study over a similar period of time. The group can then draw conclusions about what in the soil is causing the changes to occur and where it comes from. Predictions can be made about the probable increase in the effect as changes move through the levels of the ecosystem. The group can point out the source of the trouble and make recommendations to prevent its spread.

SUPERSLEUTH

Record and compare the data of three different terrestrial ecosystems.
a) How are the organisms of the area similar?
b) How do they differ?

3.4 Some Aquatic Ecosystems

All living organisms depend on water to stay alive. No terrestrial ecosystem could exist without it. Even the lichens and moss on the barren rocks need a small amount.

While many animals spend part of their lives in both types of ecosystems, some organisms live their entire lives in water. Just as a variety of terrestrial ecosystems exist to support life, so do a variety of aquatic ecosystems.

It's a Fact
Aquatic ecosystems occupy more space on Earth than do terrestrial ones.

Fig. 9

Canada is surrounded on three sides by oceans. The oceans form the world's largest aquatic ecosystem. They contain dissolved minerals which give them their salt water characteristics. Plants, animals, and microscopic organisms which live in the oceans have adapted to the salt environment. These organisms could not survive in a fresh water ecosystem.

Rivers and streams flowing inland form another type of aquatic ecosystem. Depending on the depth and the speed of the water flow, these streams and rivers are the habitats of a great variety of consumers. Fish such as trout are found in many of our northern rivers. Many of our streams and rivers are used for pleasure fishing and canoeing.

It's a Fact
Many very large rivers in Canada, such as the St. Lawrence, have been used for transportation.

Fig. 10

Although we refer to ponds and lakes as standing water, they do flow, but their current is slow. Many ponds and lakes are fed by rivers or streams and usually have an outlet. Lakes are larger bodies of water than ponds. Ponds, on the other hand, may be very small and may evaporate after a short period of time.

Fig. 11

It's a Fact
The largest inland lakes in Canada are the Great Lakes.

Fig. 12 This beaver dam has had a major effect on its surroundings.

Some ponds and lakes are surrounded by cattails and rushes. Cattails and rushes are a type of producer usually found in a corner of a lake with a slow flow of water. Sometimes animals, such as beavers, create a situation where flooding occurs and the trees in the area die. Such swamps are the habitats of many different types of consumers.

All aquatic ecosystems are based on water. The plants, animals and microscopic organisms that live there are often very different from those in a terrestrial ecosystem.

The following chart lists just a few of the living organisms found in some aquatic ecosystems.

	Producers	Consumers
OCEANS	diatoms microscopic algae phytoplankton seaweed	sharks tuna whales fish sea turtles shell fish coral shore birds
STREAMS/ RIVERS	green algae diatoms water moss phytoplankton	insects (many varieties) fish mussels, snails, crayfish frogs, turtles birds (ducks)
PONDS/ LAKES	green algae water moss submerged plants pond weeds duckweed cattails and bullrushes	fish mussels, snails frogs and turtles birds insects larvae

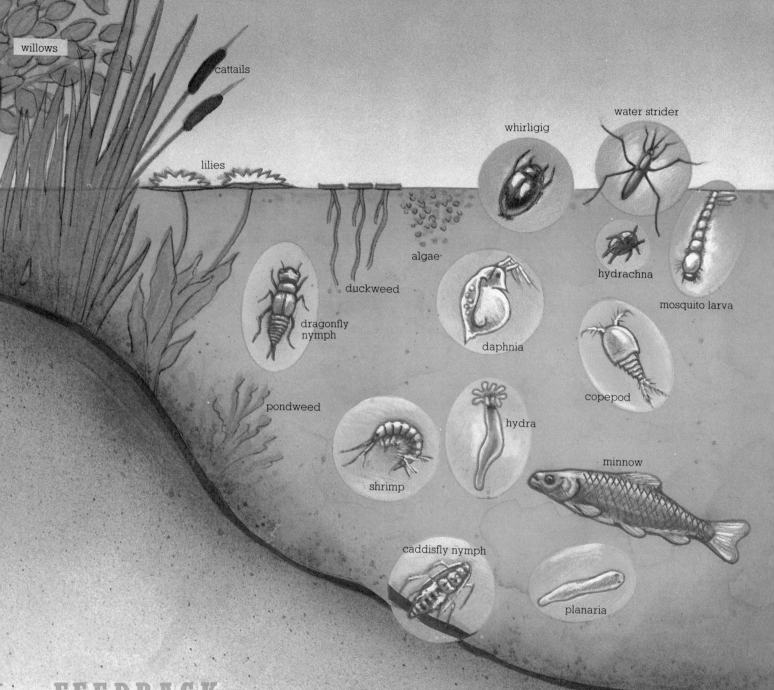

willows

cattails

lilies

whirligig

water strider

algae

duckweed

hydrachna

mosquito larva

dragonfly
nymph

daphnia

copepod

pondweed

hydra

minnow

shrimp

caddisfly nymph

planaria

FEEDBACK

1. How do oceans differ from other aquatic ecosystems?
2. What determines a stream's inhabitants?
3. Why are marshes and swamps aquatic ecosystems?
4. Give two reasons why we should maintain aquatic ecosystems.

THIS CONCERNS YOU

Does the Earth Owe Us?

By Jack Miller, Toronto Star
(Reprinted with permission — The Toronto Star Syndicate)

Life, including the human race, is not a parasite, sponging thanklessly off Mother Earth. This once was a battered, barren world, no better than today's Mars or Venus.

We made it unique, by generating a lower atmosphere in which life could flourish. And for at least 3.5 billion years, all the things that grow, fly, swim, crawl, love and wonder, have worked together unknowingly and automatically, as a master control team, keeping Earth's surface lush and alive, like the fur on a cat.

So says The Gaia Hypothesis, a scientific bombshell conceived around 1972 by lone-wolf British scientist James Lovelock.

The Gaia Hypothesis was named after the ancient Greek goddess of Earth. The idea slowly formed in Lovelock's mind after he noticed that unlike other planets, Earth's atmosphere is chemically unstable. Our air is almost all free-floating nitrogen and oxygen, with a little

Fig. 13 *Did human life help to create this scene? Do you honestly believe it will remain like this, unless humans change their polluting ways?*

carbon dioxide (CO_2) and traces of methane, ammonia, and a few other interesting gases.

The mystery lay in the fact that oxygen, in particular, is a very reactive gas. It hates the single life.

Turn oxygen loose with nitrogen, as we find them in our air here, and before long you would expect to find enormous amounts of nitrogen oxides. Similarly, oxygen combines with methane, which has carbon in it to produce CO_2.

So what's different about Earth? Life is here — that's what. Green plants take in carbon dioxide and use its carbon to make wood for their branches, throwing the oxygen back into the air. Methane, one of the trace gases, keeps getting produced by bacteria living in swamps. It bubbles into the air as fast as natural chemical

processes are wiping out the methane that was there before.

In the 1960s, the U.S. National Aeronautics and Space Administration hired Lovelock to help dream up ways for its Viking spaceship to search for signs of life on Mars, where Viking was to land in 1976. The British researcher decided there was already lots to indicate that Mars could have no life on it. All that carbon dioxide, sitting undisturbed in its atmosphere, was a strong sign.

Soon after, Lovelock started working with Boston University's Lynn Margulis, a top microbiologist. Together they developed the concept that life had changed the lower atmosphere on Earth in a way that not only made life more feasible, but kept adjusting to outside factors to keep it that way.

74

Millions of years ago, for example, the sun is believed to have been only three-quarters as hot as now. Gaia says life let the CO_2 level in the air go much higher than today, creating a stronger greenhouse effect, to make the planet as warm as it is now.

Later, as the sun warmed, the planet's living surface adjusted, reducing the CO_2 and the greenhouse, to keep the heat from rising until the seas boiled off. Also, all that free oxygen made possible the ozone layer, which protects life here by blocking the sun's ultraviolet rays (an ozone molecule is three oxygen atoms bound together).

The Lovelock-Margulis work drew some fans they had not expected. Polluters of the atmosphere used it to argue that life would adjust for the mess they were making of the air.

Most scientists tended to brush off the idea until recently. Making Gaia a symposium subject at the American Association for the Advancement of Science convention February 1988 was a sign that attitude is softening.

Think about it

1. a) What is a hypothesis?
   b) What does the Gaia Hypothesis state?
   c) Why has this hypothesis led to further scientific research?

2. a) What gases make up our present atmosphere?
   b) What useful properties does oxygen have that make it different from other atmospheric gases?

3. How do green plants help maintain a balance in our atmosphere?

4. a) How does our lower atmosphere support life?
   b) Why is it believed that there is no life on Mars?

5. a) How has the greenhouse effect been beneficial to us?
   b) If temperatures continue to rise, would you predict that the greenhouse effect will continue to be beneficial to us? Explain.

6. Some polluters have used the Gaia Hypothesis to argue that life will adjust for the mess they are making of the air.
   a) Do you think this is a reasonable argument?
   b) Why might this be a dangerous argument, even if the Gaia Hypothesis were true?

Fig. 14 *We are all familiar with scenes such as this one. Plants did not create this scene, nor did animals. Humans are the only ones capable of creating this kind of mess.*

Investigation

3.5 What's in the Water?

Aquatic ecosystems are studied a little differently from terrestrial ecosystems. The water environment does not exist entirely on its own, so you usually include the surrounding land in your study.

You need
- data book
- identification books
- string
- measuring devices
- plastic bags
- small container for water samples
- soil augers
- sieves
- pH paper
- thermometer

Find out

What relationships exist between producers and consumers in a given aquatic ecosystem?

	Station A	Station B	Station C
a) Temperature of water			
b) Temperature of air			
c) Depth of water			
d) Average depth			
e) Turbidity (muddiness) of water			
f) Direction of flow of water			
g) Source where water flows into the main body			
h) Point where water flows out of the main body			
i) pH			
j) Wind direction			

DO NOT WRITE IN THE TEXTBOOK

(Before recording any data about the area observe the appearance of the landscape. Is the area flat? Are there trees? Is it a rocky area? Since it is not always easy to find the depth of the water in the middle, much of the data-gathering is done near the shoreline.)

Abiotic Data

1. *Copy the chart on page 76 into your notebook and complete it as you do your study.* (Keep these data for future use)

Biotic Data

1. Take a sample of the water in a light-coloured bowl and examine any aquatic organisms present. You must be very patient and careful while doing this. *Sketch the appearance of these animals. Take several samples and state which organisms seem to be most plentiful in the body of water from which you took your sample.*
2. Take some water samples to be examined later in the lab under the microscope.
3. Set up a quadrat from 2 m into the water to 5 m past the water's edge.
   Record at 50 cm intervals the vegetation that is present.
4. Do a soil analysis and temperature recording as you did in the terrestrial field work. *Record all data.*
5. Look for evidence of animals in the area. *Record your findings.*

Fig. 15

6. *Using the technique you used to prepare quadrat maps in Chapter 2, sketch the pond and the area surrounding it. What happened?*

What happened?

1. Make up a chart from the field data containing the following information:
   • Name the major producer from each station.
   • the major consumer from each station.
   • abiotic factors which seemed to influence the presence of producers and consumers

	Producers	Consumers	Abiotic factors
Station A			
Station B			
Station C			

continued

2. Draw three food chains from this area.
3. Draw a food web for the surrounding area.
4. Use the microscope to examine water samples taken from the different stations.
   a) What similarities are there amongst organisms?
   b) What are the major differences amongst organisms?
   c) Sketch three different organisms seen from the water samples.
   d) Describe how each of these organisms moves about in the water.
5. If you have visited both aquatic and terrestrial ecosystems on this field trip, compare them under the following headings.
   a) Overall appearance of the area.
   b) Dominant producers in the area.
   c) Size of the producers in the area.
   d) Dominant consumers in the area.
   e) Size of the consumers in the area.
   f) Abiotic factors which have an influence in the area.
6. In groups of two to four, select one of the following topics to be presented to the class. (Use data from your field work as well as reference books.)
   a) Producers in the area
   b) Insects in the area
   c) Birds and mammals in the area
   d) General terrain of the area
   e) Food web
   f) Human influence on the area.
   g) Abiotic factors in the area.
   h) Microscopic organisms

Be prepared to describe in detail size, shape, number and characteristics of your topic. Present your findings on Bristol board, accompanied by an explanation.

Now you know

You saw that it was necessary to look at interrelationships in a terrestrial ecosystem because no part of it stands alone. Similarly, problems such as the acidification of lakes can't be understood without looking at the land around them—the soil that holds the water and the trees on which rain falls. Studies of aquatic ecosystems provide data used in a variety of ways by our governments. One such study had far-reaching results. In the 1970s, there was controversy about whether or not phosphates from detergents were causing algae to bloom in the Great Lakes. The scientific data that were available at the time served to confuse rather than clarify the issue. Manufacturers insisted that phosphates were necessary as a cleaning agent and were reluctant to discontinue their use. By adding phosphorus to one side of an experimental lake, scientists proved beyond doubt that it did indeed cause algae to bloom. As a result, laws were passed requiring soap manufacturers to produce low-phosphate dishwashing and laundry soaps—a practical application of scientific principles that had a major, observable effect.

Fig. 16 *Phosphates are an environmentally hazardous addition to lake water.*

3.6 A Lake in a Test Tube

If you test a lake, how do you know what to measure your findings against? Where is your control? In Northern Ontario, that's where. There, in the Experimental Lakes Area (ELA), the Canadian Government has set aside 46 lakes and watersheds scattered over about 200 km². It's the only area of its kind in the world, and it has set the world standard for what acid rain means to fish, frogs, and bacteria.

When ELA scientists began studying the effect of acid rain on lakes, most people believed that it threatened only fairly small areas around smelters. The scientists were able to study what happens to all the elements of a lake's food chain as it gradually becomes acidic. They discovered that, while some fish were hardier than others, no fish reproduced when the water had a pH below 5.1. They also found that some organisms in the food chain were affected at lower rates of acidity than anyone had suspected.

When they studied the de-acidification of a lake, they discovered ''natural buffers,'' bacteria on the lake bottom, that actively work to de-acidify the lake, even when the acid readings are very high. This kind of information can only be obtained by experimenting with actual lakes. Thus, Canada is making a unique contribution to environmental studies worldwide and to the health of the ecosystem and that of the humans who share it.

At the beginning of this chapter, we said that you need Earth, air, and water in order to live. You have seen, in Chapters 2 and 3, how all the parts of our ecosystem interrelate. You now know that aquatic and terrestrial ecosystems interact with each other and depend on each other. It isn't possible to make a decision about one part of the system that doesn't affect the entire system in a large or a small way. The more responsibly we humans make decisions about the many aspects of our environment that concern us today, the cleaner and healthier will be the Earth, air, and water in our world and the world we leave for our children.

Fig. 17 *This is one of Canada's experimental lakes. Here, scientists add phosphorus to one side of the lake to study its effects.*

3.7 Chapter Summary

- The two main ecosystems are aquatic and terrestrial.
- A terrestrial ecosystem has land (soil and rock), such as mountains and fields, as its base.
- An aquatic ecosystem has water, such as rivers, lakes, streams, and oceans, as its base.
- Quantitative analysis is based on specific numbers and measurement.
- Qualitative analysis is based on properties that can't be measured.
- Quadrat analysis can be used to determine interrelationships among plants and animals in a given area.
- Sampling from both aquatic and terrestrial ecosystems can be used as a basis for the summary of the interrelationships in given areas.

3.8 Are You Ready to Go On?

Do not write in the textbook.

1. a) Compare qualitative and quantitative analysis.
   b) When is each type of analysis used?
2. How do the producers in a forested area differ from the producers in a field.
3. How are mountains similar to the lichens on a rock?
4. How are data gathered from terrestial ecosystems?
5. List seven abiotic factors about which data can be gathered.
6. List two groups of biotic components about which data can be gathered.
7. a) What producers in oceans, rivers, and streams are similar?
   b) What producers in oceans, rivers, and streams are different?
8. List two producers found in ponds and lakes.
9. a) Copy the following chart into your notebook and use it to compare the aquatic and terrestrial areas.

	Aquatic	Terrestrial
Type of Ecosystem		
Abiotic Factors to be Measured		
Biotic Factors to be Measured		
Inhabitants (Producers) (Consumers)		

b) From your chart construct three food chains for the area. Expand and combine these three food chains into a food web.

c) Select the abiotic factor that has the greatest effect in the area. Why is this the most influential abiotic factor?

10. Why is it more difficult to gather data from aquatic ecosystems than from terrestrial ones?

11. You have just won a prize in a lottery. In order to qualify for your one million dollars you must be able to prove with substantial evidence that you can analyse both aquatic and terrestrial ecosystems. You will be told that you are to investigate an area along a lake shoreline that has a swamp/marsh area in the north end and a stream flowing from the south end. The shoreline has a sandy area on the east side and there is an open field with a wooded area on the west.
    a) Sketch a map to show the area.
    b) How does the swamp area affect the plants and animals of the lake?
    c) What animals might be found in the water areas?
    d) Make up a possible food web for the area.
    e) Water is the major abiotic factor in this area. List three other abiotic factors that could be measured.
    f) How could you find out how many trees on the property could be used for lumber?
    g) What adaptations do the consumers in this area have to make for winter survival?

12. Look at this sketch of an area in Northern Ontario:

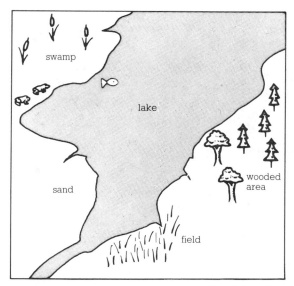

Each symbol represents 10 organisms.

symbols				
	poplar trees		fish — Bass	
	coniferous trees		hay field	
	cattails		frogs	

1. Calculate the number of trees in this area. How do the coniferous trees differ from the deciduous trees in number.

2. There has been a fungus disease in the water. How might this affect the number of fish in the water?

3. List five consumers that may visit this area and give one reason for their visit.

4. a) Make a sketch of how this area might look sixty years from now if a beaver moved into the area ten years from now.
   b) Show in your diagram what possible changes may take place.
   c) Select one producer and one consumer that the beaver would affect most and state why you made that choice.

Contents

Chapter Four

Keep It Clean

4.1 Risky Business

Many of the activities we enjoy involve some kind of risk to ourselves or others. Some risks are so small in relation to the benefit or enjoyment, we don't even consider them; while others are so great, we weigh them very carefully against the benefits before deciding on a course of action.

When the course of action involves chemicals, we have to be extremely cautious. Chemicals have brought many benefits to our lives, but with these benefits come risks, and the risks, although sometimes great, aren't always easy to observe. Some develop after many years; some develop when chemicals come into contact with other substances; some develop because certain chemical combinations are almost indestructible and stay around when we no longer need or want them.

In this chapter, you will find out about some of the benefits and risks that come with the use of chemicals. You will find out how the people in the photos are damaging their environment, and why they (and you) should care.

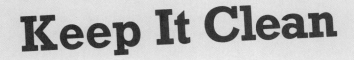

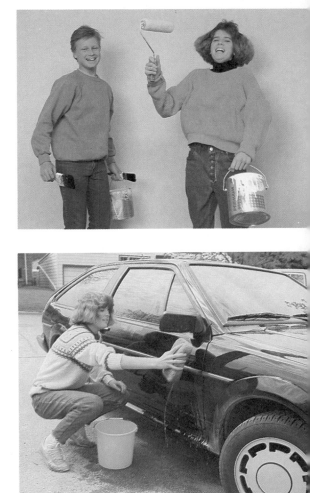

Fig. 2 All of these activities involve some risk to the environment. In some small way, they all contribute to damaging the Earth we live on, the air we breathe, or the water we drink. Does it matter?

4.2 Acids and Bases

We take for granted many of the benefits of chemicals in our lives but it isn't as easy to be aware of the risks. We need to learn something about chemicals and the way they work in order to be able to make decisions about whether to use them or not.

Science classifies information about chemicals. We can use one of the ways chemicals are classified to help us understand more about them.

Fig. 3 All of the liquids in these photos are acids. You've probably used all of them. In edible products, acids add sourness to the taste.

Fig. 4 You've probably used dishwashing liquid which is a **base**. Chemicals known as bases or **alkalis** feel slippery and produce a soapy taste. (However, it is important to remember NEVER to taste anything in the lab.)

Scientists call the measure of how acidic or basic a substance is its **pH**. To detect an acid or base, a chemist uses an **indicator** or a **pH meter**. An indicator is a substance which changes its colour when placed in an acid or base. Litmus and bromthymol blue (BTB) are common indicators in the lab. Some household substances such as tea, beet juice, and wine can also be used as indicators since they change colour when added to an acid or a base.

Here are some common substances and their pH measures. Numbers below 7 on the pH scale indicate an acid; and numbers greater than 7 indicate that the substance is a base.

stomach fluid	1.7	ACID
vinegar	2.5	
lemon juice	2.6	
wine	3.7	
tomatoes	4.5	
coffee	5.1	
milk	6.5	
blood	7.4	
seawater	7.8	
strong ammonia	11.0	
limewater	12.8	BASE

Many common substances belong to the class of chemicals known as acids or bases, so having a convenient way of detecting these groups is helpful.

Investigation

4.3 Identifying Acids and Bases

If you want to know whether a substance is an acid or a base, find out how an indicator reacts with it. If you test your indicator with a substance that you know is an acid or a base, you can observe how the indicator reacts. You can then use it to test an unknown substance.

Find out

A. How do indicators react with acids and bases?
B. How can indicators be used to identify unknown substances?

You need

- 50 mL beakers (8)
- hydrochloric acid
- distilled water
- litmus paper
- sodium hydroxide solution
- vinegar (ethanoic acid)
- fruit juice
- bromthymol blue (BTB)
- dishwasher detergent
- ginger ale
- phenolphthalein
- drain cleaner
- safety goggles

SAFETY ALERT!

Wear safety goggles. Keep chemicals off your skin: acid is corrosive.

Try this

1. *Copy the chart into your notebook. Above each indicator, write its colour before being tested.*
2. Into each of eight beakers, place 5 mL of the substance to be tested. Add 20 mL of distilled water to each sample.

Chemical	Litmus	Phenolphthalein	Bromthymol Blue	Acid/Base/ Neutral
hydrochloric acid				
sodium hydroxide solution				
vinegar (ethanoic acid)				
fruit juice				
ginger ale				
drain cleaner				
dishwasher detergent				
distilled water				

DO NOT WRITE IN THE TEXTBOOK

3. Add a few drops of the indicator to each beaker. If the indicators are already on pieces of paper, place a drop from the beaker on the paper. *Record any colour changes in the table.*

hydrochloric acid and water	ginger ale and water	drain cleaner and water	vinegar and water

sodium hydroxide solution and water	dishwasher detergent and water	distilled water	fruit juice and water

Fig. 5

4. Group the chemicals that you tested according to the colour changes that they made in the indicators. The chemicals that made the same changes as hydrochloric acid are acids. The chemicals that produced the same changes as sodium hydroxide are bases. Chemicals that produced no changes are classified as neutral.
5. *Record in a list the chemicals which are acids, bases, and neutral substances.*

What happened?

1. How can you recognize an acid?
2. How can you recognize a base?
3. What common products are acids? Have you used any today? Which ones?
4. What common products are bases? Have you used any today? Which ones?

Now you know

Acids and bases are very large groups of chemicals. To determine the presence of an acid or a base you can use an indicator, provided you know what the colour change in the indicator means.

Many sour-tasting foods contain acids. The acid in soda pop gives the drinks a sharp, crisp taste. Without it, they would be syrupy and unpleasantly sweet.

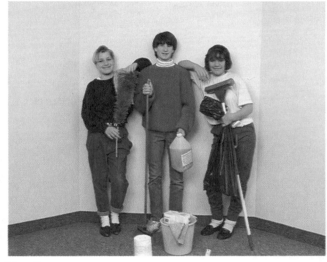

Fig. 6

Bases tend to feel and taste soapy. Many cleaning products that you often use in your home feel slippery. However, some products feel slippery because they contain oil. Just as acids and bases can easily be confused by their appearance, they can also be incorrectly identified by the way they feel.

SUPERSLEUTH

Obtain some other indicators from your teacher and test some food samples to see if they are acids or bases.

4.4 Using Acids and Bases

Acids and bases have many useful properties. However, they must be used carefully. The presence of even a small amount of an acid or a base can start a series of other reactions. Such chemical situations are described as ''trigger reactions.'' Some trigger reactions cause major changes in the environment.

An example of a trigger reaction involves the effect of acids on lakes. Slight changes in the acid content of a lake make tremendous differences in the ability of the lake to support animal and plant life.

Changes in the acid content of soil can also be crucial. To produce a beautiful lawn or a high-yield crop, soil must contain the needed nutrients. It must also be in a condition that will encourage plants to use the nutrients it contains. Different plants require varying levels of acid. If the soil has too much acid, much more fertilizer is required for a healthy crop. To farm efficiently, a farmer must measure the acid content of the soil. If needed, a substance called lime is spread on the soil to lower its acid content.

Investigation

4.5 Soil Tests

Designing tests to identify the presence and quantity of a chemical in a sample is an important area of scientific research. For the purpose of growing crops, soil must contain the nutrients plants need in order to grow. The main indicators of a soil's fertility are: how much nitrogen, phosphorus, and potassium it contains and its acidity.

Find out

A. How much nitrogen, phosphorus, and potassium are in a sample of soil?
B. How are the above nutrients affected by acid conditions?

You need

- potting soil
- 2 large containers (about 2 L)
- distilled water
- pH paper
- dilute sulfurous acid
- soil test kit
- filter paper
- funnel
- stirring rod
- safety goggles

SAFETY ALERT!

Wear safety goggles. Keep chemicals off your skin: acid is corrosive.

Try this

Part A

1. *Copy the table into your notebook.*

	Potting soil	Acid-washed potting soil
pH		
Nitrogen		
Phosphorus		
Potassium		

2. a) Prepare a sample of soil by adding 500 mL of soil to a large container and washing the soil with 500 mL of distilled water.
   b) Add the water to the soil and stir the mixture. Pour off (decant) the water through the filter paper, keeping the soil in the beaker. Repeat the washing twice more.

Fig. 8

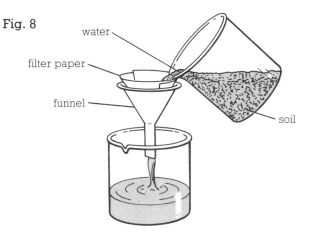

water
filter paper
funnel
soil

3. Follow the directions very carefully on your soil test kit to measure the content of nitrogen, phosphorus, and potassium. *Record the measurements in your chart.*

continued

Part B

1. Place 20 mL of soil into a small beaker. Add 30 mL of distilled water and stir. Let the mixture stand for 5 min. *Measure and record the pH of the water.*
2. To a large container add 500 mL of potting soil. Add 500 mL of sulfurous acid to the soil sample and stir the mixture. After 5 min pour off the dilute sulfurous acid. Repeat the acid wash twice more.
3. To the soil sample, add 500 mL of distilled water and stir the mixture. After 5 min pour off the water. Repeat the wash.
4. Analyse the acid-rinsed sample with the soil test kit for nitrogen, phosphorus, and potassium. *Record the measurements in your chart.*

What happened?

1. How did the nutrient content of the acid-washed sample compare to that of the other sample? Record your answer in your notebook.
2. What values did other students obtain?
3. What influence did the acid wash have on the nutrients in the soil sample?
4. What is one of the changes in the environment possibly caused by acid rain?

The ability of soil to support healthy plants depends on the nutrients available. Dilute acids remove these important chemicals more readily than does neutral water. The greater the acid content of the rain, the greater the damage will be.

The environment, which supports all living things, would be greatly altered if the soil were unable to nurture plants. Not only would the food chain be destroyed in that area, but the bare ground would then be easily eroded by wind and water.

4.6 Acids From The Fuels We Burn

North Americans, on average, use more energy per person than anyone else in the world. Much of this energy comes from fuel which is burned to heat or air condition the buildings they live and work in.

When a fuel is burned, the particles which make up the fuel combine with oxygen in the air. Heat is released and the products of burning, mainly carbon dioxide and water, are put back into the air we breathe. These two substances are not normally harmful to the environment. However, most, if not all, fuels contain impurities. The impurities in the fuel can react during burning and their products are also released. Because such huge amounts of fuel are used each day, the quantity of gas pollutants in our atmosphere is greatly magnified.

One of the more common impurities in fuel is sulfur. Sulfur combines with oxygen during burning to produce sulfur dioxide gas. The more sulfur the fuel contains, the more sulfur dioxide it will produce. Some kinds of coal, oil, and natural gas contain very little sulfur while others have a high sulfur content.

Sulfur dioxide gas is harmful to living things in two ways. The gas itself can kill living tissue. Since it is a gas, it can be spread over many areas by wind. When dissolved in water, it produces sulfurous acid. A major problem occurs when the gas dissolves in water vapour in clouds and then falls to the Earth as acid rain or snow. Sulfur dioxide is the gas largely responsible for acid rain, although oxides of nitrogen in car exhausts also play a part.

Acid rain damages the environment in several ways. Soil loses its ability to produce crops and plants die. Acid rain and snow also kill our lakes, dissolve buildings, and prevent maple trees from producing the sap needed for maple sugar. There have been attempts to protect the environment by building high smokestacks. This helps only the communities near the sulfur-producing companies, since the pollutants don't disperse harmlessly into the atmosphere but affect other communities both as a gas and as acid rain. In order to keep sulfur dioxide damage to a minimum, we have to keep as much of the gas as possible from getting into the air. We can do this either by washing it out of smokestack gases or by removing the sulfur from the fuel before it is burned.

Many new factories have installed **scrubbers**. Scrubbers clean the impurities from the products of burning so that fewer are dumped into the environment. However, scrubbers are very expensive to install, so older factories, especially, are not being fitted with them as quickly as they should be. This is true of coal-burning factories in the Ohio Valley in the United States, for example. The sulfur found in coal is very difficult to remove and, since many of the factories don't have scrubbers, they dump thousands of tonnes of sulfur dioxide annually into the atmosphere. In Canada, we experience it as acid rain.

Fig. 9

Sulfur can be removed more easily from some other fuels than it can from coal. In Canada, natural gas has sulfur removed from it before being carried by pipelines from the West to the East.

A great deal of money is being spent by industry to find out how to further reduce industrial pollutants. A balance is needed between the requirements to run a business and the critical need to lessen acid rain.

FEEDBACK

1. How are the risks of chemicals found in fuels magnified?
2. What is one method for cleaning dangerous chemicals from the gases produced during the burning of fuels?
3. Which gas is primarily responsible for acid rain?
4. What is the source of the sulfur dioxide?
5. How can the sulfur dioxide be kept out of the environment?
6. Why is a tall smokestack an inadequate solution to air pollution problems?
7. In a few sentences, describe why a balance is needed between the critical need for less acid rain and the great expense of removing dangerous chemicals from stack gases.

Fig. 10 Before the big smokestack was built in Sudbury, people even had difficulty in growing grass in their yards near the factories. Since the smokestack was built, Sudbury has become a beautiful city with plenty of greenery. The company using this stack has installed many devices to scrub impurities from the stack gases.

Chemical Technician

Are you interested in lab work. Do you want to work in the chemical industry? Then this could be you.

The chemical technician who works testing and analysing the properties of a substance begins training in high school. In addition to studying basic chemistry, a technician must also complete courses in physics and mathematics. After high school a two or three year program at a college or technical school is necessary. Finally, after being hired, the chemical technician continues learning on the job and through additional courses. As long as knowledge and technology keep changing, the technician's job will keep changing too.

Having worked for five years in a laboratory investigating the contents of samples, you, as a technician, may decide that you would like a change in your career. With your training and experience, you could easily move to different work in production units where you would operate a chemical process.

An alternative would be to become part of a technical sales team involved with the sale of manufactured products. Your

Fig. 11 *A chemical technician has a variety of interesting job possibilities to pursue that can involve further training and specialized skill development.*

laboratory experience will be helpful in understanding customers' needs. Having experience in lab work, you could trouble-shoot or assist in setting up a process to use your product. Customers not only pay for a product; part of their money pays for service that is part of a marketing strategy.

Another new direction your laboratory technician's training and experience could take you is into the field of public affairs and communications. Communicating technical information is an important part of most chemical companies' marketing strategies

today. Brochures, newspaper items, plant tours, all require the technical knowledge and experience for communicating with the public and customers. Many times business decisions have to be made by people who have limited technical knowledge. They need the technical expertise and communication skills of an experienced technician to make the best decision.

You may not have or want to have the same job for forty years. Training as a chemical technician provides experience which can lead to continued growth. Will this be you?

93

Investigation

4.7 Testing for Sulfur Dioxide

A problem can't be solved if no one knows it exists. Science can indicate existing problems and help with their solution. Scientists can detect the presence of dangerous pollutants such as sulfur dioxide. In this investigation, you will discover how the acid properties of sulfur dioxide can be used for its detection.

Find out

A. What are the properties of sulfur?
B. What are the properties of sulfur dioxide?

SAFETY ALERT

Wear safety goggles. Keep chemicals off your skin: acid is corrosive.

The following investigation can only be attempted when there is a fume hood or other safe means of removing the sulfur dioxide gas from the working area.

You need

- paper
- sulfur flowers
- distilled water
- deflagrating spoon
- fume hood
- gas bottle
- glass plate
- litmus indicator
- Bunsen burner
- beaker
- safety goggles

Try this

1. *Copy the chart below into your notebook.*
2. Place a small amount of solid sulfur onto a piece of paper.
3. Examine the easily-observed properties such as colour, odour, and texture. (A magnifying glass or microscope may help you see the individual particles.) *Write your observations in your chart.*
4. Mix a small quantity of the sulfur into a few millilitres of distilled water. Test the water to see if it shows acid or basic properties (see the previous investigation on page 86 for the method.) Does the sulfur produce an acidic, basic, or neutral solution? *Write your answer in your chart.*
5. Place a small quantity of sulfur in a deflagrating spoon. In a fume hood or other appropriate place, heat the sulfur using an open flame such as a Bunsen burner.
6. Notice carefully the colour changes in the sulfur as it is heated. *Describe the process below the chart in your notebook.*
7. When the sulfur begins to burn with a light blue flame, lower the deflagrating spoon into a bottle containing 5 mL of water. Keep the spoon out of the water. After 1 min, remove the spoon and extinguish the flame by immersing the spoon in a beaker of water.

Chemical	State	Odour	Colour	Texture	Acid Test
sulfur					
sulfur dioxide					

Fig. 12

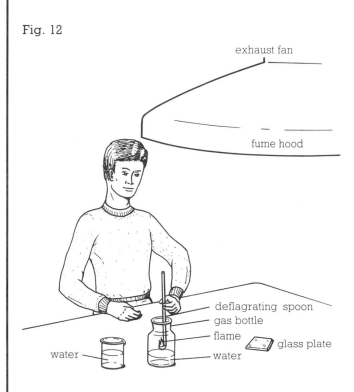

8. Cover the bottle with the glass plate and shake it to mix the water and the gases produced. This process is to help dissolve some of the sulfur dioxide gas in the water.
9. Test the contents of the bottle for the presence of an acid or base. *Record your observations in your chart.*

What happened?

1. Does sulfur or sulfur dioxide have the stronger odour?
2. Are the individual particles of the solid smaller or larger than those of the gas?
3. In water, which substance produces acid properties?

Now you know

The properties of elemental solid sulfur are different from those of the gas it forms when it is burned in air. When ignited, the yellow solid melts and darkens as it burns. The light blue flame is a pretty colour but the odour of the gas produced is certainly not pretty. You can often notice the sharp odour while lighting a safety match or when near some heavy industries.

The acid produced when the sulfur dioxide gas dissolves in water is largely responsible for the acid rain destruction of our lakes and forests. Sulfur as an element has no effect on water. The molecules of sulfur are very stable. The molecules of sulfur dioxide react easily with water to produce acid properties.

The properties of these two substances, pure sulfur and sulfur dioxide, are very different.

The property of acidity alone is not enough to identify sulfur dioxide, since many other compounds have the same property. However, the element that we burned was sulfur, so we are probably safe to assume that the compound that tested as acidic was sulfur dioxide. We need *both* pieces of evidence: a) that we burned sulfur, and b) that the resulting compound was acidic, in order to identify the compound as sulfur dioxide.

4.8 In Our Environment: Manufacture, Recycle, Reuse

Sulfur dioxide presents such a problem in our environment, we would NEVER burn it intentionally, right? Wrong! Sulfur IS an unwanted contaminant in fuels and certain mineral ores. But, it is also one of the world's most important industrial chemicals, used in producing fertilizer and sulfuric acid which is used in manufacturing detergents and synthetic rubber.

In order to manufacture sulfuric acid, sulfur must be burned to produce an oxide. As you have seen, sulfur is removed from natural gas before the gas is piped across Canada. Where possible, the sulfur used to manufacture sulfuric acid in Canada is obtained this way.

Fig. 13 This mountain of sulfur could be used to produce useful sulfuric acid.

It's very beneficial to us and our environment when the unwanted contaminant of one resource is the starting material for making another.

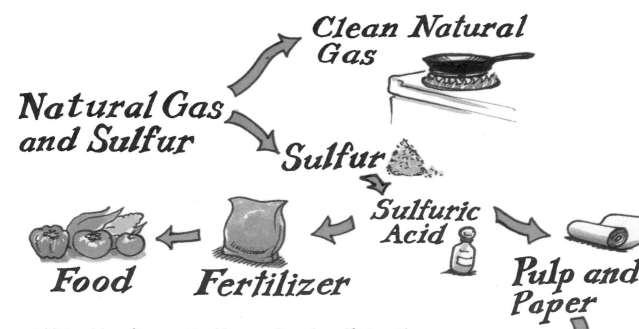

Additional benefits are gained by recycling the sulfuric acid which was used in a manufacturing process but was not totally consumed. The "spent" acid is remanufactured into a pure substance by the removal of impurities that it picked up during its first use.

Researchers look for ways of reusing the substances used in manufacturing processes. Many processes, such as burning sulfur and the manufacture of synthetic rubber, use water to remove heat. Where possible, the hot water that is produced is used to heat buildings and in other manufacturing processes. By reusing substances, removing impurities, and recycling processes, manufacturing industries reduce their expenses and also reduce the amount of material that must be disposed of.

FEEDBACK

1. For what purpose is sulfur burned intentionally?
2. What is one important source for the sulfur used in the manufacture of fertilizer?

4.9 Hard Water Isn't Always Ice

What is hard water? It is water containing dissolved minerals. Hardness in water is a natural result of the movement of rain water to the taps in our homes. When rain, which is naturally slightly acidic from the carbon dioxide in the air, washes over limestone, marble, or chalk rocks, some of the substances in the rocks dissolve. The dissolved minerals from the rocks are mainly calcium carbonate and magnesium carbonate. The degree of water hardness is determined by the amounts of these, and similar salts, which are in water. The more acidic the rain, the more rock it will dissolve. So water hardness is also determined by the acidity of the rain in the area.

The salts which make the water hard can precipitate out of the water under some conditions. The solids produced plug the pipes in our homes, line the kettles in which water is heated, and reduce the effectiveness of soaps.

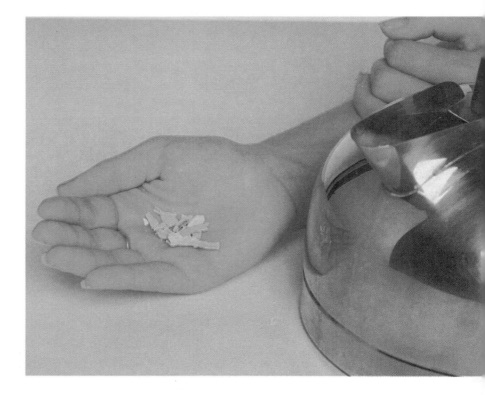

Fig. 14 Kettle scale forms inside a kettle when hard water is boiled in it over a period of time.

Hard water provides a good example of science producing risks and benefits. Science has contributed to the production of chemicals which help to make the water hard. To help solve the problem of washing with hard water, synthetic detergents were developed but this development was a mixed blessing. Detergents were able to wash well in hard or soft water because of the cleaning power of phosphates with which they were made. Unfortunately, the phosphates from these detergents didn't break down in the environment. They encouraged the growth of algae in the streams and lakes where the water eventually ended up. The algae grew so plentifully that some types covered enough lake surface to prevent sunlight from getting through, upsetting each lake's natural balance. Phosphates, which had at first seemed beneficial, had very harmful long-term effects.

For this reason, some governments have banned the use of phosphates in detergents. To get the benefits of detergents without damage to our environment, detergents were developed which could be easily broken down by living organisms.

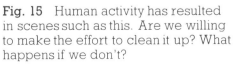

Fig. 15 Human activity has resulted in scenes such as this. Are we willing to make the effort to clean it up? What happens if we don't?

4.10 Water Hardness—Good and Bad

Find out

A. What are some properties of hard water?
B. What effect does acid rain have on hard water and soft water?

SAFETY ALERT!

Wear safety goggles. Keep chemicals off your skin: acid is corrosive.

You need

- 25 mm × 200 mm test tubes (4)
- 150 mL hard water (tap water)
- 150 mL soft water (distilled water)
- eyedropper
- soap solution
- test tube rack
- detergent solution
- dilute hydrochloric acid
- 150 mL beakers (2)
- pH meter and pH paper

Try this

1. *Copy the following table into your notebook.*

Condition	Soft water	Hard water
soap		
detergent		
pH		
pH of acid		

DO NOT WRITE IN THE TEXTBOOK

2. To 25 mL samples of hard and soft water in large test tubes, add 10 drops of soap solution. Shake the samples vigorously for 15 s and then compare the suds produced in each. *Record observations of the suds and appearance of the mixtures.* Do not throw away these samples until after step 3.

3. To two more 25 mL samples of hard and soft water in large test tubes add 10 drops of detergent solution. Shake the samples vigorously for 15 s and then compare the suds produced to each other and to the samples used in step 2. *Record your observations in your table.*

4. Measure the pH of 100 mL samples of hard and soft water. *Record the pH in the table.*

5. Add 10 drops of dilute hydrochloric acid to the samples of hard and soft water. Measure the pH of the water once again. *Record the measurements in your table.*

Fig. 16

hard water and soap solution   soft water and soap solution   hard water and detergent solution

soft water and detergent solution

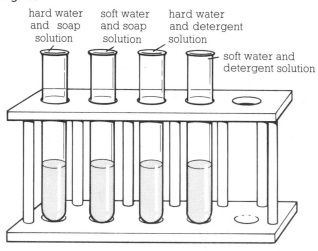

1. How does soap react with hard and soft water?
2. How does detergent react with hard and soft water?
3. How does the pH of hard and soft water behave upon the addition of dilute acid?

Now you know

Soaps react poorly in hard water, forming scum which can clog pipes and create a general nuisance.

Detergents which perform the same job as soaps work in both hard and soft water.

One beneficial property of hard water is its ability to buffer the change in pH resulting from the addition of a strong acid. Hard water requires more acid to effect the same pH change as soft water.

Acid rain is a much more complex solution than hydrochloric acid. It contains small amounts of all the dissolved gases and solids that are in the air. Thus, the results of acid rain on hard and soft water are similar but not exactly the same.

The effect of acid rain on lakes, buildings, trees and the rest of the environment is not fully known. But the more that is learned, the worse the problem seems to be.

SUPERSLEUTH

If quantities of acid rain are available, redo step 5, using the rain as your water sample.

4.11 What Goes Up Must Come Down

Fig. 17

Many different substances escape into the atmosphere every minute of every day. Some are the result of natural events, such as volcanic eruptions. Others are the result of chemical reactions, such as burning fuel for heating our homes. Many are the result of the chemical products that we use every day. Spray cans are used for paints, insecticides, waxes, oils, hair sprays, oven cleaners, and deodorants. Each spray is propelled out of its can by the pressure of a chemical. The products that you choose to use and the propellant that delivers them dump many chemicals into the air and cause many stresses on the world you live in.

Some substances dumped into the air, water, and land combine with each other in ways never imagined by scientists, producing new chemicals which are both unplanned and toxic

Fig. 18 *Scientists test various
surfaces to find out how they react to
acid rain.*

to the environment. An example of this happens when
sunlight reacts with nitrogen oxides from car exhaust to
produce ozone. Ozone is a form of oxygen that damages living
and non-living things alike. (Ozone at high altitudes absorbs
harmful solar radiation. We need it there. At the Earth's
surface, it becomes a problem).

Just as you use soap and water to clean dirt from your
hands, rain washes dirt and toxins from the air.

Because acid rain kills the living things in a lake it is
defined as a form of toxic rain. A common name for toxins in
the environment is pollutants.

People seldom intend to pollute the air. Pollution usually
results from lack of knowledge. Many people don't realize that
the manufacturing of products that make their work easier and
improve their lifestyle cause pollution. Such products are easy
to sell and become widely used. However, people now know
the importance of a clean, safe environment. One of the big
challenges facing the chemical industry is to keep from putting
more stress on the environment while making the products
that people want to buy. Sometimes the high costs of having
clean manufacturing methods keep people from acting quickly
enough to prevent pollution.

4.12 Pesticide or People Killer?

In 1874, a super bug-killer was developed that killed disease-carrying insects. Its wide use after World War II probably made tremendous growth of the world's population possible. In the 1950s and 1960s, this insecticide was used extensively throughout the world. It seemed the perfect answer to the problem of insects which ate crops and also carried disease. The insecticide was DDT.

Many years after its development, DDT was found to be collecting in the fat of birds and fish. DDT couldn't kill *all* insects, so birds and fish ate DDT in some of these surviving insects. The DDT killed some of the birds and fish, and others were no longer able to reproduce successfully. Also, because natural predators, as well as pests, were killed, the insect pests were then easily able to increase rapidly. DDT appeared to threaten human health and the ecosystem. Therefore, the Government of Canada banned the use of DDT in 1969, although permits for its use are still issued. Permits can be obtained only if other methods of killing pests have failed.

Many Third World countries have warm climates with huge numbers of insects which destroy crops and carry diseases. Therefore, making a decision to ban an inexpensive chemical insecticide like DDT would likely produce great hardship for the people who live there. Using DDT carries with it a risk to the environment, but, because of the benefits such a chemical has in reducing human suffering, it is still used widely.

Fig. 19 *This girl is not intentionally polluting the environment, but sprays like these do add toxic chemicals to the air.*

Think about it

1. Do you think people should continue to use DDT or should it be banned worldwide?
2. Under what conditions would you consider using a chemical that would kill black flies or mosquitoes?

Fig. 20

4.13 **Where Can I Dump This?**

Garbage . . . garbage . . . garbage . . . and more garbage. Every one of us is responsible for the huge piles of garbage that threaten to clog our cities and deface the countryside.

Many individuals give little thought to what happens to garbage. For most of us, a truck comes by and efficiently removes our garbage once or twice a week. The truck then takes the garbage to a landfill site or incinerator. At the landfill site the loads of refuse are soon covered. However, after a limited number of loads, the site is full and another must be found.

Fig. 21

Trying to locate landfill sites is a great problem for our local governments, since nobody wants one as a next-door neighbour.

Landfill sites have to be carefully chosen for several reasons. To reduce the need for transportation, disposal should ideally occur where the waste is made. This is not practical in our cities. Also, as rain water runs into dumps, it can dissolve toxins. These toxins can easily get into water supplies with disastrous results. Therefore, to minimize the risks of toxic substances, landfill sites must be a safe distance from drinking water supplies.

Burning garbage is perhaps the answer to full landfill sites. However, as you know, the products of burning are filling the air and threatening the existence of all living things.

Fig. 22

Fig. 23 *Residents in some communities are very concerned about incinerators that spew toxic gases into our air.*

Incineration might seem to be the best short-term solution to our garbage problem but in the long term, we must find new uses for the mountains of garbage we are making. Research can show us how to recycle much of what we now call waste. People are beginning to take the time to bundle up newspapers and put them out for collection and recycling. They are cleaning out used cans and bottles, removing their labels, and taking them to a local depot or depositing them in boxes provided by the community. People also need to change their buying habits and lifestyles, demanding that manufacturers use less packaging, so that there is much less need for both landfill and incinerators.

FEEDBACK

1. Why is garbage disposal a problem?
2. Why can't new landfill sites be opened if the old ones are full?
3. a) What could consumers persuade manufacturers to do?
   b) Why might the manufacturers be reluctant to co-operate?

Fig. 24

Fig. 25

Will This Be You?
Environmental Technical Specialist

Can you see yourself as a well-trained, well-respected, caring and responsible technical specialist? In this position, you will be working on spill reporting, the registration of waste products, and the disposal of industrial wastes. To earn your way to this level of employment, you will need to succeed in a college program in which you will learn basic chemistry, physics, and environmental studies. After completion of your diploma, you will gain experience and knowledge on the job in a large complex network of interconnecting chemical industries.

The company who hires you might do so by placing an advertisement such as this one:

In such a position, what would you be expected to do? The company above produces rubber used in chewing gum and vehicle tires. If hired your first work would be to learn the manufacturing processes and the testing processes that they use. Then, as an environmental technician, you would be responsible for taking samples of the air, water, and perhaps even the soil around the plant.

As a member of the technical team, you will work with experienced technologists and scientists. On the team your job will be to take samples and record data accurately. As you gain experience on the team you will be encouraged to carry out testing on the samples to analyse them for the kind and amount of specific compounds present. This will involve the basic skills learned in high school and college as well as on-the-job instruction in the use of specialized equipment.

If the process is disturbed and the product must be disposed of, it will be your job to offer advice to the team or carry out a solution to the problem.

If an accident results in a spill, you will have to protect people and the environment quickly. After the immediate danger is passed, you will have to monitor the effects of the spill, perhaps for years, keeping accurate records on testing as it is completed.

Your training will continue throughout your career; you will be sent on up-grading courses and conferences so that you can keep up-to-date. Your employer will want you to be able to give the best possible advice by collecting and understanding the most accurate information available. In return you will be well-paid and respected for your contribution.

A technical specialist does much more than collect and analyse samples. The specialist must understand the issues associated with his or her work. Will this be you?

Fig. 26 *An environmental technical specialist might find a rewarding job with a large chemical company.*

4.14 Testing: A Clean Bill of Health?

Doctors usually recommend regular checkups so that any problems can be solved when they are still in the early stages and easy to correct. A medical examination usually includes tests designed to give clues to how well your body is functioning.

Similarly, scientists test our environment. Tests are usually run on samples of air, water, and soil. The results provide clues to any problems that may be about to happen. Environmental technologists test with instruments and by observing what is living in the sample area. Some living species are very sensitive to certain parts of their environment. For example, the kinds of fish living in a lake or river provide clues to the health of the water. Some species of algae are present in water with low oxygen content. And, where sewage is in high concentration, coliform bacteria become more numerous.

A. Testing Our Air

Testing the air is one of the important tasks of government technologists. Making sure that the air is safe to breathe requires a great deal of sensitive and expensive equipment.

Measuring air quality is difficult, due to the problems of sampling and testing gases for small quantities of a chemical.

Some test kits are available to make measurements of air content but they are not very common.

Fig. 27 Cars pollute our environment. It's our responsibility to minimize the pollution by keeping the car well-maintained, using automobile anti-pollution devices, and leaving the car at home whenever possible.

SUPERSLEUTH

In many areas, the government agency that monitors the quality of the environment is pleased to demonstrate how it does its job. Contact the people who are responsible in your region and ask for a demonstration.

Alternatively, visit a government laboratory or the laboratory of a local business which monitors the environment.

B. Testing Our Water

We can test our water to see if it contains certain chemicals that living things may use as nutrients. However, if the water contains an excess of one substance, its balance is upset, and the water may become toxic. Some substances that scientists test water for are:

• Oxygen

Respiration requires the intake of oxygen so oxygen is important in determining what plants and animals the water can support. Some plants and animals will only live in oxygen-rich water while others thrive in low-oxygen environments.

Fig. 28 *Scientists test water to ensure that it contains a balance of substances and no unacceptable impurities.*

• Nitrogen

When living things grow, they require nitrogen. Nitrogen can be found in water as part of ammonia and as part of nitrates. If the nitrogen content in a water supply gets too high, it becomes a pollutant responsible for algal blooms. The nitrogen compounds in water can be formed by sewage, fertilizer run-off, and the decay of dead plants and animals.

• Phosphorus

Phosphorus, like nitrogen, is needed for plant growth, and also like nitrogen, it is a pollutant if its concentration becomes too high. High phosphorus content often leads to algal bloom. Phosphorus comes from many of the same sources as nitrogen: sewage, decaying plants and animals, fertilizer from farms and lawns.

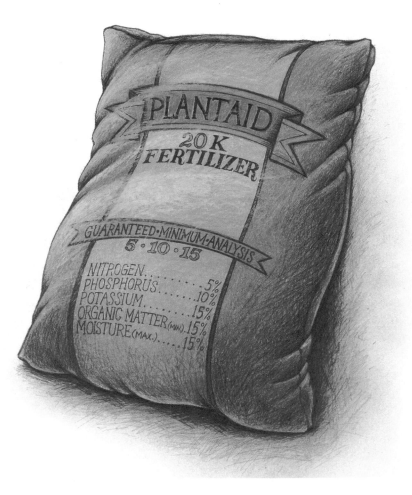

4.15 Water From Different Sources

Find out

What is the pH and the oxygen, nitrogen, and phosphorous content of several samples of water?

You need

- water test kits
- water samples
- 10 mL sulfurous or hydrochloric acid

Fig. 29

Try this

1. *Copy the following chart in your notebook.* (Make a chart for each different sample of water, such as from a stream, swamp, aquarium, lake, and lab water supply.)
2. Compare the measures of the various samples.

	oxygen	nitrogen	phosphorus	pH
Sample/ source				
Measure				
Trial 1				
Trial 2				
Trial 3				
Average				

DO NOT WRITE IN THE TEXTBOOK

3. Add 10 mL of dilute acid to the samples and retest to compare their contents.

What happened?

1. How did the results of samples from different sites compare?
2. What do the test results indicate about the sample?

Now you know

Water test kits can provide information about the health of any water sample. If you find evidence of an unsuspected toxin in a sample, make sure to notify the local government offices for further testing.

111

THIS CONCERNS YOU

What a Waste!

As we process our Earth's resources into what we want or need, we create waste. A carrot is a healthy snack but even the process of preparing the carrot for eating produces wastes. The water used to wash the carrot, as well as the peelings, must be disposed of. Most of the products we want require much more complex processes to produce than a carrot snack. Consequently, the wastes produced during these processes are much more hazardous.

Handling of hazardous waste is controlled by government regulations which cover:
- waste production
- storage
- packaging
- transportation
- disposal

Waste, such as sewage, which can't be recycled or reused must be treated so that it can't harm us or our environment. This process is called neutralizing.

With such careful regulation, why is it that we see so many headlines and hear so many news reports about spills that pollute our air and water? We read about residents in urban areas who are concerned about dangerous chemicals contaminating the soil on which their homes and gardens are built. These chemicals leak out of old landfill sites and infect the soil for many years. Toxic gases still belch out of old factory chimneys that don't have scrubbers to clean the gases that pass through them.

Just how are chemical wastes disposed of? The following pattern is used in the disposal of liquid chemical wastes. Before a waste is accepted for treatment, chemists and technicians measure its quantity and take samples while it is in the customer's plant. The samples are taken to laboratory facilities in Sarnia and analysed to determine if the waste can be treated and what the by-products of treatment will be. In addition to deciding how to neutralize the material, this analysis process provides a "fingerprint" for future identification.

Transportation of the material is part of the management program and so an appropriate vehicle and trained people must be hired to pick up and deliver the waste.

An identification code and the nature of the waste is sent to government specialists so they can monitor the waste.

On arrival of the tank trucks at the plant, a sample of the waste is again taken by a technician. The "fingerprint" of this latest sample is matched to the original sample. Only if the shipment has not changed will it be unloaded and treated.

The first step of treatment is to unload the truck and place the

Fig. 30 *Rats thrive in our garbage dumps. Rats can be a cause of disease among humans.*

waste in storage tanks.

Organic wastes are piped to a specially designed incinerator where they are used as fuel to create a temperature of 1300°C. This high temperature destroys the organic substances. Some waste organics do not burn easily. They are injected into this very hot flame so that they too are destroyed. It takes less than 2.5 s for this reaction to take place!

Burning organic wastes in the incinerator can produce acids. The acidic gases formed in the incinerator are cooled by a spray of water and mixed with alkaline inorganic wastes, so that they are both neutralized.

Solids produced by this neutralization are filtered from the incinerator flu gas. The remaining flu gas, which is mostly carbon dioxide and water vapour, is then released to the atmosphere through a tall stack.

The whole process is monitored and recorded to ensure that it is adequate. As in many industries, automatic sensors shut down the process if they detect a problem.

Since inorganic liquid waste can't

be made safe by incineration, another method is used. Acid waste is neutralized by mixing it with alkaline waste. The salts are then mixed with the fine ash from an incinerator to form a solid cement-like product which is more easily managed.

Finally the solid clay-like material formed in the treatment process is buried in very deep, secure cells. These cells are designed to imprison the hazardous material for life. The cells are dug 20 m deep into a 41 m clay deposit. Such sites are chosen so that rain or ground water can not wash the waste out into our environment. The diagram below shows what a formidable prison the cells are. As in other prisons, the area around the site is monitored closely. Even rain water that falls on the work site must be collected, monitored, and treated before it is released to the environment. Any changes in the ground water could indicate that wastes may be leaking from the cells into the environment.

Working around such material is not what most people dream of, but as long as living creatures produce wastes, waste disposal will be necessary.

Think about it

1. How much waste do you produce? (Hint: what other snacks do you eat besides carrots?) How can you reduce the amount of waste you produce?
2. Industry is irresponsible about disposing of hazardous wastes and is not willing to lower its profits to protect the public's safety. Do you agree? Discuss.
3. Many problems with chemical waste disposal are with us today because we once didn't understand how toxic and longlasting such wastes were. As a result, we didn't take as much care in disposing of them as we should have. Give two examples and indicate how our approach to these wastes has changed.
4. In a small group, research recent and current problems with hazardous wastes that are discussed in the media. Find out what the problem is, what caused it, its effect on the environment, and what is being done to clean it up. Present your findings in a report, accompanied by illustrations and/or photos.
5. A manufacturer has been charged with dumping hazardous chemical wastes into a nearby stream. The manufacturer now faces a fine which will probably not act as a deterrent since safety measures would cost much more than the fine. How would you go about convincing the manufacturer to use a safer method of dispose of wastes?

Fig. 31

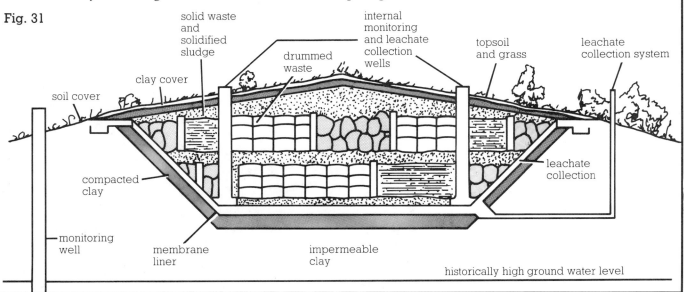

soil cover
clay cover
solid waste and solidified sludge
drummed waste
internal monitoring and leachate collection wells
topsoil and grass
leachate collection system
compacted clay
leachate collection
monitoring well
membrane liner
impermeable clay
historically high ground water level

4.16 A Modern Product— A Modern Problem

Each year, the number of cars, trucks, motorcycles, bicycles, and other vehicles is growing. Almost all of these machines need rubber tires of some sort. In fact, more than seven million tires are manufactured around the world each year. A large number of tires is not itself a problem. However, dealing with the old, worn-out tires *is* a problem. The part of a tire which is worn away on the road is only a very small part of its whole structure.

People want tires to last many years. Science has made rubber compounds which can remain solid and stable for 50 years. When buried in a dump the tire will stay unchanged for probably hundreds of years.

What can be done with these millions and millions of tires? Only a very small market exists for remanufactured tires. How to dispose of the rest is a major research problem for the chemical industry and waste disposal authorities.

It's a Fact
Rubber can still be made from the sap of certain plants, but the product is inferior and tires made from it are unable to meet the requirements of highway speeds and heavy loads.

Fig. 32 Bicycles, motor cycles, cars, trucks, aircraft—all use rubber tires. What happens to them all?

We use chemicals to manufacture the synthetic rubber in tires. Synthetic rubber is made from crude oil, salt, and carbon. The oil is piped from the wells in western Canada to southern Ontario through the Trans-Canada Pipeline. In chemical factories, the crude oil is heated and separated into its components.

The simple small molecules separated from crude oil are joined together into long chains called **polymers**. The polymers are treated with chlorine that is taken from salt (sodium chloride). The resulting complex molecules are long, strong, and hard on the environment. The product that is made lasts for years and, with care, can travel 1 000 000 km. Like other chemicals, rubber used in tires has its benefits, but it also imposes risks on the environment.

FEEDBACK

1. If rubber tires, made from 1946 on, last for 50 years, how many tires are in disposal sites this year?
2. Where does the rubber go that is worn from the tires of vehicles?
3. What are two natural resources from which synthetic rubber is made?

You are part of a very complex environment. The things you do, the chemicals you use, and the products you buy make a difference. Water, soil, and air (and the impurities we put into them) all influence each other. In order to maintain the planet in a condition which can support life, we must understand how these different aspects of the environment affect each other.

The long life people now expect is partly due to chemicals which improve food production and decrease disease. Our environment and our chemistry can co-operate for a healthy and prosperous lifestyle. But we must learn to manage our resources and technologies wisely if this is to be achieved. We still tend to act before we have all of the necessary information. Some of the damage that results can't be repaired.

Fig. 33 In these distillation columns, crude oil is separated into its components.

If money is made available, researchers may find ways to protect and repair our environment. On a personal level, we can all make an effort to reuse manufactured goods, recycle those that can't be re-used, and discard only the smallest amount of waste possible.

4.17 Chapter Summary

- All activities involve some risk. With skill and knowledge we can reduce risks and increase benefits.
- Acids and bases are two important classifications of substances. Acids and bases are measured on the pH scale. Measures greater than 7 are bases; below 7 are acids.
- Acids and bases can be identified by the use of indicators such as phenolphthalein, bromthymol blue, and litmus.
- Acid content of a soil affects its ability to grow plants.
- Soil washed with acid such as acid rain is reduced in nutrients.
- Acids are unwanted products of burning most fuels. If they can be removed from a fuel before burning, the damage they cause can be reduced.

- One substance responsible for a large part of acid rain is sulfur dioxide.
- All chemicals can be both beneficial and dangerous depending on their use. Sulfur can become a pollutant but it can also be used in manufacturing fertilizer and paper for books.
- ''Hard'' and ''soft'' are terms used to describe the mineral content of water.
- Acid rain is a very complex mixture of the gases found in our air and dissolved in water.
- Testing of our environment is necessary. Air, water, and soil must be sampled and their contents identified.
- Disposal of unwanted material is a growing problem.
- Society is beginning to look seriously at re-using and recycling materials, as an alternative to some kinds of waste disposal.

4.18 Are You Ready To Go On?

Do not write in the textbook.

1. Explain the terms ''risk'' and ''benefit.''
2. Name two properties of an acid.
3. Name three properties of a base.
4. Arrange the following in order from strongest base (highest pH) to strongest acid (lowest pH). You may use the list on page 85.
   - vinegar
   - milk
   - blood
   - wine
   - limewater
5. From the information given below write the colour of the indicator listed that would be expected for each sample.

Chemical	Litmus	Phenolphthalein
hydrochloric acid		
limewater		
ginger ale		
sodium hydroxide		

6. From the following description decide if the substance is an acid or a base:
   A person splashed a little of this liquid on a plate of potato chips. The chips gained a pleasantly sour taste.
7. What effect does a washing with dilute acid have upon a sample of potting soil for plants?
8. How can the little bit of sulfur in fuels be such a great problem?
9. List three effects of acid rain on the environment.
10. Unscramble the words listed below. Write each unscrambled word in your notebook.
    a) dcias
    b) sseab
    c) ttsse
    d) leufs
    e) ccylere
    f) serue
    g) skir
    h) kaalli
    i) lusmit
    j) tuenral
    k) fuursl

11. Decide if the following are true or false. If the statement is true, copy it into your notebook. If it is false, rewrite it so that it is true.
    a) Wine is an acid.
    b) Seawater is an acid.
    c) If a chemical is slippery it is always a base.
    d) A chemical that turns litmus red is a base.
    e) A lemon contains an acid.
    f) Only living things are affected by acid rain.
    g) DDT, like all pesticides, has no benefits.

12. Describe how to test if a gas is sulfur dioxide.

13. In your notebook write the names of two uses for the sulfur removed from natural gas.

14. Describe in your notebook what is meant by the terms ''hard'' and ''soft'' water.

15. What is one benefit of hard water?

16. Describe one problem associated with hard water.

17. Why should we care about the substances that we put in the air?

18. Is the following true or false? Explain your choice.
    - You can always tell if a company is damaging the air by the colour of the smoke from its chimney.
    - Finding a place to dump the garbage from a city should not be a problem because Canada has a great deal of land that is not being used.
    - If water is clear and colourless, it is probably good to drink.

19. How are the people in the photos on page 83 damaging their environment?

Contents

Chapter Five

It All Depends

5.1 Back To The Basics

What are the most important things in your life? Nice clothes? Good friends? Your family? Fun times? Finding happiness? All of these needs, and others, are very real. However, not one of them is absolutely essential for your survival. The basic things you need for staying alive are:

- food nutrients to supply energy and substances for growth, repair, and proper cell functioning.
- oxygen gas to release the energy from the food so that you can use it.
- water, which all cells need so that they can be fat, full and crisp — a condition necessary for life processes like respiration, growth, and repair.

All these substances must enter your cells. Carbon dioxide and excess water and other poisoning cell wastes must leave your cells.

OUTPUTS

EXCESS WATER   CARBON DIOXIDE   CELL WASTES

LIVING CELL

INPUTS

WATER

OXYGEN

FOOD NUTRIENTS

119

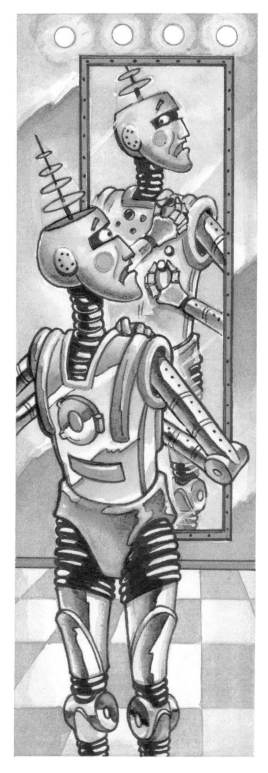

Doesn't sound too interesting does it? Actually, how your body works to keep you alive is very exciting. Your body is an intricate machine, finely tuned to adjust to surrounding changes to meet your cells' needs.

In this chapter, you will find out how your body gets food nutrients and oxygen gas into all its sixty million million living cells and how it removes carbon dioxide, excess water, and other wastes from them. To do so, it depends on some of its systems. Four of your body's systems will be considered:

- the circulatory system
- the gas exchange, or breathing, system
- the digestive system,
- the waste removal, or excretory, system.
- You will have the opportunity to see the parts of some of these systems first-hand during the investigation in which you dissect a preserved frog whose internal organs look rather like your own. You will also find out what sorts of conditions cause your body systems to become unwell, and what sorts of things you can practise to keep or gain back a healthy body.

FEEDBACK

1. Name four of your body's systems.
2. a) What substances do your body cells have to take in to stay alive? What life processes occur with the help of these substances?
   b) What substances do your body cells have to get rid of to stay alive? Why?

Fig. 3 *Your body is an intricate machine.*

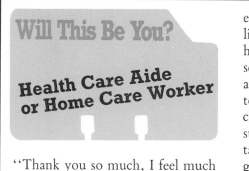

Health Care Aide or Home Care Worker

"Thank you so much, I feel much better now. It was so thoughtful of you to do that for me." It is heartwarming to know that some action of yours has made someone else feel better, especially if that someone is no longer able to do all the things he or she used to be able to do because of age or failing health.

One of the fastest growing career opportunities involves helping elderly people with their daily living requirements, in their homes or in housing facilities for senior citizens. As a health care aide or home care worker you get to do just that. You assist your clients with their daily activities, such as dressing, keeping clean, taking meals, moving around, going to appointments. You may be required to keep health records such as temperature readings, pulse and breathing rates, fluid intake and output. If your client lives at home, your job will include meal planning and preparation, food shopping, housecleaning, and laundry. Always, the mental and physical well-being of your client will be your first concern.

For these kinds of careers, it is best to have a high school diploma and to be interested in a wide variety of things. There are programs at community colleges and elsewhere that can help you to become better care givers.

Because you may have to wheel your client about or assist her or him to move or walk, some physical strength and stamina are also needed. Being genuinely interested in and caring bout others are very important. Having lots of patience is a must too.

Knowing that someone else is a little happier, better cared for, and healthier because of your efforts is a very rewarding experience. Will this be you?

Fig. 4 *Home care workers help people who are ill but do not need hospitalization.*

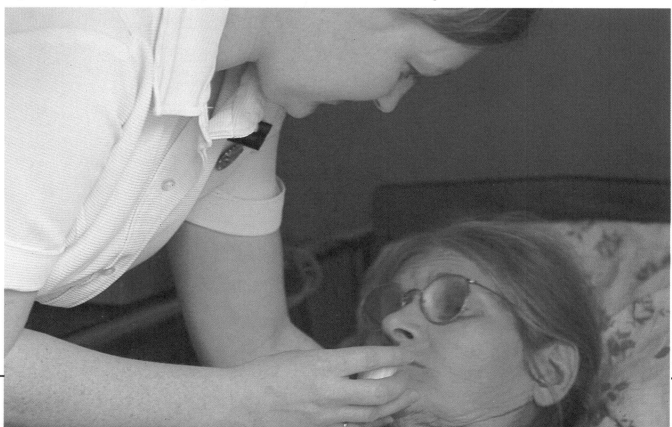

5.2 The Highs and The Lows

How do food nutrients and oxygen gas get into cells? How do carbon dioxide and other wastes get out? You can set up a cell-like system to see how this exchange probably takes place. Water will represent food nutrients and oxygen gas. Molasses will represent carbon dioxide and other cell wastes. It is quite easy to see diffusion occurring both into and out of a cell-like system at the same time.

Find out

Can molasses and water move in opposite directions through a membrane-like material?

You need

- 25 cm dialysis tubing to imitate the action of cell membrane.
- tap water (a very high concentration of water molecules)
- molasses (a very high concentration of sugar molecules dissolved in some water)
- funnel
- metric ruler
- 1 m glass tubing
- elastic
- support stand
- 600 mL beaker

Try this

1. Open the length of dialysis tubing and tie one end.

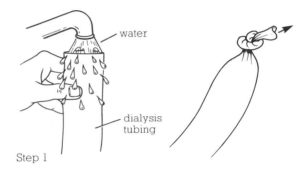

Step 1

Fig. 5

2. Using the funnel, place an 8 cm depth of molasses into the dialysis tubing bag.

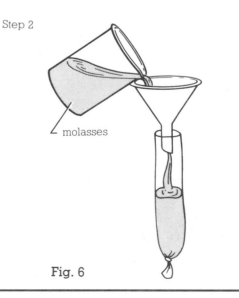

Step 2

Fig. 6

122

3. Insert the piece of glass tubing into the molasses in the dialysis tubing bag. Using the elastic, close the dialysis tubing tightly around the glass tubing. Rinse thoroughly to remove all traces of molasses from the outside of the assembly. Check for leaks. Correct any that exist.

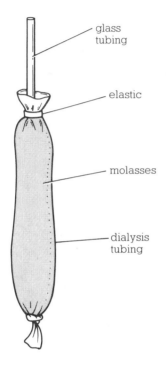

glass tubing

elastic

molasses

dialysis tubing

Fig. 7

4. Place the dialysis-glass tubing assembly in the beaker and support it upright. Cover the dialysis tubing with water.
5. *Draw a diagram to illustrate this completed assembly. Label the water, the molasses, the position of the top surface of each, and the colour of each. Title this diagram "The Beginning."*
6. After half an hour, observe any changes that have occurred. *Record your observations in the form of another labelled diagram, titled "After Half an Hour."*
7. Clean up your work area.

What happened?

1. What evidence indicates that water passed through the membrane? In what direction did the water go?
2. What evidence indicates that molasses passed through the membrane? In what direction did the molasses go?
3. The spreading of a substance from an area of high concentration to an area where its concentration is low is called **diffusion**.
   a) Show that water diffused by relating its movement to its areas of concentration.
   b) Do the same for molasses.
4. Under what conditions can molasses and water move in opposite directions through a membrane-like material?

Now you know

Over time, the molasses rose inside the glass tubing. This happened because water diffused into the dialysis bag from the beaker, so that the contents increased in volume and rose up the tube. Also, the water in the beaker became brown, like dilute molasses, because molasses diffused outward through the dialysis tubing. Water and molasses diffused in opposite directions at the same time. (NOTE: if this system were left long enough, the concentrations of both water and molasses would equal out throughout the entire system and diffusion would seem to stop.)

5.3 **The Ins and Outs of Cell Life**

Your body's cells are surrounded by extracellular fluid (ECF). As long as their environment contains food nutrients, water, and oxygen gas in concentrations greater than what's inside the cells, these substances will diffuse into the cell. For the poisonous carbon dioxide and other cell wastes made inside cells, the opposite must occur. They must diffuse outwards into the extracellular environment. It is important that the concentrations of the chemicals be kept low in the ECF so that this outward diffusion can occur. Thus the ECF surrounding cells must be kept high in food nutrients and oxygen gas, and low in carbon dioxide and other cell wastes.

Fig. 8

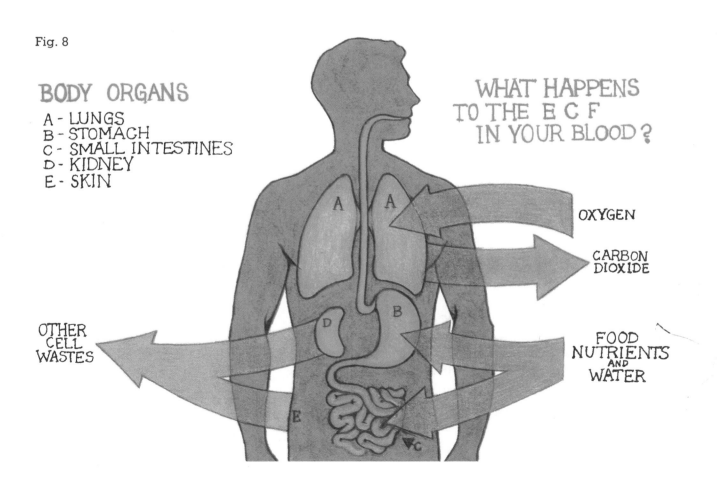

BODY ORGANS

A - LUNGS
B - STOMACH
C - SMALL INTESTINES
D - KIDNEY
E - SKIN

WHAT HAPPENS TO THE E C F IN YOUR BLOOD?

OXYGEN

CARBON DIOXIDE

OTHER CELL WASTES

FOOD NUTRIENTS AND WATER

Because living cells continuously remove food nutrients and oxygen gas from their environment and add poisonous wastes to it, the ECF is both a source of dinner and a sewer! So fresh ECF must be continuously brought to these cells. Just like the water in a slow-moving swamp, your blood continuously flows and oozes through your body. It brings fresher, cleaner ECF to all your body cells and carries away the stale ECF to be cleaned and freshened. Specialized organ systems of your body are responsible for certain aspects of the freshening and cleaning processes.

1. a) Draw a picture that illustrates a cell in ECF, and the location of the high concentration region of each of the kinds of substances that must go in and out.
   b) Using arrows, show the direction in which each of these substances moves.
2. Living cells continuously change the contents of their extra-cellular fluid. Describe these changes.
3. Why are your body cells continuously endangering their lives?
4. Look at figure 8 for help in answering the following questions:
   a) To what part of your body does the blood carry stale ECF so that the carbon dioxide can be removed from it and oxygen gas can be added to it to freshen it?
   b) To what part of your body does the blood carry stale ECF so that it can be replenished with food nutrients?
   c) Poisonous cell wastes other than carbon dioxide are made into urine and sweat and removed. Through what part of your body does the blood take stale ECF so that it can be thoroughly cleansed of these poisonous cell wastes?

5.4 **The Double Circuit Treadmill**

In a complex animal like you, the circulatory system is the transport system for moving the substances that cells need and the wastes they produce. The major organ of your circulatory system is the **heart**. This thickly muscled organ pumps blood through blood vessels called **arteries**. These thick muscular-walled tubes carry blood away from the heart into tiny **capillaries**. Capillaries are thin-walled tubes that pass close to all cells of the body. Nutrients, gases, and cell wastes pass between the blood in the capillaries and the ECF surrounding your body cells. Then the blood still remaining in the capillaries flows into another set of large blood vessels, the **veins**, whose job it is to carry the blood back to the heart.

Fig. 9 *Nutrients, gases, and cell wastes pass between the blood in the capillaries and the ECF.*

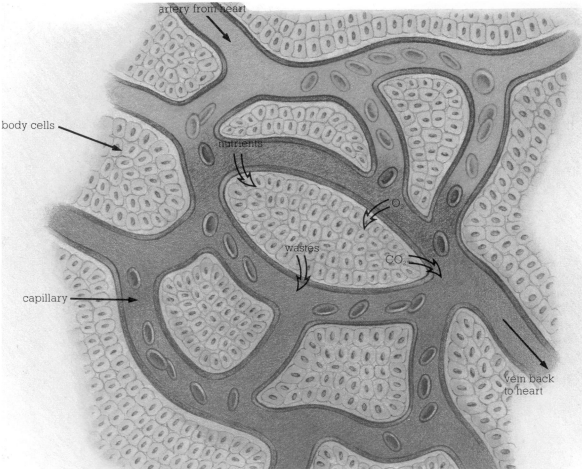

The circuit your blood actually follows resembles a lopsided figure eight. Your heart is divided into two halves, from top to bottom. Blood entering the right side of your heart is pumped into arteries that end in capillaries in the lungs. Carbon dioxide diffuses out of the blood here, and oxygen gas diffuses in and gets attached to **red blood cells**, which carry it to other parts of the body. The veins bringing blood back from the lungs enter the left side of the heart.

The oxygen-rich blood is now pumped into the largest artery in your body, the **aorta**. From there, it is pushed into a huge maze of other arteries that carry it to all of the rest of your body except the lungs.

- Some travels through your digestive system, picking up nutrients as it does.
- Some goes through the kidneys and skin, the **excretory** organs of your body where cellular wastes are removed.
- A lot gets into the capillaries surrounding your brain cells, and the muscle cells all over your body. In these regions the blood supplies oxygen gas and nutrients to those cells, and collects the carbon dioxide and other cell wastes from them. Blood from all these parts of your body then flows through veins back to the right side of your heart.

Right side of heart to lungs, to left side of heart to somewhere else in the body, to right side of heart again—this double circuit treadmill very efficiently moves your blood all through your body, keeping it supplied with oxygen gas and nutrients, and keeping it cleansed of carbon dioxide and cellular wastes.

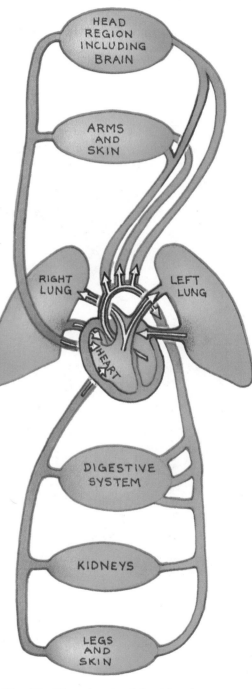

Fig. 10 *The circuit of the blood around the body*

127

It is important to keep the muscles of your heart wall strong and healthy so that they can keep pumping for a lifetime. It is also important to maintain the health of your arteries and veins, keeping the muscles in their walls well toned, and their insides, where the blood flows, clean and smooth-walled. Doing exercises that make your circulatory system work faster for short periods of time, and eating good nutritious foods are excellent ways to do this.

Fig. 11a *Major external blood vessels of the heart*

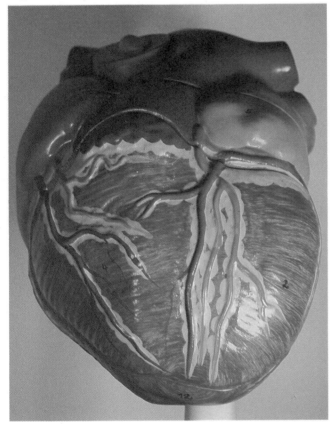

Fig. 11b *Inside the heart*

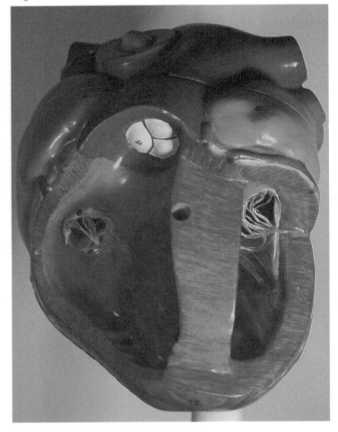

FEEDBACK

1. Important parts of your circulatory system are: arteries, capillaries, heart and veins. Copy and complete the chart shown below to match the part to the description.

Description	Part of the circulatory system being described?
tubes that carry blood back to the heart	
pumps blood	
tubes that carry blood away from the heart	
tiny, thin-walled tubes	
large, thin-walled tubes	
a thick, muscled organ	
thick, muscled tubes, like the aorta	
tubes close to every body cell	
allows substances to pass between the blood and the body cells	

2. Trace the diagram on the right into your notebook. Then use figure 10 to help you do the following:
   a) Place these labels in their correct places on the diagram: aorta, artery to lungs, capillaries around body cells, capillaries in lungs, heart, vein from body cells, vein from lungs.
   b) Place arrows on the diagram to demonstrate the figure eight pattern of your circulation.

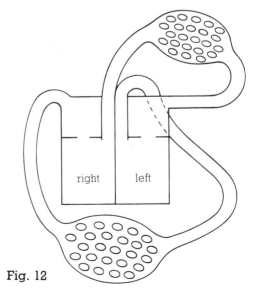

Fig. 12

129

Activity

5.5 The Light of Your Life

You can't see your cells using oxygen to get the energy they need from food nutrients. However, you can watch a candle using oxygen to produce heat and light energy from the candle wax. What does the burning candle do to the air around it?

You need

- candle
- half a petri dish to mount the candle in
- glass jar big enough to fit over the candle in its dish
- tray with some water in the bottom
- matches
- wooden splint
- some limewater
- beaker tongs

1. Design an investigation to demonstrate what a burning candle does to air. Use the equipment listed (ask your teacher for anything else you may also wish to use).
2. Perform your experiment to make sure that it works.
3. *Prepare a lab report, describing how you did your investigation and what you found out.*

Think about it

As a candle burns, it uses up oxygen gas from the air and produces carbon dioxide. Your body cells are rather like burning candles. They use oxygen gas molecules during the process called **respiration** to get the energy out of the nutrients you have eaten and they produce carbon dioxide and water. Your cells use this energy in their activities. For example, your brain cells are using energy now as you read.

1. a) In what ways is respiration in your body cells similar to burning candles?
   b) In what ways is it different?

 *Investigation*

5.6 Used Air, Anyone?

You know what a burning candle does to air. How can you see what the process of respiration does to it?

 *Find out*

What happens to air while it is in your lungs?

You need

- sanitized plastic bags (2)
- twist ties (2)
- 20 mL limewater
- short candle
- 600 mL beaker
- watch with second hand or minute timer

SAFETY ALERT!
Use each bag only once, then discard it.

Fig. 13

 *Try this*

1. Sit quietly at your desk. Breathe normally. Count the number of breaths you take in one minute. *Record your findings.*
2. Inhale normally, then seal a plastic bag around your nose and mouth. Exhale into the bag. Inhale and exhale this same air from the bag until breathing gets uncomfortable, counting the number of times you are able to do so.

SAFETY ALERT!
Stop breathing into the bag when it becomes uncomfortable to blow up the bag one last time.

3. Rest for a few moments until your breathing returns to normal. Then repeat step 2 for the second plastic bag. Use a twist tie to tightly close each bag of "used" air.
4. What happens to your breathing rate as you use the same air over and over again? *Record your findings.*
5. *Record the appearance of the inside of the bag.*

continued

6. Carefully untie one of the bags, opening only a corner. Add about 20 mL of limewater, without letting much of the gas escape from the bag. Reclose the bag tightly. Shake the bag to get the gas in it to mix with the limewater. What happens to the limewater? *Record your obervations.*
7. Anchor a short candle in the bottom of the beaker. Light the candle.
8. Untie the second bag of used air. Pour the used air over the candle in the container. *Record your observations.*

Fig. 14

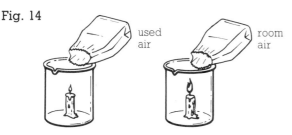

used air

room air

9. Relight the candle. Fill the bag with the air from the room. Pour this air over the candle as you did in step 8. *Record your observations.*
10. Clean up your work area.

What happened?

1. You can't breathe the same air for very long. Your body does something to the air. What do the results of this investigation tell you about changes that occur in the air as you breathe?
2. What was the purpose of pouring the bag of ordinary air over the lighted candle flame?
3. a) What happens to breathing rate as the amount of carbon dioxide increases?
   b) Explain why your breathing rate increases when you exercise. Give as much detail as possible.

4. Look at the following analysis of the amounts of gases in inhaled and exhaled air:

Gas	Inhaled air	Exhaled air
oxygen	20%	16%
carbon dioxide gas	0.03%	4%
water vapour	varies with the humidity	always higher than inhaled air

Suppose the exhaled air is inhaled again, as in this activity. Predict the percentages of oxygen and carbon dioxide in the air when it is exhaled a second time. *Record your predictions.*

Now you know

Moisture collects inside the bag as you breathe in and out repeatedly. This moisture is water. When you exhaled repeatedly, the carbon dioxide in your breath caused the candle flame to flicker, dim, and possibly be extinguished. Ordinary air does not have this effect.

So you remove oxygen gas from each breath you take and add carbon dioxide and water vapour to it. The oxygen gas goes into your bloodstream and the carbon dioxide and water come from your bloodstream.

5.7 The Great Gas Exchange: On the Way In

Before your body cells can use oxygen gas molecules in respiration, these molecules have to get from the atmosphere to the ECF surrounding your cells. Part of the journey — lungs to heart to body cells — has already been discussed. Now for the journey from atmosphere to lungs.

It's a Fact
Both food and air pass through the throat or pharynx.

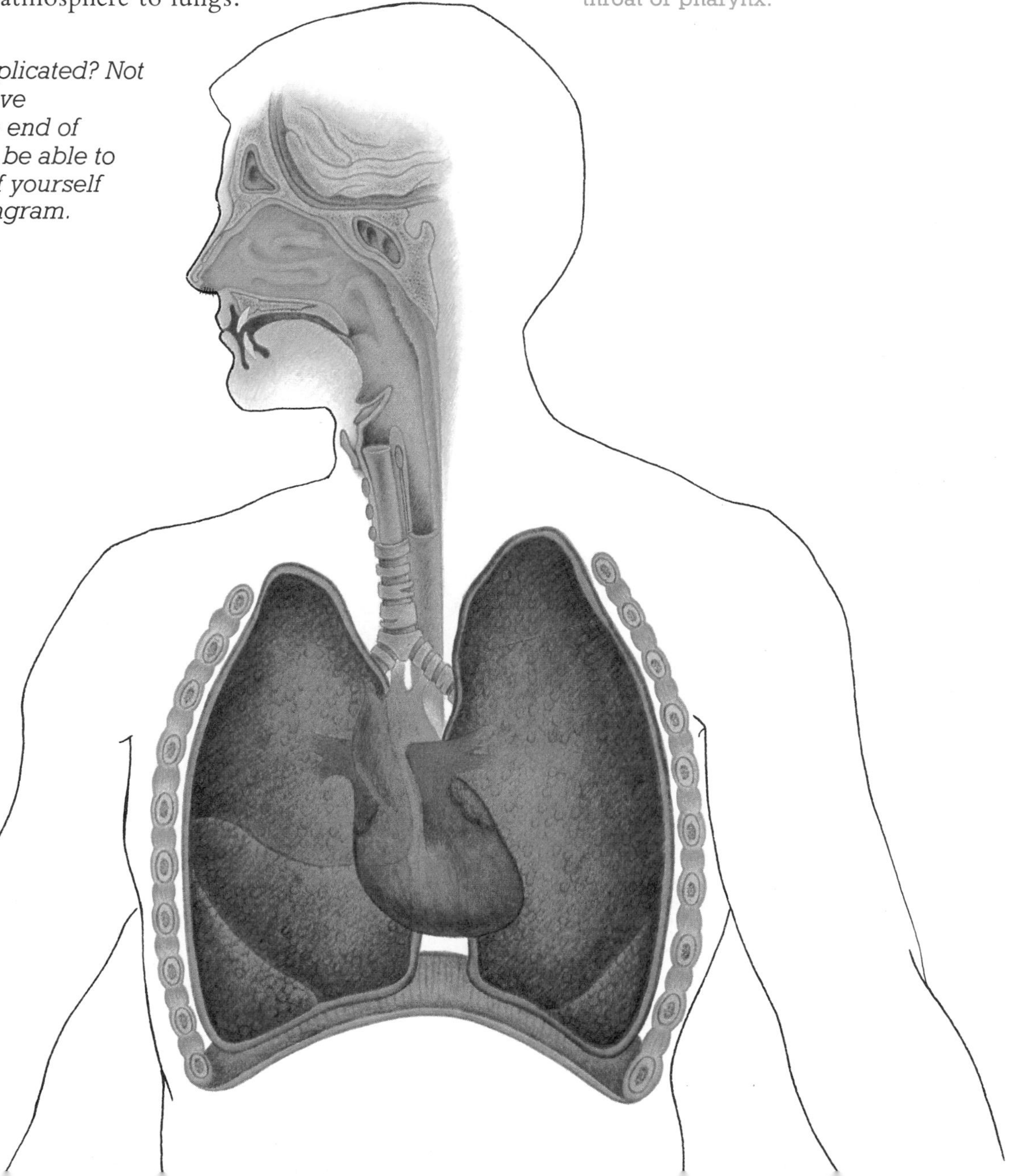

Fig. 15 *Looks complicated? Not really. When you have completed up to the end of Section 5.9, you will be able to name all the parts of yourself illustrated in this diagram.*

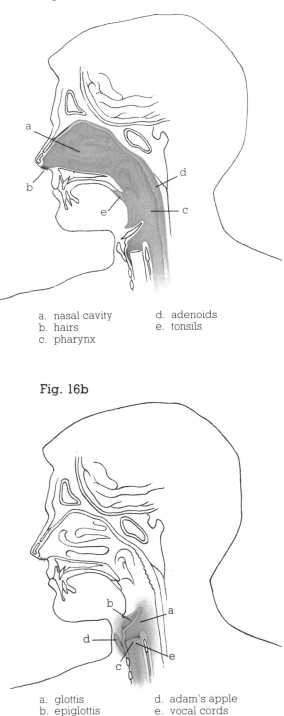

Fig. 16a

a. nasal cavity   d. adenoids
b. hairs   e. tonsils
c. pharynx

Fig. 16b

a. glottis   d. adam's apple
b. epiglottis   e. vocal cords
c. larynx

When you breathe in through your nose, oxygen gas molecules in the air near your nose are pushed into the **nasal cavities**. Entering your nose, the oxygen molecules are in a forest of hairs, which are wet with mucus. These hairs look something like your eyelashes or eyebrow hairs, only shorter. It's very warm and humid inside the nose. As the air is drawn through the nose passages, dirt and germ particles (viruses and bacteria) get stuck on the mucus. Cleaner, warmer, and more humid air, containing the oxygen gas molecules, then passes from the nose into your throat or **pharynx** located at the back of the mouth. The walls here are hairless, smooth, warm and moist.

On the walls of the pharynx are **adenoids** (just where the nose passages and pharynx meet) and **tonsils** (one on each side of the pharynx, just about where the root of the tongue is attached).

Air is further cleaned, warmed, and moistened while it is in the pharynx. The tonsils and adenoids trap and destroy a lot of the viruses and bacteria that are still in the air. Sometimes these glands become swollen, sore, and inflamed as this happens.

This cleaner, warmer, moister air that still contains the oxygen gas molecules is then drawn into the opening of the windpipe. This opening, called the **glottis**, has a trapdoor-like flap on it called the **epiglottis**. When you swallow, the back of your tongue pushes your epiglottis closed over the glottis to prevent food and drink from getting into the windpipe. When you breathe in, the epiglottis flap is up, the glottis is open, and air passes into the windpipe. If you swallow and laugh or talk at the same time, the epiglottis will be open, some of your food or drink may "go down the wrong way," and you could start to choke.

The bump at the top of windpipe is your **larynx**, or voicebox. You can feel this bump on your neck. You call it your **Adam's apple**. There is a pair of **vocal cords** in the passageway of your larynx. When you speak, sing, or cough, air passes over the vocal cords causing them to vibrate to produce the desired sound. You can feel these vibrations if you touch your Adam's apple while singing or speaking. The walls of the larynx are moist and warm to further condition the passing air.

The inhaled air next enters your windpipe or **trachea**. The walls of this ten centimetre-long tube in your neck contain rings of **cartilage**. You can feel their ridges when you rub up and down your neck just below the Adam's apple. These cartilage rings keep your soft-walled trachea open while you breathe. The inside surface of your windpipe is also wet and warm. There are no hairs like those in your nose, but there is a carpet of microscopic **cilia** that completely lines the trachea.

As air containing oxygen gas molecules passes down your trachea, more dust, dirt, and pollutant particles get trapped in the wet mucus on the walls. The cilia beat, in rhythm, in an upward direction and move the dirtied mucus towards your larynx and glottis. This dirty mucus collects there and every once in a while you cough to expel it into your pharynx, then swallow it or spit it out.

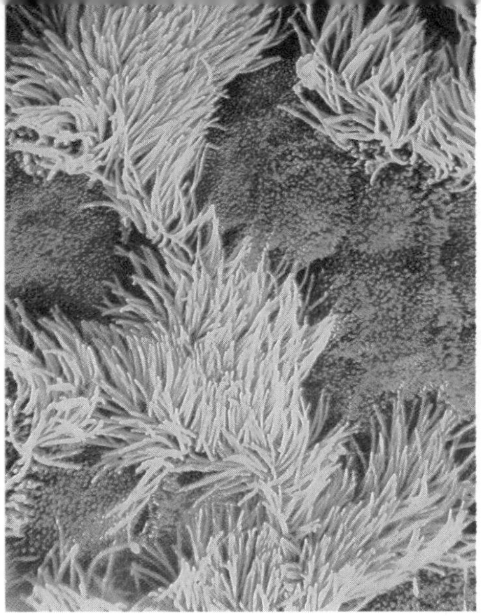

Fig. 17 *Cilia are microscopic finger-like extensions outward from the surface of cells.*

FEEDBACK

1. a) What is the technical name for the inside of your nose?
   b) What does each of these structural features do to the air passing through the nose?
      • mucus
      • hairs
   c) What makes the inside of your nose warm?
   d) List three ways in which air is different after it has passed through your nose.
2. What happens to air while it is in the throat?
3. a) Distinguish between the epiglottis and the glottis.
   b) How does your tongue prevent food from "going down the wrong way"?
4. a) What is your larynx?
   b) Where is it?
   c) What is located inside it?
   d) Why is it important?
5. Your trachea:
   a) What is it?
   b) How can you locate it in your throat?
   c) How long is it?
   d) Why do its walls contain rings of cartilage?
   e) What happens to air passing through to it?
6. Why is mucus so important in your breathing system?

Fig. 18

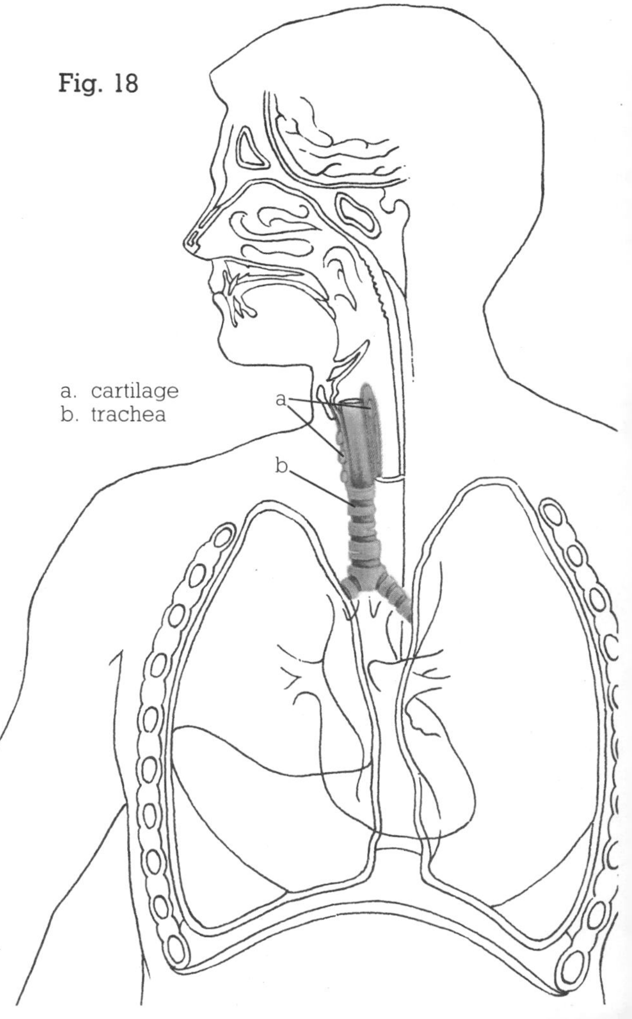

a. cartilage
b. trachea

5.8 The Great Gas Exchange: In the Lungs

After passing through your trachea nicely warmed, moistened, and much cleaner air enters your **bronchi**. These are two tubes that branch off the trachea, one going into each lung at the point in your chest that is about at the top of the breastbone. The bronchus walls are just like those of the trachea, and they do the same jobs.

Each bronchus then branches over and over again inside its lung. The smaller tubes formed are called **bronchioles**. These are miniature versions of the bronchi, which carry out the same functions. Air, still with all the oxygen gas molecules in it, is really clean, warm, and moist, when it reaches the end of the tiniest bronchioles.

Fig. 19

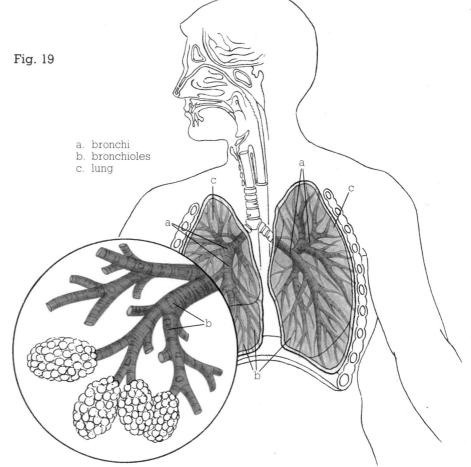

a. bronchi
b. bronchioles
c. lung

The tiniest bronchioles end in grape-like clusters of flat, curved cells, called **air sacs** or **alveoli**. Each alveolus is surrounded by a network of tiny blood vessels called capillaries. It is here, finally, inside the alveoli, that the oxygen gas molecules diffuse from the air through the flat cells of the alveoli and get into the red blood cells of the blood. The function of all the other parts of the breathing system is simply to warm, clean, and moisten air, and to get it to these thin-walled alveolar sacs.

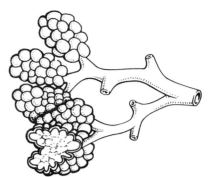

Fig. 20b *Alveoli*

Fig. 20a *Inside the alveoli, oxygen gas molecules diffuse into the red blood cells.*

a. lung
b. alveoli
c. capillaries

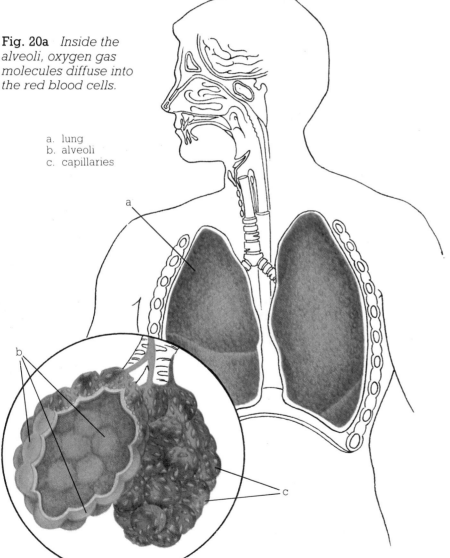

So, each of your **lungs** is like a full bag, containing one bronchus, a forest of bronchioles, and about 150 million alveoli. The lungs' major function is to allow gas exchange with the blood to take place at the alveoli. All these spongy structures are enclosed in a thin-walled smooth coating called the **pleura**. The pleura is smooth and slippery wet. It allows the surface of the lungs to expand, contract, and slide around inside your chest cavity without rubbing against anything else. This means you don't feel your lungs moving inside your chest cavity; you just feel the cavity getting bigger and smaller as air goes in and out.

FEEDBACK

1. a) What are your bronchi and bronchioles?
   b) How are they alike?
   c) How do they differ from each other?
   d) What is their job?
2. a) What are your alveoli?
   b) Where are they found?
   c) How many does your body contain?
   d) What are they made up of?
   e) What happens in your alveoli?
3. a) What are your pleurae?
   b) What is their function?
4. What part of your lungs makes them spongy in texture?

5.9 The Great Gas Exchange: On the Way Out

The story of carbon dioxide's journey from your cells to the outside world has almost all been told, too. Carbon dioxide diffuses from all the body cells and travels in the blood to the lungs. It then diffuses through the alveoli cells into the air in those air sacs. From there it travels the reverse journey through the breathing tubes when you breathe out and is exhaled into the air outside your body.

Think about it

1. Copy this chart into your notebook, and complete it.

Breathing system		
	cilia	hairs
Where are they found in the breathing system?		
In what ways are they the same?		
In what ways are they different?		
What is their function?		

2. Copy this diagram of a greatly enlarged alveolus with its capillaries into your notebook. Use arrows to show the direction the oxygen gas (O_2) diffuses, and the direction the carbon dioxide (CO_2) diffuses. Title the diagram.

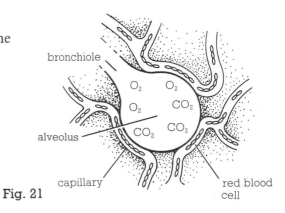

bronchiole

O_2 O_2

O_2 CO_2

CO_2 CO_2

alveolus

capillary

red blood cell

Fig. 21

3. Imagine that you are small enough to be a molecule of carbon dioxide gas as it travels from a red blood cell in your lungs to the air outside your nose. What pathway would you follow? Copy this pattern into your notebook, then fill it in.

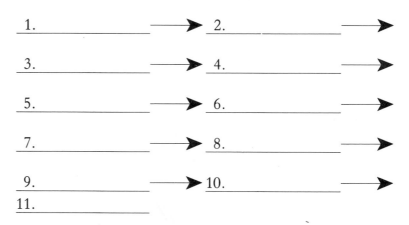

1. _____ ⟶ 2. _____ ⟶

3. _____ ⟶ 4. _____ ⟶

5. _____ ⟶ 6. _____ ⟶

7. _____ ⟶ 8. _____ ⟶

9. _____ ⟶ 10. _____ ⟶

11. _____

Do this by rearranging these parts of your breathing system in their correct order: alveoli, blood, bronchi, bronchioles, capillaries, glottis, larynx, nasal cavities, pharynx, red blood cell, trachea.

4. Trace figure 15 onto a page in your notebook. Correctly label all the parts identified by letters. Draw arrows to show the pathway of the air. Give your diagram a suitable title.

5.10 Making a Model of the Chest Cavity and Lungs

You have seen the path that air takes into and out of your lungs. But just how does your breathing system take air in and push it out again? You can make an apparatus that demonstrates how air is moved into and out of your lungs.

You need

- clear, stiff-walled plastic bottle
- rubber stopper with glass tubing inserted
- piece of elastic sheet to cover bottom of the bottle
- elastic
- string or tape
- scissors or knife
- small balloon

Try this

1. Cut the bottom off the plastic bottle.
2. Fasten the elastic sheet over the bottom of the bottle.
3. Use the elastic band to fasten the small balloon to the end of the glass tube. This balloon represents the lungs.
4. Insert the rubber stopper tightly into the bottle.
5. Carefully pull the elastic sheet outwards. *Describe the effects of this action on the balloon, perhaps by using a diagram.*

6. Carefully push the elastic sheet inwards. *Describe the effects of this action on the balloon, perhaps by again using a diagram.*

Think about it

1. Which direction of air movement does the balloon filling with air represent? What is the shape of the elastic sheet at this time?
2. Which direction of air movement does the emptying of the balloon represent? What is the shape of the elastic sheet now?

Fig. 22

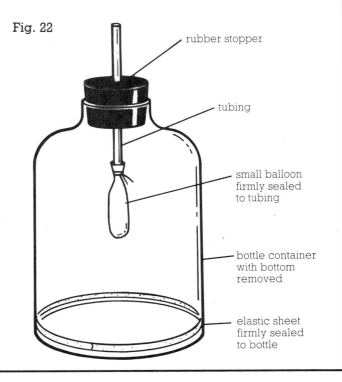

rubber stopper

tubing

small balloon firmly sealed to tubing

bottle container with bottom removed

elastic sheet firmly sealed to bottle

5.11 Moving It

Air pressure is the force that moves air into and out of your lungs when you breathe in (inhale) and breathe out (exhale). Your own breathing motions simply change the size of your chest cavity. During breathing in, you make your chest cavity bigger. This means there is less pressure on the air in your lungs. Higher air pressure in the atmosphere pushes air into your lungs, an **inhalation**. During breathing out, you make your chest cavity smaller. Now the pressure increases on the air in your lungs. This lung pressure is higher than atmospheric air pressure and air is pushed out, an **exhalation**.

Muscles change the size of your chest cavity so that air pressure can make you inhale and exhale. The major muscle involved in breathing is the **diaphragm**. (In the activity, the elastic sheet performed the function of the diaphragm). This muscle curves upward and covers the bottom of the chest cavity. When you inhale, the diaphragm contracts and flattens, making the chest cavity larger. A set of muscles between your ribs is also involved in breathing. Feel along one of your ribs

It's a Fact
The meat on spareribs is the muscles between the ribs of the pig or cow from which the ribs came.

It's a Fact
Many yoga exercises are designed to improve diaphragm breathing.

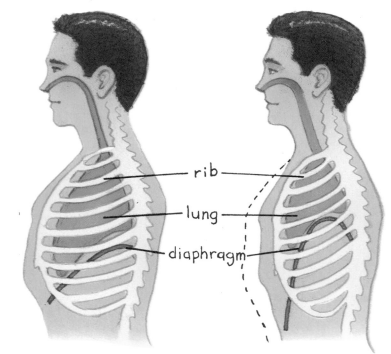

INHALATION   EXHALATION

relaxed (exhalation)

contracted (inhalation)

Fig. 23 *The diaphragm*

Fig. 24

and notice how it slopes downwards to the front. When the muscles between your ribs contract, they lift your rib cage upwards and outwards. This also increases the size of your chest cavity, and you inhale.

To breathe out, you just relax the diaphragm and rib muscles. The chest cavity gets smaller and air is pushed out of the body.

FEEDBACK

Copy and complete this chart in your notebook.

	Breathing in	Breathing out
What do you make your diaphragm and rib muscles do?		
What happens to the size of your chest cavity as a result?		
Which way does air pressure now push air?		
Is this an inhalation or is it an exhalation?		

5.12 **Diaphragm Breathing**

Can you feel your diaphragm working? Try this activity to find out.

1. Sit comfortably with your stomach muscles relaxed.
2. Breathe out all the air you can. Press your finger tips up under your rib cage.
3. Now breathe in deeply. Observe and describe the movement of your diaphragm. Observe and describe the movement of your rib cage. *Record your observations.*
4. Now try breathing in as much as possible, using only your diaphragm. Moving your stomach down and out in an exaggerated manner helps. (Your ribs shouldn't move.) Then try breathing as much as possible using only your rib cage. (Your stomach shouldn't move.) Which type of breathing moves more air in and out? Which type is easier to perform? *Record your findings.*
5. Which breathing muscles do you use more strongly when you sigh? yawn? Do one or the other to find out. *Record your findings.*

Think about it

1. Which type of breathing seems to move more air in and out of your lungs, normal breathing or diaphragm breathing?
2. List some activities for which you would need to use diaphragm breathing.
3. a) What kind of position is your body often in when you want to sigh or yawn?
   b) What happens to the amount of air you breathe in when you sigh or yawn?
   c) Use these data to explain why you sigh or yawn.

Fig. 25

Investigation

5.13 Of Vital Concern

How deep is a deep breath? You might be able to answer this question after measuring your **vital capacity**. Vital capacity is the volume of air that can be pushed out of your lungs after inhaling as deeply as possible. In this activity, you will measure the vital capacity of your lungs. You will analyse data obtained from classmates to discover factors that might affect the vital capacity of lungs.

Find out

How much air can your lungs hold?

You need

- large 6–8 L glass bottle
- 500 mL measuring device
- large shallow pan
- 1 m flexible tubing
- small glass plate
- waterproof marking device
- some antiseptic solution

SAFETY ALERT!

Make sure that anything that goes into your mouth has first been sterilized in the antiseptic solution and rinsed in clean water.

Try this

1. Mark off the large glass bottle in 0.5 L intervals. Do this by measuring 500 mL of water into the bottle and then marking the water level on the bottle. Repeat until no more complete 0.5 L amounts can be added.

Fig. 26

2. Fill the shallow pan three-quarters full of water. Slide one edge of the pan over the edge of the sink. Tip the pan slightly towards the sink by putting a wedge under the pan.
3. Close the mouth of the bottle tightly, using the small glass plate. Carefully tip the bottle upside down so that its mouth is under water in the shallow pan. This will probably require teamwork.

sink

Fig. 27

4. Hold the bottle vertically and remove the glass plate. You should now have a full bottle of water, upside down.
5. Raise or tip the bottle slightly without letting any water escape. Push one end of the rubber tube into the mouth of the bottle. Feed the tube up as high as possible into the bottle.
6. Dip the free end of the rubber tubing in the antiseptic solution and then rinse it in some water. This makes the tube end sanitary.
7. To find your vital capacity, first inhale as deeply as possible. Next put your mouth tightly around the sanitized end of the tubing. Then breathe out SLOWLY through the tube into the bottle, exhaling as much air as you can.

Fig. 28

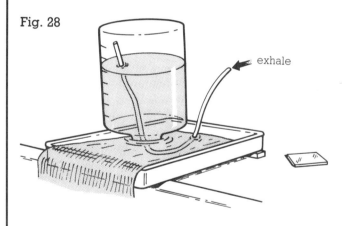

exhale

8. When you have forced out all the air you can, quickly bend the tube in two and pinch it shut. Remove the tube from your mouth and from the bottle.
9. *Record the amount of air you exhaled into the bottle.* This volume is your vital capacity.
10. Repeat steps 2 to 9 for each person in your group.
11. Clean up your work area.

146

What happened?

1. A milk bag holds about 1.25 L. About how many empty milk bags could you blow up with one full breath?
2. a) Vital capacity could be affected by the amount you exercise. Record the vital capacities of classmates who are physically active (jog, swim, ski, play sports, etc. at least five hours a week). Then record vital capacities of those who are not physically active.
   b) How does the amount of physical activity affect vital capacity?
3. a) What other factors could affect the vital capacity of the lungs?
   b) Choose one of these factors. State a hypothesis about its effect on vital capacity. Prepare a suitable chart and collect the necessary data from your classmates to test the hypothesis.
   c) What do the data tell you about your hypothesis?
4. How does your vital capacity compare with the other members of your group? Suggest reasons to explain the differences you find.
5. a) Suggest some ways that the vital capacity of a person's lungs could be increased.
   b) Why would a larger vital capacity be an advantage?

Fig. 29

You probably have a vital capacity ranging from 3 L to 6 L. You can fill from two to five 1.25 L milk bags with one large breath. A physically active lifestyle has a positive effect on your vital capacity. Many other factors, including height, weight, your sex, smoking, length of sleep, playing a wind or brass instrument, and the type of physical activity, could affect your vital capacity.

Testing a hypothesis as to what factor might affect vital capacity will need a great amount of data. You may have been unable to test your hypothesis because there just weren't enough data available from among your classmates. Also, your hypothesis may not be supported by the data available. Such a situation is a wonderful opportunity in science, because you automatically ask the questions: ''Why?'' or ''How come?'' Then you set out to answer these questions. This is the best kind of scientific process there is.

5.14 So What Can Go Wrong?

Exercising in fresh air, eating properly, drinking plenty of fluids, getting proper amounts of sleep, and humidifying the air you breathe—these are all ways of taking good care of yourself. By doing so, you allow the parts of your breathing system to accomplish their task of warming, moistening, and cleaning the air that reaches the gas exchange surfaces of the alveoli. The cleaning part of their job involves dealing with viruses and bacteria, dirt and dust, and other pollutants. All of these can be harmful to you in varying degrees.

Colds
Certain viruses find the moist linings of your nose an ideal home. When they begin to multiply, your body's defences turn on. Part of the defence is an increased production of mucus to help flush out the viruses. This produces the runny nose and watery eyes you usually experience during a cold. The blood vessels and mucous linings in the nose passages also swell, giving your nose a reddish tinge. The swelling also narrows the air passages inside your nose, so that breathing through your nose becomes more difficult. To make matters worse, some of the mucus may trickle down your throat, causing you to cough. The infection can spread into that region, causing a sore throat (**pharyngitis**). Your adenoids and tonsils may also swell as they attack and destroy the infection (**adenoiditis**, **tonsillitis**).

Fig. 30 *People who suffer from breathing problems such as asthma can use inhalators for temporary relief.*

Laryngitis

Some viruses and bacteria infect the larynx. The vocal cords become irritated and sore. They may swell in size, making it difficult or impossible to produce sounds. Until the condition clears up, you may have to speak in whispers or not at all. Often laryngitis is not particularly painful and will disappear in a few days.

Bronchitis

Sometimes, infections such as the common cold extend into the trachea, bronchi, and bronchioles. To help fight the infection of viruses or bacteria, extra mucus is produced which makes breathing difficult. Frequent coughing is necessary to help clear the mucus from these passages. Often, a wheezing or whistling sound can be heard from the chest. It is always wise to seek medical attention when you develop any infection in the breathing tubes of the chest cavity.

Emphysema

This is becoming a serious killer among the aging, and among those exposed to industrial pollutants and smoke. These pollutants gradually wear away the walls separating the alveoli from one another. This results in less gas exchange area in the lungs. Faster and deeper breathing must occur to compensate for the lost gas exchange surface. As the elastic nature of the lungs decreases, breathing becomes harder work. Over time, less and less oxygen gas gets into the blood stream. Weakness sets in and the body's systems become unable to function. Death results.

Lung cancer

In any cancer, normal body cells are changed and destroyed. Abnormal cells grow and spread, causing tumors, in the lungs and perhaps throughout the body. Cancer in the lungs can block or destroy the alveoli. Gas exchange with the blood becomes much more difficult. There is overwhelming evidence that inhaling cigarette smoke greatly increases your chances of developing lung cancer.

FEEDBACK

1. a) When you have a cold infection your body produces extra mucus. Why does this help to get rid of the cold?
   b) What cold symptoms does this mucus production cause?
   c) Why does a cold infection often cause you to have a sore and swollen throat?
   d) List things you can do to prevent yourself from getting a cold.
2. a) What causes bronchitis?
   b) Why do you cough a lot when you have bronchitis?
   c) What telltale breathing sound does a doctor, who suspects your chest infection may be bronchitis, listen for?
3. a) What can you do to prevent yourself from developing emphysema when you get older?
   b) Why does a person not recover from emphysema?
4. a) What lifestyle habit can you practise to lower your risk of developing lung cancer?
   b) What does lung cancer do to your lungs?

Fig. 31 *This is what lung cancer does to a lung.*

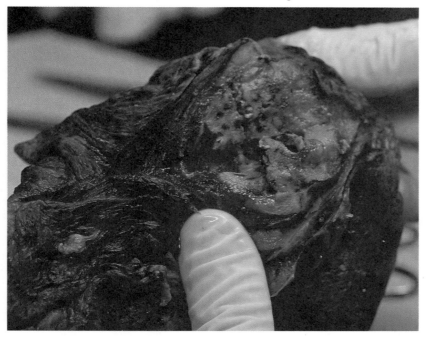

5.15 **Those Strange Sounds**

Every once in a while, your diaphragm may go into spasms of contractions. The reason for this isn't clear, but the result is that you **hiccup**. When the diaphragm muscle contracts suddenly, it flattens out and air rapidly rushes into your lungs. To stop this rush, the epiglottis clamps down over the trachea, producing the "hic" sound. The air flow is stopped so quickly by this action that your body suffers a jolt. The "cup" sound is produced by the air rushing out by the epiglottis as it relaxes.

If you are forced to sit quietly for a while, your breathing may become slow and shallow. You may become bored or very sleepy and begin to sigh or yawn. A **sigh** is a small gasp of air drawn deeply into the lungs. A **yawn** involves a sudden gasp of air drawn deeply into the lungs. The increased intake of air lets you be more alert for a while. Then, the slow, shallow breathing pattern resumes, and soon you are sighing or yawning again.

The surface of the windpipe near the epiglottis is very sensitive to touch. Any bits of matter such as food, or dust, or mucus from a runny nose that touch this area cause quite a reaction. An explosive blast of air, the **cough**, is released by your lungs. The purpose of the cough is to blow the bits of matter out of your windpipe. This prevents any blocking of the windpipe. The speed of the air through the windpipe is so great it can reach 100 km/h during a cough. The air is set in

Fig. 32 *Can you look at this photo without yawning?*

motion by a sudden upward thrust of the diaphragm and an inward push by the muscles of the rib cage. Frequent coughing can make these muscles tired and sore.

Cough remedies work in different ways. Some act to turn off the cells that produce the mucus in the nasal and sinus passages. If no mucus trickles down the throat the cough reflex isn't turned on. Other remedies turn off the part of the brain that sends the nerve signal to start the cough action. Sometimes other parts of the brain are also turned off. As a side-effect of this, you may feel sleepy and dopey.

Sneezes are similar to coughs. A sneeze is a blast of air that cleans matter, like dust or mucus, out of the nasal passages. A sneeze is triggered by something irritating the surface of the nasal passage. Air speeds up to 167 km/h have been recorded during a sneeze.

FEEDBACK

1. What causes the "hic" and the "cup" of a hiccup?
2. Why does your body make you sigh or yawn?
3. Compare coughs and sneezes for their similarities and differences.

SUPERSLEUTH

Write a short speech, letter, or radio commercial, or design a poster to discourage students from smoking.

5.16 Breathing Without Lungs

As you now know, your breathing system contains branching tubes that end in very delicate, thin-walled alveoli buried deep in your lungs. In these air sacs you exchange oxygen and carbon dioxide with your blood. You have to keep your gas exchange surfaces clean, warm, and moist. Usually, only dust, dirt, germs, and harmful chemicals which are in the air you

It's a Fact
Harmful chemicals, like cancer-causing agents and other pollutants in smoke can stop or disrupt the normal life activities of the alveolar cells.

151

breathe can reach them. The wet, cilia-lined surfaces of most of your breathing tubes warm, moisten and clean the air passing through them. Other animals have gas exchange surfaces which are in very different places in their bodies.

Tadpoles and fish exchange oxygen and carbon dioxide with the air that is dissolved in the water they swim in. They don't move water into and out of lungs as you move air. Instead, their thin gas exchange surfaces are feathery-looking gills on either side of the body, just behind the head. As the tadpole or fish swims, water passes over these gills and gas exchange with the blood happens on the gill surfaces. Next time you have the chance to observe swimming tadpoles or fish, look for these pink (because they are so full of blood) feathery structures. They are quite exposed, like whiskers, on

Fig. 33 *Inside a fish gill*

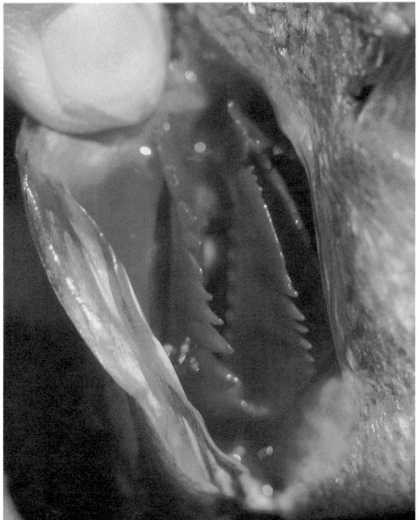

tadpoles. On fish, they are protected by flaps of muscle-covered skin. You can watch the fish drawing water into its mouth and out through its gills, coordinating the opening and closing of each.

The gas exchange surface of the earthworm is even more exposed and vulnerable than that of the tadpole or fish. It is its skin! Earthworms live in damp soil that contains air pockets. The soil's moisture keeps the earthworm wet, so that it can exchange oxygen and carbon dioxide through its skin with the air in the soil. (The oxygen and carbon dioxide molecules dissolve in the moisture on the worm's skin.) When the surface soil gets too dry, the earthworms dig deeper to find moister soil. The opposite situation can also occur. After a heavy rain, the soil can get so water-logged that the air is driven out of it. Then the earthworms have to come up to the surface; otherwise they would suffocate and drown.

It's a Fact
Single-celled **protist** organisms really keep it simple. They use their cell membranes as gas exchange surfaces.

FEEDBACK

1. In what kinds of conditions do you cough and sneeze more? Explain why.
2. A goldfish will die of suffocation if it gets out of the water in its bowl, yet it doesn't suffocate and drown as long as it's in water. Why?
3. Why are earthworms found on sidewalks and pavement during and after heavy rains?
4. Copy this chart into your notebook. Complete it.

Organism	Where does it live?	How does it exchange gases with its environment?
human		
earthworm		
tadpole or fish		

153

5.17 You Are What You Eat

You've probably heard this saying, and it is very true. You ARE what you eat. **Nutrients** are the food molecules that your cells need to keep you alive and healthy. Inside your cells these molecules help to provide energy, to build and repair body parts, and to control chemical reactions.

The six nutrients that your body needs are:
- carbohydrates (sugars and starches)
- proteins
- fats and oils
- water
- minerals
- vitamins

The amounts of these nutrients that make up your body are shown in figure 34.

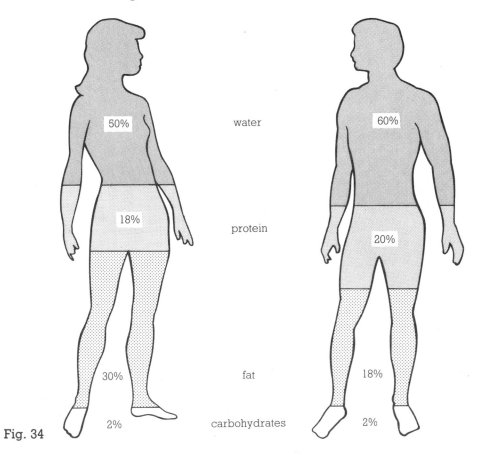

Fig. 34

Nutrients You Need		
Nutrients	Examples of Foods That Contain These Nutrients	What They Do
carbohydrates	bread, sugar, honey, potatoes, cereals, corn, rice, fruit, candy	• provide your body's main source of quick energy • supply energy to cells • store excess carbohydrates as fat
proteins	meats, milk, fish, cheese, eggs, peanut butter, vegetables	• used in repairing cells and building new cells • make up cell organelles, bones, hair, nails, muscles, and other tissues
fats, oils	butter, milk, ice cream, and fat, vegetable oil, cheese, peanut butter	• make up cell organelles • provide good energy reserve • insulate the body
water	vegetables, fruits, milk and other liquids most foods have water in them	• makes up most cytoplasm, extra-cellular fluid and blood • transports materials • dissolves materials so that chemical reactions can occur
VITAMINS: vitamin A	carrots, spinach, beets, sweet potatoes, butter	• help in proper growth • let you have good night vision
vitamin B (twelve types)	green and yellow vegetables, foods made from whole grain cereals	• aid in energy release from carbohydrates during respiration • allow your nerves to work properly
vitamin C	oranges, grapefruit, lemons, limes, tomatoes, and vegetables like spinach, and lettuce	• needed for growth • helps make blood vessels, teeth and gums strong
vitamin D	liver, fortified milk, made by your skin when exposed to sun	• aids in proper growth and maintaining bones and teeth
vitamin E	milk, butter, leafy vegetables, eggs	• needed for the proper functioning of many of the body's chemical reactions
vitamin K, (manufactured by bacteria in your intestines)	green vegetables, tomatoes	• helps your blood clot properly after you cut yourself
MINERALS: sodium chloride	table salt, salty-tasting foods	• assists you to digest your food • helps your nerve and muscle cells to work correctly
potassium and magnesium	fruits, and vegetables	• assist your muscles to contract
calcium and phosphorus	milk, cheese, eggs	• strengthen bones and teeth
iron	liver, meats, eggs, vegetables	• lets your red blood cells carry oxygen gas
Note: your body needs many more minerals as well		

FEEDBACK

Refer to page 155 to help you answer these questions.

1. Suppose that for lunch you have a peanut butter sandwich made with bran bread, a glass of milk and an orange.
   a) List the nutrients you would obtain.
   b) List the nutrients you would not obtain.
   c) Add items that would supply these missing nutrients.
2. Potatoes, corn, or rice are the major staple foods for much of the world's population. What major nutrient do these foods supply to humans?
3. If fruits and vegetables were not available for you to eat:
   a) What nutrients might be missing from your diet?
   b) List five different changes that could occur in your body and in the way you feel.
4. As a member of a sports team, like basketball or hockey:
   a) Why is it important to eat foods rich in magnesium and potassium?
   b) Why should some fats and oils be included in your diet?

Fig. 35

5.18 Out of the Food and Into the Cells

Imagine a juicy hamburger loaded with all the extras you really love. Sounds good? Can you smell it? Is your mouth watering? Has your stomach started to rumble? Do you suddenly feel hungrier than you were? The sight and smell of food can trigger your digestive system into activity, especially if you haven't eaten for a while and really like the food before you.

Food contains the nutrients you need. But food molecules are usually too big to go directly into your body cells. **Digestion** is the process that breaks your food into its nutrient molecules. These nutrient molecules are small enough to enter body cells by diffusion.

It is the job of the organs of your digestive system to break your food into nutrients that can enter your bloodstream and be taken to all your body cells. In the next part of this chapter, you will follow that amazing process.

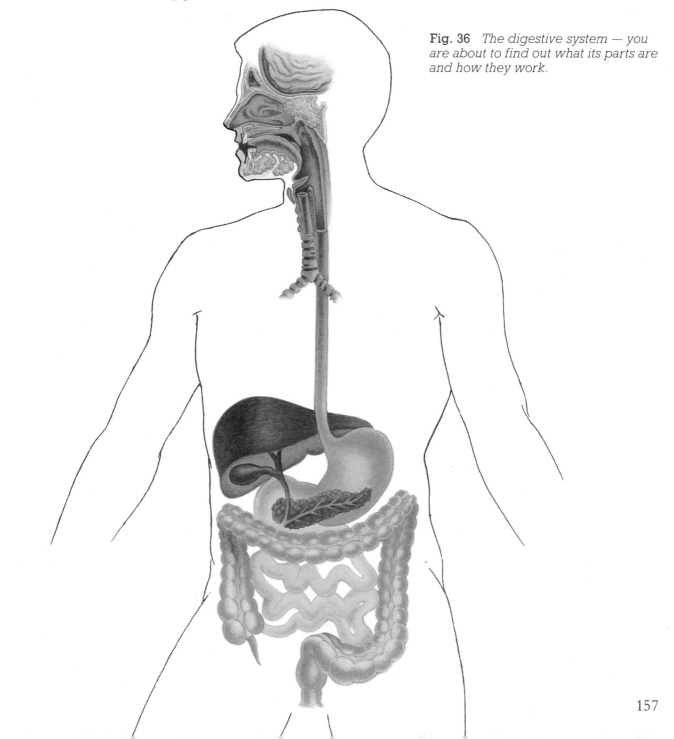

Fig. 36 *The digestive system — you are about to find out what its parts are and how they work.*

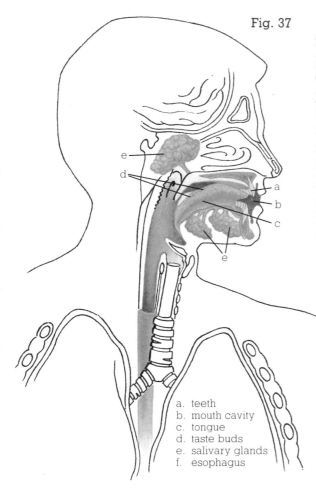

Fig. 37

a. teeth
b. mouth cavity
c. tongue
d. taste buds
e. salivary glands
f. esophagus

In your imagination, take a bite of that hamburger. Your front teeth, called **incisors** and **canines**, cut and tear bite-size portions from the food. Then you chew it. The next time you chew gum or a food that needs a lot of chewing, watch yourself in the mirror. Your lower jaw moves down and up and from side to side as you chew. As this happens, the broad, flat teeth at the sides of your mouth, your **molars**, grind the food into smaller chunks. At some time, you have probably bitten your **tongue** while you have been chewing. This happens because your tongue continuously moves while you chew, pushing food between your molars to grind it up. Because your jaw muscles exert a lot of force on the food while it is being chewed, a tongue bite can be very painful.

Taste buds embedded in the upper surface of your tongue help you to taste your food.

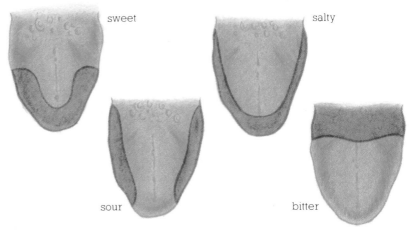

Fig. 38 *Taste regions of the tongue*

When you chew, **saliva** is squirted into your mouth from the **salivary glands** located in the sides and floor of your mouth. Saliva softens and moistens food and contains an enzyme that starts to break starch into sugar.

When your food is chewed and moist enough, your tongue forms it into small balls, about the size of large marbles, and pushes them to the back of your mouth. The food then passes into the **esophagus**, a flexible, rather flat muscular tube connecting the mouth to the stomach. **Swallowing** moves the food from the mouth to the stomach. A series of muscular contractions, called **peristalsis**, occur along the esophagus to squeeze the balls of food along this tube.

muscles contracting
(later)
ball of food
muscles relaxing

Fig. 39 *This is how peristalsis takes place inside the esophagus.*

Mucus is produced by glands in the walls of the esophagus. Mucus lubricates the food and the esophagus so that the food balls slide along easily.

The food balls from your bite of hamburger pass from the bottom of your esophagus into the side of your **stomach**, where they stay for about four hours. The stomach is a flexible bag-like structure in which several events occur:

- **Gastric juice** is released into the food from glands in the stomach wall. Enzymes in this juice act on the protein in the hamburger, digesting it into smaller molecules. Acid in the gastric juice helps kill germs that may be in the food.
- Glands in the stomach wall also produce mucus to protect the stomach from the acid and enzymes which will destroy the wall if they come into contact with it.
- Peristalsis by the strong muscles in the stomach walls grind, squeeze, and churn the food, to thoroughly mix it with gastric juice. The food becomes quite liquid and quite acidic.

At the bottom of the stomach is a ring of muscle called a **sphincter**. It opens and closes, allowing small squirts of food to enter the **small intestine**. This part of your digestive system is only about two centimetres in diameter but it is about seven metres long. Two major activities take place in it:

- digestion of your food into its nutrient molecules is completed
- the nutrients are absorbed into your bloodstream.

To accomplish the digestion process, enzymes are added to the food. Special glands in the wall of the small intestine produce some of these enzymes. More enzymes come from the **pancreas**, entering the small intestine through a small tube, the **pancreatic duct**. Peristalsis by the muscles of the small intestine's wall mix these enzymes with the food. The enzymes digest the carbohydrates, proteins, and fats in the food into their small nutrient molecules. Fats and oils are difficult to digest, because they are rather sticky and gummy. They get sloshed and swished into small droplets by peristalsis. Then they get coated with **bile**, a greenish liquid manufactured by the **liver**. Bile is stored in the **gall bladder** and travels through the **bile duct** into the small intestine. There it acts like a detergent on fats and oils, coating them so that they stay

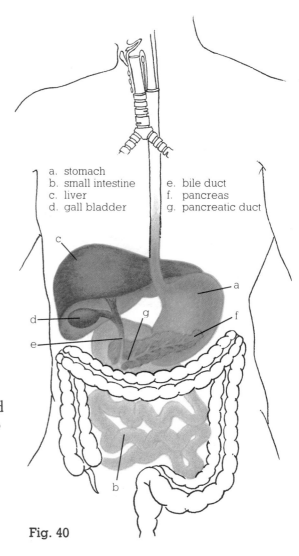

a. stomach
b. small intestine
c. liver
d. gall bladder
e. bile duct
f. pancreas
g. pancreatic duct

Fig. 40

159

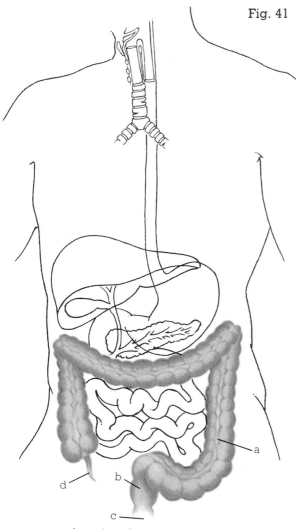

Fig. 41

a. large intestine
b. rectum
c. anus
d. appendix

in small drops. Fat-digesting enzymes from the pancreas and the small intestine can digest the fats and oils more quickly, as a result. Bile also neutralizes stomach acid.

The useful small nutrient molecules, like glucose, that result from the breakdown process of digestion, now diffuse through the lining of the small intestine into the bloodstream. The blood carries these important molecules to all cells of the body, using the double circuit route of the circulatory system already described. This process of **absorption** in the small intestine needs a great deal of surface area so that it can happen as quickly as possible. The inside lining of the lower end of the small intestine is folded into thousands of microscopic-sized finger-like ridges, called **villi**. Inside each villus is a network of capillaries through which the blood flows.

Food remains in the small intestine for about twelve hours. By that time, only the parts of the food that cannot be digested and much of its water content still remain in it. This watery, rather brownish mixture enters the side of the **large intestine**, a tube which is 5 cm wide and 1.5 m long.

The main function of the large intestine is to absorb water from the waste material passing through it. This water passes into the bloodstream, conserving water, so that you don't have to drink so much of it.

As water is absorbed from the undigested parts of food, what remains becomes thicker and thicker. Finally, after twelve to fourteen hours, it piles up in a thick mass called **feces**. The feces are stored temporarily in the **rectum**. During the process of **defecation** they are released through an opening, the **anus**, at the end of the large intestine. The anal opening operates by the opening and closing of a sphincter muscle there. You learn to control the actions of this muscle.

FEEDBACK

1. What is digestion, and why is it necessary?
2. What are incisors, canines and molars and what job does each do?
3. What job does your tongue do as you chew your food and after you have finished chewing?

4. Name two ingredients that saliva adds to the food you are chewing.
5. What does peristalsis accomplish during swallowing?
6. What is the job of each of these in your stomach?
   - enzymes
   - stomach acid
   - mucus
   - peristalsis
7. Describe the small intestine:
   a) What are its two major activities?
   b) How do the pancreas and liver help it?
8. a) What happens during the process of absorption?
   b) What are villi? Where are they found? Why are they important?
9. Your large intestine:
   a) What is in the brownish mixture that enters it?
   b) What are its two functions?
10. What is the function of each of the following:
    - rectum
    - anal sphincter

Think about it

1. Imagine that you are a bit of that big juicy hamburger as it travels in your digestive system until its nutrients enter your blood. What pathway would you follow? Copy this pattern into your notebook, then fill it in.

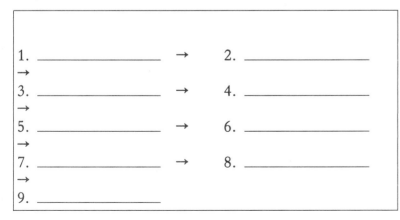

Do this by rearranging these parts of your digestive system in their correct order: anus, esophagus, large intestine, lips, small intestine, rectum, stomach, teeth, tongue.

YOUR BODY'S BACTERIA COULD FILL A SOUP CAN. SUBTRACT THOSE WHICH LIVE IN THE GUT AND THE REST COULD ALL HIDE IN A THIMBLE.

2. Trace figure 42 onto a page in your notebook. Correctly label all the parts identified by letters. Also draw arrows to show the pathway of food. Remember to give your diagram a suitable title.

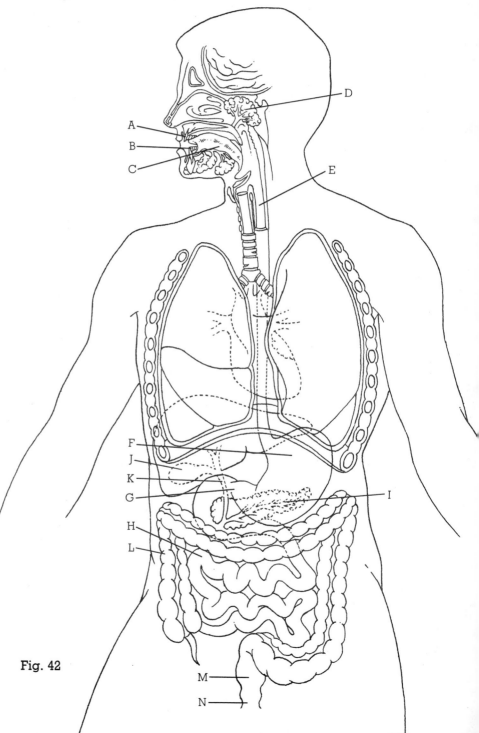

Fig. 42

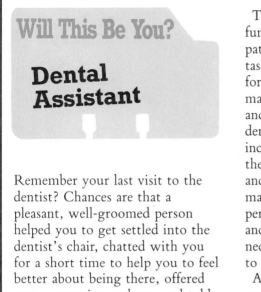

Dental Assistant

Remember your last visit to the dentist? Chances are that a pleasant, well-groomed person helped you to get settled into the dentist's chair, chatted with you for a short time to help you to feel better about being there, offered you a magazine perhaps, and told you that the dentist would be with you in a few moments. That was the dental assistant.

The dental assistant's primary function is to assist the dentist as patients are treated. Technical tasks include preparing the patient for treatment, preparing materials, maintaining a clear operating area, and passing instruments to the dentist. Other responsibilities include developing X-rays, keeping the office and reception room neat and pleasant, greeting patients, managing the appointment book, performing simple book-keeping and accounting, ordering necessary supplies, and attending to correspondence.

A dental assistant who is courteous and thoughtful with patients, in the office or on the telephone, is important to the success of a dentist's practice.

Good physical health and stamina are essential because the assistant has a busy and active day. There is a certain amount of nervous strain associated with the work since some patients are not at their best when visiting the dentist.

It is still possible to become a dental assistant with on-the-job training. Most dental assistants, though, are trained by going to community college or dental assistant school. A high school diploma is necessary.

Trained dental assistants are in demand. They usually begin at a moderate salary which increases according to work experience.

Will this be you?

Fig. 43 *A dental assistant might prepare a patient for further dental work by cleaning his or her teeth.*

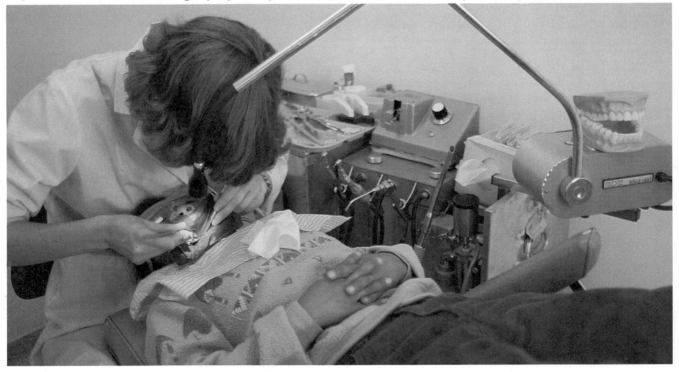

5.19 Enzymes in Action on Proteins

You know that enzymes are added to your food during digestion to help break the food down into nutrients your body can use. Your body contains hundreds of kinds of enzymes. Each enzyme controls a specific kind of chemical change. Some break large molecules apart. In Chapter 1 you performed an investigation that involved the enzyme amylase in your saliva. This enzyme digests starch molecules into sugar molecules that your body cells can absorb and utilize. Other enzymes join small molecules together to make larger ones. This happens when you grow, or repair damaged cells and tissues.

In fact, enzymes control all the chemical reactions that make you alive, and this is a very good thing. For example, a large slice of

chocolate cake contains about the same amount of chemical energy as one half a cup of gasoline. This is enough energy to raise your body temperature about 10°C, a fever that would kill you! Luckily, enzymes in your body slow down the speed at which energy in food is released. This means that you burn food, but the food won't burn you.

Each enzyme works best under certain conditions like temperature, acidity, and the presence of specific chemicals. In this investigation you will see the action of the enzyme **pepsin**, a protein-digesting enzyme found in gastric juice. Gastric juice also contains hydrochloric acid.

Find out

Are both the enzyme pepsin and hydrochloric acid necessary to digest a protein, like egg white?

You need

- safety goggles
- test tubes with rubber stoppers (4)
- test tube rack
- labelling equipment
- 10 mL graduated cylinder
- 40 mL water
- eyedropper
- 20 drops acid
- 20 mL pepsin enzyme solution
- equal-sized cubes cooked egg white protein (4)

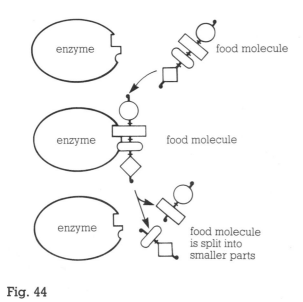

enzyme

food molecule

enzyme

food molecule

enzyme

food molecule is split into smaller parts

Fig. 44

Handle acid with care since it is corrosive. If any spills, immediately rinse the area with lots of water.

Try this

1. What is your prediction concerning the Find Out question? *Record your prediction*.
2. Label the test tubes as shown in the diagram.
3. Identify the test tube rack with the names of the members of your group.
4. Prepare each test tube as shown in figure 45.

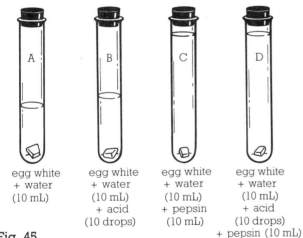

A	B	C	D
egg white + water (10 mL)	egg white + water (10 mL) + acid (10 drops)	egg white + water (10 mL) + pepsin (10 mL)	egg white + water (10 mL) + acid (10 drops) + pepsin (10 mL)

Fig. 45

5. In your notebook, record what the contents of each test tube look like. *Label this information "Beginning of Investigation."*
6. Set the four test tubes in the test tube rack.
7. Store the test tubes in a warm place, preferably at 37°C for at least 24 h.
8. After at least 24 h, examine each test tube carefully. *In your notebook record what the contents of each test tube look like. Label this information "After 24 h."*
9. Clean up your work area.

What happened?

1. How could you tell that some egg white was digested?
2. Why was test tube A the control in this investigation?
3. What substances seem to be necessary to digest egg white protein?
4. What is significant about the temperature 37°C?
5. a) Answer the Find Out question.
   b) Did your results support your prediction?

Now you know

Egg white protein is not affected by water (the control), or acid, or pepsin. It is only when all three are present that digestion occurs. 37°C, normal body temperature, is the temperature at which pepsin works fastest. Since digestion is a rather slow process, food remains in your digestive system for more than a day before you discharge its remains from your body.

Animals are not the only organisms that produce enzymes that digest proteins. Plants do as well. For example, pineapple and papaya fruits each contain such enzymes. An enzyme from papaya, called papain, is one of the main ingredients in meat tenderizers.

SUPERSLEUTH

1. Design and carry out an investigation to show the effect of temperature on the ability of pepsin to digest protein.
2. Design and try out an activity to show the effects of pineapple juice and/or meat tenderizer on protein.

5.20 So What Goes Wrong?

Many problems that can affect the digestive system are preventable with a healthy diet and lifestyle. Knowing something about the problems helps you to make wise decisions.

Everyone worries about **halitosis**, bad breath. Halitosis can be caused by ill health, dental problems, or eating certain foods. It can be prevented by frequent, thorough cleaning of your teeth to remove the food particles caught between them and the **tartar** and **plaque** built up on them. These substances are the waste products of bacteria that always live in your mouth, feeding on the food caught between your teeth. These waste products are the cause of bad breath. Halitosis also occurs when you develop cavities, holes eaten through the tough enamel surface of the teeth by lactic acid, a waste product of the bacteria living in your mouth. The decaying material in the cavity can produce strong, unpleasant odours. Halitosis also occurs when you eat food containing strong spices, like garlic or onions. Practising good dental hygiene and avoiding highly spiced foods are ways to prevent halitosis.

Eating a lot can stretch your stomach to its fullest. Gastric juices make the contents very acidic. The stomach churns and squeezes to mix the food and the gastric juices. Sometimes the stomach is so full that part of this acidy mixture is pushed back up the esophagus. The acid irritates the inside wall of the esophagus. You might feel this as a burning sensation in the region just below your heart. You have **heartburn**.

Fig. 46 *When food and gastric juices are pushed back up the esophagus, you suffer from heartburn.*

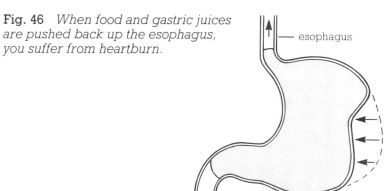

esophagus

Sometimes the stomach or intestine gets irritated. When this happens, your brain senses that all is not well and you feel ill. This nausea can be relieved by throwing up or **vomiting**. Backward contractions in the stomach, and strong squeezes by the abdominal muscles push the food up the esophagus and out of the mouth. You have to be careful that none of this food gets sucked into the windpipe by accident. This is called **aspiration** and can cause suffocation.

You may have noticed that your mouth and throat become very dry when you get nervous or tense. This happens because of a reduction in the amount of mucus being produced. The same situation occurs in your stomach and small intestine. Usually the insides of the walls of the stomach and small intestine are continuously coated by a thick layer of protective mucus. If the amount of mucus you produce decreases, **ulcers** can develop. These are sores that develop in the walls that line the inside of the stomach or small intestine. They occur when the enzymes and acid in the digestive juices come into contact with the walls, destroying cells that line them. Sometimes a hole is "eaten" deep into the wall and bleeding occurs. In a really serious case the damage may make a hole right through the wall. This is a **perforated ulcer**, a very serious problem, because the enzymes and acid of the stomach content can now damage other body organs besides those of the digestive system.

To prevent an ulcer from forming, or to give an ulcer a chance to heal, try to reduce the stress and nervous tension that prevent your body from producing its digestive fluids normally and efficiently. Plenty of rest, and daily exercise are two good stress and tension relievers. Spicy foods tend to increase the amount of acid produced, which increases the problem. Your doctor may recommend that you drink milk every few hours. Milk has a tendency to coat the inside walls of the stomach. It takes a long time for enzymes to digest milk, so that the milk coating acts like a substitute mucus coating for a short while.

At any given time, one quarter of the blood that leaves your heart is passing through your liver, the largest organ in the body. It operates continuously to keep your blood cleansed of any toxic substances. It also stores very valuable substances, like glucose and fat-soluble vitamins, until cells somewhere in your body need them, then it releases them back into the blood. Every second you wear out 30 million red blood cells! The debris of these cells is filtered out of the blood by your liver. Most of the debris is converted into bile and passed into the small intestine through the gall bladder and bile duct. Sometimes the liver produces more bile than it can get rid of. The bile breaks down in the liver. Some of the substances from this breakdown go into the bloodstream and act like poisons, turning the skin slightly yellow. This liver disorder is called **jaundice**.

The liver also filters out the excess amounts of the substance called **cholesterol** and sends it along the bile duct. Sometimes the cholesterol contributes to the crystallization of salts in the gall bladder, producing tiny **gallstones**. Occasionally, a gallstone leaves the gall bladder and blocks the bile duct. This causes intense pain as the pressure from the bile builds up. Often surgery is needed to remove the gallstones.

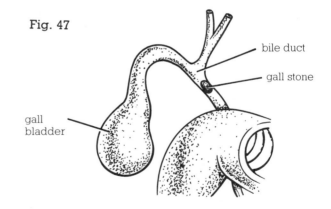

Fig. 47

bile duct

gall stone

gall bladder

Hepatitis is a very serious virus infection of the liver. The liver's normal functions are greatly disrupted causing very serious illness. The patient could die. Hepatitis occurs more frequently among people who inject non-medical drugs into their bodies.

Recall that one important product of the digestion of carbohydrates is the nutrient, glucose. Glucose is the simple sugar that is the energy source for all your cells' activities. Before your cells can use the glucose molecules they must diffuse from the blood through the cell membranes. This diffusion cannot occur without **insulin** also being present in the blood. Insulin acts like the key to open doors into cells.

Insulin is a hormone produced by certain cells in the pancreas. The disease called **diabetes** occurs when the pancreas does not produce enough insulin. The cells do not get enough glucose to function properly.

Until the early 1920s, people with diabetes usually died from the disease. A Canadian discovery provided for a way to control it. Three Canadians, Frederick Banting, Charles Best and John Macleod, identified a lack of insulin as the cause of diabetes. They separated insulin from the pancreas of animals during their research at the University of Toronto. On January 11, 1922 they gave the first injection of insulin to a human suffering from diabetes. That person showed remarkable improvement in health. In 1923 Banting and Macleod received the Nobel Prize for their discovery of insulin. Dr. Banting divided his share with Best. Thanks to the research of these pioneers and of subsequent researchers around the world, diabetics can now live quite normal lives.

Fig. 48 *Frederick Banting and Charles Best*

Sometimes the **appendix** becomes infected with bacteria. Fluids build up and pain occurs. The condition is known as **appendicitis**. An operation is often necessary to remove this diseased organ. If the appendix were to rupture, bacteria could be released inside the body to infect other organs, a very serious condition known as **peritonitis**.

Diarrhea results when the large intestine doesn't absorb enough water from the indigestible food remnants passing through it. The feces produced are very loose and watery. There are several causes of diarrhea, for example, a change in diet, bacterial or viral infections, stress. Severe prolonged diarrhea can result in dehydration of your body cells. Death could result. Always be sure to drink lots of fluids if you are suffering from diarrhea.

Sometimes too much water is removed from the waste material passing through the large intestine. The feces that collect in the rectum are drier and harder than normal. Elimination of the feces is difficult. This condition is known as **constipation**. To prevent it make sure you eat lots of whole grain products, fruits and vegetables and bran, foods that contain a lot of fibre, and drink lots of liquids.

The outer layer of your stomach and intestines is made up of strong muscles. These muscles carry out peristalsis, squeezing and pushing around the food to make it mix with digestive juices and to move it along. The sloshing around that results produces the **gurgles** that you can hear and sometimes feel.

Several hours after a meal, the stomach empties. The stomach muscles stop contracting for another hour or so. When they start up again, their squeezing and pushing result in **hunger pangs**.

At times, pockets of air or other gases get caught in the food passing through your digestive system. This can happen if you eat quickly, gulping down your food or drink. The pockets of air in your stomach rise to the top of your stomach and collect in the dome there. Every once in a while a peristalsis contraction in the wall of this dome pushes some of the air back up the esophagus. This air often makes a noise as it comes back up. You call these noises **burps**, or if they are loud and prolonged, **belches**. Burps and belches often make you feel better because getting rid of the pockets of air relieves the pressure inside, and the stomach wall is not stretched as much.

Certain kinds of foods, like egg yolks, beans, soya-based foods, foods that contain sulfur, cabbage, Brussels sprouts or squash cause the bacteria growing in your large intestine to produce gases, like carbon dioxide and hydrogen sulfide (rotten egg gas). These gases collect in pockets in the wastes passing along, and peristalsis eventually moves them to the rectum, from which they are expelled along with the feces. This condition is known as **flatulence**, passing wind.

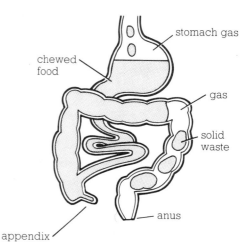

Fig. 49

FEEDBACK

1. a) What are tartar and plaque?
   b) What causes tooth cavities?
   c) What is halitosis? What are its causes, and how can you prevent it?
2. What happens that causes aspiration, when vomiting occurs?
3. a) What are ulcers? Why do they develop?
   b) How can you avoid getting an ulcer?
4. a) What substances does your liver store for you until you need them?
   b) From what substances does it make bile?
5. What causes:
   a) the yellow tinge you may develop if you get jaundice?
   b) hepatitis
6. a) What part of your body makes insulin?
   b) Why is insulin important to you?
   c) Name the disease that results if your body can no longer produce enough insulin.
7. What causes diarrhea and constipation, and how can each be prevented?

SUPERSLEUTH

Obtain a copy of "Nutrient Value of Some Common Foods." Use it to identify foods high in cholesterol that should be avoided.

171

5.21 It's Time to Have a Look—The Dissection of a Frog

It would be rather inconvenient to examine most of the organs of your own breathing and digestive systems. However, there are many animals with the same basic internal parts that you have for these two systems. The parts are even arranged very much like yours. The frog is one such animal.

In this investigation you will perform a detailed study of some of the internal organs of a frog, as you follow the steps of this **dissection**. Do the dissection carefully, following the steps exactly and asking for help whenever you think you need it.

You need

- preserved frog
- dissecting surface
- dissecting pins (8)
- scissors
- forceps
- probe
- eyedropper
- ruler
- microscope slide
- stereo microscope
- disposable plastic gloves
- damp paper towels
- plastic bag
- labelling materials

Find out

What do the internal organs of a frog look like?

Fig. 50

SAFETY ALERT!

- Wear plastic gloves, if they are available, to protect your hands from the chemicals in which the frog was preserved. If no gloves are available, wash your hands frequently.
- Work in a well-ventilated area to avoid breathing the fumes of the preserving chemicals.
- Each day when you finish your work, remove the frog from the dissecting surface and wrap it in damp paper towels. Put it into a plastic bag, and close the bag to make it air tight. This keeps the frog in good condition for the entire time you are dissecting it. Remember to label the bag with the names of the people in your group.
- Thoroughly rinse and dry all your dissecting equipment at the end of each session to keep it from rusting.
- Wash your hands thoroughly, using soap and water, after each session.

Try this

Part A: An Initial Look

1. Rinse the preserved frog thoroughly in cold running water to remove preserving solution.
2. Study the frog's skin. *Describe what the skin looks like, and how it feels.*
3. Study the frog's head to locate the position of the eyes, nostrils, and eardrums. *Trace the outline of the side of a frog's head shown in figure 51. Put in and label the position of an eye, nostril, and eardrum.*

Fig. 51

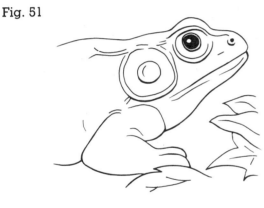

4. Compare the feet of the frog to your own feet, for similarities and differences. *Record your findings. Labelled diagrams could be a good way to do this.*

Fig. 52

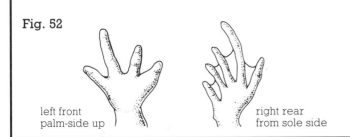

left front palm-side up

right rear from sole side

Part B: The Grand Opening

1. Lay the frog on its back (**dorsal**) surface on the dissecting surface. You may wish to anchor it to that surface, using pins, so that it will not slide around.

Fig. 53

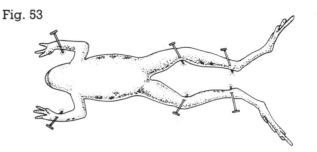

2. The frog's skin is attached quite loosely to its muscles. Use forceps to gently hold the skin free of the muscles on the belly (**ventral**) surface (see figure 54). Use the scissors to make a small crosswise nick through the skin at the point (X) (figure 54). Cut lengthwise from this nick to make a cut (incision) from where the hind legs join all the way to the chin (Y) (figure 55). Then make sideways incisions through the skin from a to b, and c to d, as shown in figure 55. Two flaps of skin result. Any liquid that oozes out is preserving fluid and it can be sponged up with paper towel.

Fig. 54

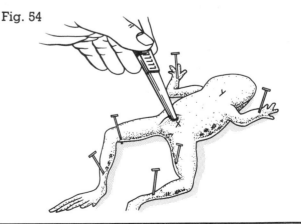

continued

Fig. 55

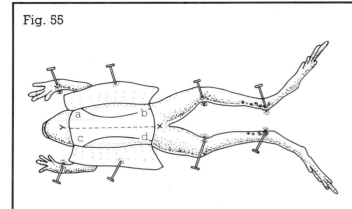

Fig. 56

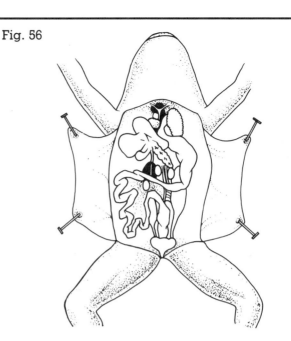

3. Open these flaps of skin like the pages of a book. They may have to be separated from the body wall underneath in places where they are attached. Use a point of the forceps, probe, or scissors to do this. Anchor the flaps to the dissecting surface using pins. If they won't anchor easily, cut them off, wrap them in paper towel and discard them in the place specified by your teacher. (See figure 55)

4. Find the blood vessels under the skin. Observe the muscle layer which is the belly (**abdomen**) wall. There is a large blue vein located in the mid-line of this wall.

5. Repeat the X to Y cut of step 2, this time through the abdomen wall. Do not let the scissor points damage the organs lying just underneath. Extend the cut up towards the jaw. When you get close to the front legs, cut slowly and carefully. This is the region where the heart and lungs are, which you don't want to damage. Also, the breastbone between the front legs must be cut through carefully.

6. Make the a to b and c to d cuts of step 2 in the muscle wall as well, so that the flaps of muscular tissue can be separated from the organs underneath. Anchor these muscle flaps to the dissecting surface or cut them off if they won't anchor easily.

7. Next, dissect the head region of the frog so that the mouth will open easily or stay open. Slip the point of the probe into the mouth at the very front and open the jaws a bit. Then use the scissors to cut the skin and muscles a little at the corners of the mouth so that the jaws will stay open. Do this without damaging the very large tongue which nearly fills the frog's mouth.

Fig. 57

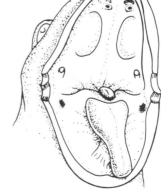

174

Part C: Take a Deep Breath

1. *Trace this diagram carefully into your notebook. Label the skin on the diagram.*

Fig. 58

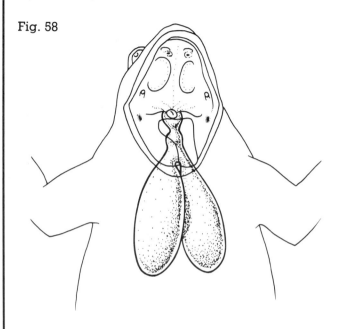

2. Look in the mouth to find the inner opening of the nostrils. They are two openings in the roof of the mouth at the sides of the bumps that are teeth. Pass the pointed end of a pin through a nostril on the outside of the head to have it come out the internal opening. Do this on both sides. You have located the frog's nose passages. *Label the position of the internal nostrils on the diagram. Draw in and label the position of the nose passages.* Remove the pins.

3. Next, locate the slit-like opening in the floor of the mouth, under the tongue. Insert the open end of the eyedropper into this opening. If you have located the correct opening, squeezing the bulb of the eyedropper may inflate the lungs with air. The opening you have found is the glottis. *Label the position of the glottis on the diagram.*

4. Locate the trachea by GENTLY inserting the probe through the glottis into the beginning of it. Be careful not to damage anything. With the forceps GENTLY move the body organs around so you can see the trachea. Trace the path of the trachea to the branching bronchi and the lungs. Look carefully. They are small and are underneath the liver, heart, and stomach which are lying on top of them. The lungs will probably be embedded in yellow finger-like deposits of fat. They look like large, wrinkled raisins. *Label the position of the trachea, bronchi, and lungs in the diagram.*

Fig. 59

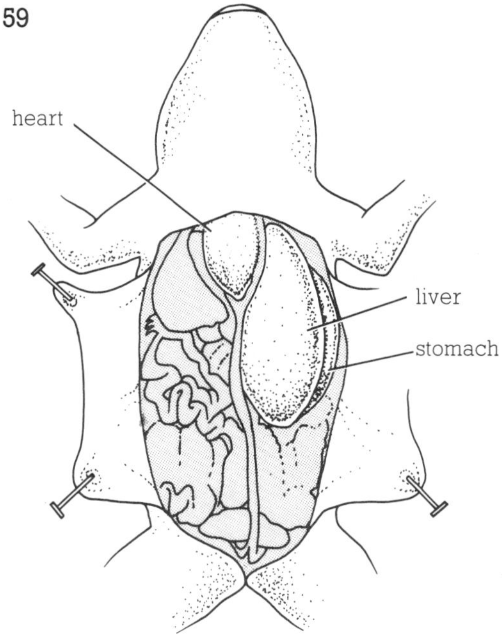

heart
liver
stomach

5. Determine if the frog has a diaphragm. *Record your findings on the diagram.*

6. Using the forceps and scissors, cut open a lung and observe the insides. *Describe the appearance of the inside of a frog's lung.*

7. *Give the diagram a suitable title.*

continued

Part D: The Food Processor

1. *Trace this diagram carefully into your notebook.*

Fig. 60

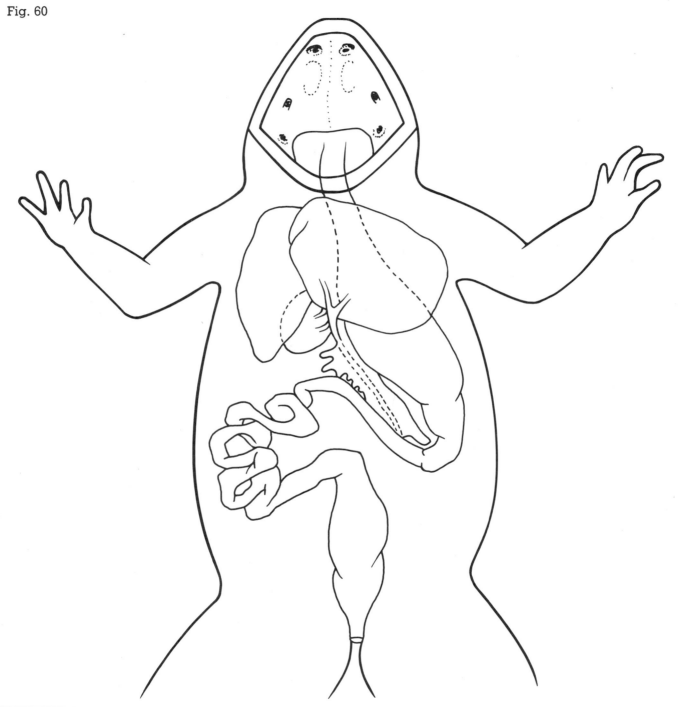

2. Observe the inside of the frog's mouth. Use the probe to locate the teeth. Be sure to rub along the jaw lines, and over the roof of the mouth especially over the two bumps between the internal openings of the nostrils. *Label the position of the teeth on the diagram. Record which way the teeth are pointing.*

3. Observe the frog's tongue, especially its tip and where it is attached to the lower jaw. *Into the diagram, draw the frog's tongue, what its tip looks like, and where it is attached to the mouth. Label all of these.*

4. Inside the mouth, locate the position of the eyeballs. *Draw in and label the position of the eyeballs in the diagram.*

5. Gently use the probe to find the opening of the esophagus at the back of the mouth. If you get the correct opening, you can gently pass the probe down the esophagus and into the stomach. *Label the opening of the esophagus and the esophagus itself in the diagram.*

6. The stomach is a fairly large organ, slightly J-shaped, and situated on the frog's left side. Find the stomach in your frog. *Label the stomach in the diagram.*

7. The small intestine begins at the bottom of the stomach. Find this tube in the frog. *Label the small intestine in the diagram.*

8. The wider, bottom portion of the frog's digestive system consists of the large intestine and the rectum. Find these parts in the frog. *Label the large intestine and the rectum in the diagram.*

9. The anus is the opening of the rectum to the outside of the frog. Locate this on your frog. *Label the anus in the diagram.*

10. Locate the frog's liver. This large organ is located almost under the bone between the front legs, and under the heart. Count the number of sections in the liver. *Label the liver in the diagram, and include the number of sections it has. Draw in and label the heart, as well.*

11. Find the gall bladder, the small sac attached to the middle section of the liver. *Label the gall bladder in the diagram.*

12. The pancreas may be hard to find. Locate the area in the frog where the small intestine joins the stomach, and using forceps, lift the intestine there. The flat, yellowish organ that you see is the pancreas. Don't get confused with the fingers of yellow fat that may be all over the place there. *Label the pancreas in the diagram.*

13. Tease away the membrane tissue that keeps the small intestine looped up. Straighten out the small intestine and measure its length in centimeters. *Record its length beside its label.*

Part E: What Was for Lunch?

1. Remove the stomach by making cuts a and b, as shown in figure 61.

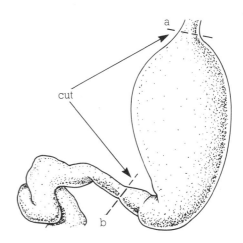

Fig. 61 *Stomach*

continued

2. Insert the tip of the scissors at the a end of the stomach. Cut the stomach open from a to b. Use the stereo microscope and a microscope slide to examine the stomach's contents. *Describe these contents.*

3. Clean out and discard the contents of the stomach. Then examine the inside lining of the stomach with the stereo microscope. *Describe how the inside of the stomach looks.*

4. Next, cut through the small intestine at the point where it joins the large intestine. Remove the small intestine. (You may have to cut more of the thin membrane that attaches the intestine to the rest of the body organs.)

5. Cut open a small piece of the intestine. Use the stereo microscope to examine its inner surface, and locate the villi. *Describe this inner surface. A diagram would be a good way to do this; be sure to label the villi.*

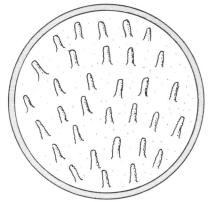

Fig. 62 *Villi*

6. Finally, cut open the large intestine. Use the stereo microscope to examine its contents. Try to figure out what kind of material the frog could not digest, and what kinds of things the frog had eaten. Consult with other groups. *Record your findings.*

What happened?

1. How does the skin on a frog's arm or leg compare to your own?

2. How do a frog's ears compare to your own?

3. Compare the air pathway of the frog from atmosphere to lungs to your own air pathway.

4. Frogs have very few teeth, certainly not enough for chewing their food (usually flying insects). What would a frog use its teeth for?

5. a) Compare where the frog's tongue is attached to where your own tongue is attached.
   b) How does this arrangement help a frog to catch its food?

6. When a frog swallows, it depresses its eyeballs into its mouth cavity. Why would this help it swallow?

7. a) Compare the food pathway of the frog from mouth to anus to your own food pathway.
   b) In what other ways is the frog's digestive system similar to your own?

8. a) Why was the frog's gall bladder difficult to find?
   b) What fluid is stored in the gall bladder?

9. What had the frog eaten?

10. a) What nutrient do you absorb into your blood through the large intestine?
    b) Why is it not necessary for a frog to keep this nutrient in its body?

11. Trace all of the diagrams in figure 63, and the frog's body outline in figure 60. Position all the cutouts where they belong in the frog's body outline. Tape them in place. Colour the organs of each system. *Label all the organs. Give your finished diagram a suitable title.*

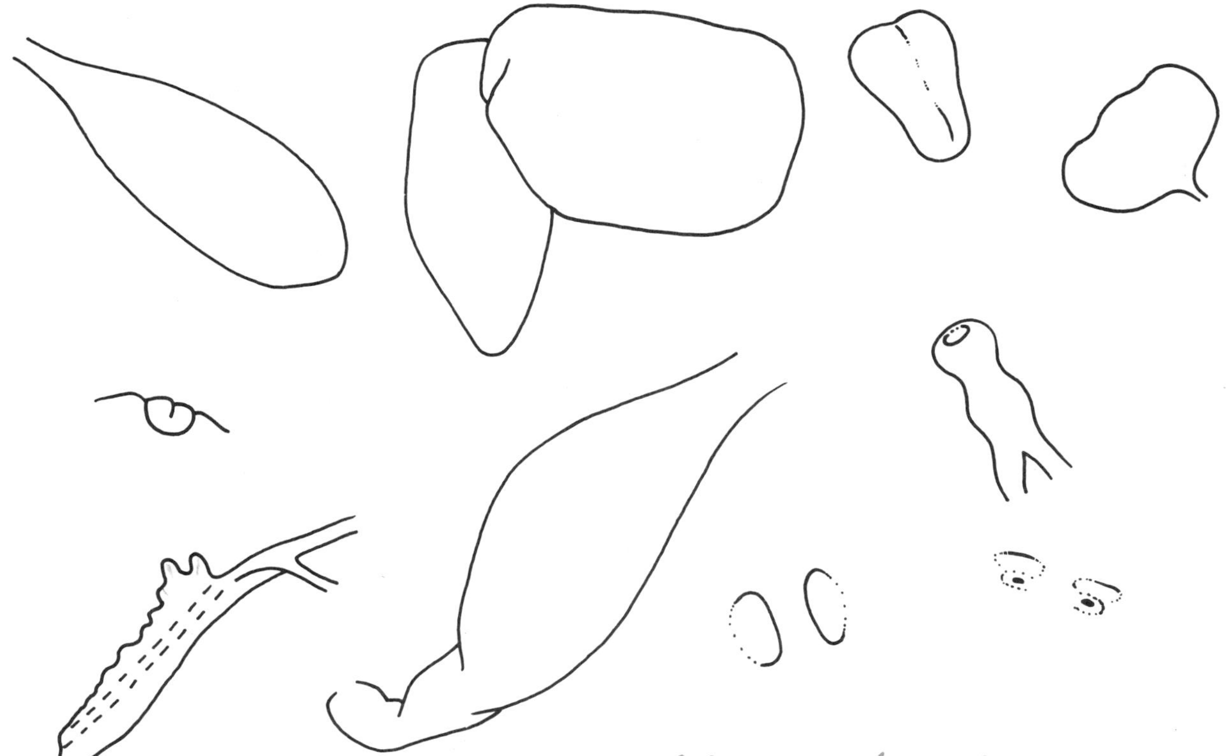

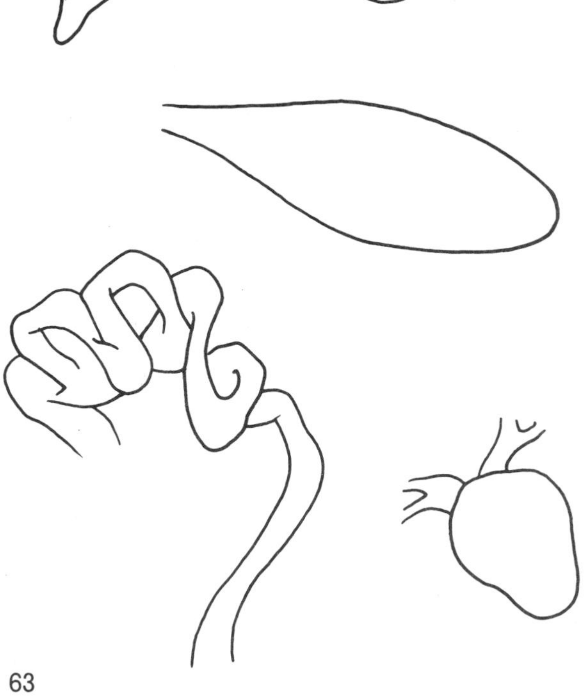

Fig. 63

Congratulations! You have successfully dissected a frog. Perhaps you liked the project, or perhaps you are very glad it is finished.

Frogs have many specialties to allow them to breathe and to eat in water. The external nostrils have flaps to close them and are raised above the snout, so that the frog can float almost submerged but still able to breathe. The frog's eyes are positioned so that it can see while floating. The tongue is marvelously adapted to catch the frog's meal, flying insects.

The frog is very similar to you in many parts of its breathing and digestive systems. The frog's body organs are located in almost the same places yours are. Because of these similarities you have been able to see somewhat the way you look inside. This is why dissections are done.

5.22 You Can't Beat The System

Your body is the most incredible machine on Earth. No computer can match your brain. No car engine uses fuel as efficiently as your muscles use food. No building is as well designed as your skeleton. You are absolutely wonderful!

Part of this wonder starts with the way your body is organized into **systems**. A system is a collection of parts that work together to accomplish a certain purpose. Each system in your body has only one main task to perform. Thus each system can have structures (they are called **organs**) that are specialized for this task.

Complex animals like humans have eleven organ systems:
1. The Skeletal System provides a frame to support and protect other systems.
2. The Muscular System creates movement.
3. The Circulatory System transports oxygen gas, nutrients, and waste products throughout the body.
4. The Breathing System makes oxygen gas available to your blood and removes carbon dioxide and excess water from it.
5. The Nervous System responds to the environment and controls actions of many parts of your body.
6. The Digestive System changes the food you eat into molecules that your body can use.
7. The Excretory System removes waste products.
8. The Reproductive System produces sperm or eggs, and has the ability to produce babies.
9. The Endocrine System, made up of glands, controls certain chemical reactions.
10. The Lymphatic System helps to drain fluid from your body tissues, and helps fight infections.
11. Skin covers and protects all the body's systems.

No system can operate on its own. Each depends upon all the others. The failure of part of one system can have serious effects on all the other systems. Good physical health means all your systems are working properly.

1. Trace figure 64 into your notebook.
2. Read the description of each system. Locate the systems on the diagram by finding their numbers.
3. Choose a colour for each system and colour in the systems on the diagram.
4. Add to the diagram a key to connect the name and function of each system to the colour you used to identify it.

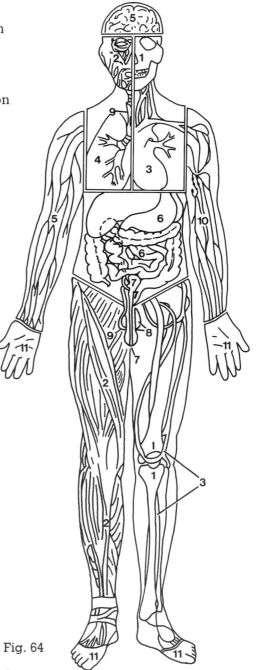

Fig. 64

181

THIS CONCERNS YOU

The Ten-million-dollar Man

"The reason I'm wheeling around the world is to create a greater understanding of the potential of disabled people." This was said by Rick Hansen, "The Man in Motion."

At the age of fifteen, Rick became a paraplegic, a person paralyzed from the waist down. This happened during a truck accident when he was struck in the back as he was thrown from the vehicle, and his spinal cord was damaged. But Rick never let his disability get him down. He became one of the finest wheelchair athletes the world has ever known. And he realized a dream—to establish a $10 000 000 fund that would be used to:

- increase awareness about the abilities of disabled people
- finance spinal cord research
- show the importance of sports and recreation in the rehabilitation of disabled persons.

Rick realized that dream before he was thirty. He circumnavigated the world, hand powering his wheelchair 40 073 km, a distance that is the actual circumference of the Earth. His two-year trip raised

Fig. 65

more than ten million dollars, and the Rick Hansen Man in Motion Canadian Trust Fund for Spinal Cord Research, Rehabilitation and Wheelchair Sport was established.

Your spinal cord is like a telephone cable, the brain is the central switchboard and your toes, fingers, arms, legs, and the other parts of your body are like telephone receivers. Your spinal cord is about the thickness of a pencil, and contains millions of nerve cells that pass down through the middle of the bones (vertebrae) of your backbone.

Though protected by these

vertebrae and cushioned by cerebral spinal fluid, the cord can be crushed by the whiplash of a car or motorcycle accident or the jolt of diving into shallow water and hitting a submerged object. If your spinal cord is crushed, your brain is unable to receive signals from, or send messages to, all the parts of the body below the region of injury. If the damage occurs in the neck, you become a quadriplegic, your body is paralyzed from the neck down. If the injury occurs further down the spinal column, you become a paraplegic, like Rick.

Fig. 66

Teams of scientific and medical researchers are working hard to develop successful treatments and cures for spinal cord injuries:

- Doctors are seeking ways to partially reverse or at least halt spinal cord damage within the first 24 hours of the accident. This increases the chances of recovery, and may prevent paralysis.

- Ways to get damaged nerve cells to regenerate, that is to grow back again, are beginning to be discovered. This means that the brain can once again control the muscles that were paralyzed.

- Electrical impulses from outside sources are being used to make paralyzed limbs move.

- Exercise programs and equipment to enhance muscle movements are being developed. It is very important to keep paralyzed muscles healthy and toned up and able to move, even though the brain can't direct these movements.

It costs a great deal to do such research.

Think about it

1. What would your life be like, what problems in everyday living would you have, if you were:
   a) a paraplegic, using a wheelchair in order to get around?
   b) a quadriplegic?

2. What precautions can you take to prevent spinal cord injury while driving or riding a car, truck, motorcycle, or all terrain vehicle like a snowmobile?

3. What precautions can you take to prevent spinal cord or head injuries when swimming?

4. List body conditions other than being paralyzed that may disable a person.

5. Part of Rick Hansen's dream was to increase awareness about the abilities of disabled people. Make a list of these abilities.

6. What would you do if you had $10 000 000?

7. Rick Hansen established the Man in Motion Canadian Trust Fund to provide funds for spinal cord research, for rehabilitation of the spinal cord disabled, and for promotion of wheelchair sports. There have been discussions about how much of the fund should be given to each area. If you were in control of the fund, how much would you grant for each area? Give reasons to support your amounts.

183

5.24 Chapter Summary

- Your body's cells need food nutrients, (carbohydrates, fats and oils, water, minerals and vitamins), oxygen gas and water. They get rid of carbon dioxide, poisonous wastes, and excess water.
- The process of diffusion allows substances to travel between your cells and the extra-cellular fluid surrounding them.
- Your circulatory system is made up of your heart, arteries, capillaries and veins. It transports the substances that your cells need and the waste products they produce.
- Respiration in your body cells uses oxygen to get energy out of the nutrients you have eaten and produces carbon dioxide and water.
- Your lungs take oxygen gas out of the air and put carbon dioxide and water into it.
- Gas exchange between air and your body takes place through your alveoli, in your lungs.
- To get to your alveoli, air first travels through your nose, pharynx, larynx, trachea, bronchi, and bronchioles. The air is cleaned, warmed, and moistened as it travels this pathway by hairs, adenoids, tonsils, cilia and mucus.
- Digestion is the process that breaks food into its nutrient molecules. It takes place mostly in your stomach and small intestine.
- Acid in your stomach helps to kill most bacteria and viruses in your food.
- Enzymes from your stomach, small intestine, and pancreas, and bile from your liver help cause digestion.
- Food nutrients are absorbed through the villi of your small intestine into your blood and carried to all your body cells by your circulatory system.
- Undigested food molecules pass through your large intestine and rectum and leave your body through the anus.
- Your body consists of eleven important systems that all interact to keep you alive.

5.25 Are you Ready to Go On?

Do Not Write in the Textbook

1. Copy each statement into your notebook, filling in each blank with the correct word.
   a) The basic things you need for staying alive are _____ , _____ and _____ .
   b) Substances can enter and leave cells by the process called _____ .
   c) For gas exchange, humans use _____ , earthworms use _____ and tadpoles and fish use _____ .

2. Choose the correct completion, then rewrite each of the following sentences in your notebook.
   - When exhalation occurs:
   a) air pressure pushes air into your lungs
   b) lung pressure pushes air out of your lungs
   c) air pressure pulls air out of your lungs
   d) lung pressure pulls air into your lungs.
   - An explosive blast of air released by your lungs is a:
   a) sigh b) yawn c) cough d) song.
   - Muscular contractions that move food inside your digestive system are called:
   a) absorption   c) digestion
   b) swallowing   d) peristalsis.
   - Under what conditions does egg white protein get digested?
   a) when it's in water
   b) when it's in water that is acid
   c) when it's in water that contains pepsin enzyme
   d) when it's in water that is acid and contains pepsin enzyme.
   - Dust and dirt particles are removed from inhaled air by:
   a) alveoli b) villi c) capillaries d) cilia

3. In your notebook, match the terms to their descriptions.

184

Terms: arteries, capillaries, heart, red blood cells

Descriptions:

a) the pump of your circulatory system
b) the thick-walled tubes that carry blood away from your heart
c) the thin-walled tubes where substances pass between the blood and the extra-cellular fluid around all your body cells
d) these cells carry gases in your blood

4. Describe the figure 8 pattern of your blood's circulation pathway.
5. What is the difference between gas exchange and respiration?
6. In your notebook match the terms to their descriptions.

Terms: alveoli, bronchioles, bronchus, epiglottis, glottis, larynx, nasal cavities, pharynx, trachea

Descriptions:

a) the air passages in the nose
b) the throat
c) the opening of the windpipe
d) the flap that opens and closes the windpipe
e) voice box, where the vocal cords are
f) the windpipe
g) the breathing tube that enters each lung
h) the smaller air passage tubes in the lungs
i) air sacs, where gas exchange between blood and air occurs

7. Name the six nutrients your body needs.
8. In your notebook, match the terms to their descriptions.

Terms: canines, incisors, large intestine, liver, molars, small intestine, stomach, taste buds, tongue, esophagus

Descriptions:

a) your teeth
b) pushes food around inside your mouth
c) let you taste your food
d) embedded in the upper surface of your tongue
e) the only part of your digestive system that is located in your chest
f) peristalsis happens here
g) where gastric juice works
h) its contents are very acid
i) the longest part of your digestive system
j) where digestion of food is completed and absorption takes place
k) manufactures bile
l) covered on inside surface with villi

9. Trace the pathway of a drop of blood from the time it enters the right side of your heart until it enters one of your villi.
10. Why is saliva so important?
11. Trace the pathway of a molecule of ice cream as it travels in your digestive system until its nutrients enter your blood.
12. In your notebook, match the terms to their descriptions:

Terms: appendicitis, aspiration, belches, bronchitis, cancer, constipation, emphysema, flatulence, halitosis, hepatitis, jaundice, laryngitis

Descriptions:

a) bad breath
b) food getting sucked into the windpipe
c) liver disorders
d) causes a wheezing and whistling sound in your chest
e) disorders of the large intestine
f) the noises caused by trapped gas in the digestive system
g) tumors that block and destroy alveoli
h) unable to speak
i) loss of alveoli

13. Why dissect a frog?
14. List arguments (reasons) you would use to try to convince your closest friend why it is a good idea not to smoke.
15. For how long is food in the digestive system after you swallow it?
16. What lifestyle habits can you practise to keep systems of your body in a healthy state?

Contents

Chapter Six
Keeping a Good Thing Going

6.1 What's So Special About You?

Do you think of yourself as someone special? Do you feel that there is no one else in the entire world who is exactly like you? You're quite right. You are the product of many different factors, all of which combine to make you a unique individual.

Fig. 2 *Individuals inherit traits like skin, hair, and eye colour, blood type, hair texture, and body build from their parents.*

Some factors are **hereditary**—such as the traits or characteristics, noted in figure 2 that you inherit from your parents. Some factors are environmental—these may be social, cultural, or physical factors. The characteristics they produce are **acquired** characteristics. For example, an accomplished musician may come from a family that enjoys music as a social activity; a good athlete probably grew up in the company of people for whom athletics were important. Cultural factors probably determine your native language and may affect your choice of clothes. Physical factors, such as diet and exercise, may affect your weight, your muscle development, and the condition of your heart.

Fig. 3 *Inuit drum dancing is a form of dancing that is an acquired characteristic.*

FEEDBACK

1. Explain the difference between hereditary characteristics and acquired characteristics.
2. List three of your characteristics which were inherited.

3. a) Name three of your characteristics that you believe were influenced by environmental factors.
   b) Name a characteristic that can be influenced by both hereditary and environmental characteristics.
4. Light intensity is an environmental factor that can affect acquired characteristics. Sunlight is influenced by the weather. Name two other environmental factors that are influenced by the weather, and that may affect the characteristics of plants.

Fig. 4 *These flowers are influenced by a number of environmental factors.*

Investigation

6.2 A Variety of Traits

Humans have thousands of traits. Some, such as hand structure, vary little from one individual to another. Others, such as eye colour, vary considerably. Brown, blue, hazel, grey, and green are common. How are such varied characteristics inherited? You can easily investigate a number of variations in humans by examining the people in your class.

Find out

A. What are some variations of traits in humans?
B. Which are inherited traits?
C. Which are acquired characteristics?

You need

• a class full of students.

Try this

1. *Copy the chart on page 190 into your notebook. Make it a full page in size.*
2. *In the "trait" column, list the different variations for each trait. For example, the variations in hair colour would be black, brown, blond, and red. Here are suggested variations for each trait:*
   Hair length — long, medium, short
   Eye colour — list at least three colours
   Skin colour — list at least two colours
   Wears eye glasses — yes or no
   Fingernails — short or long

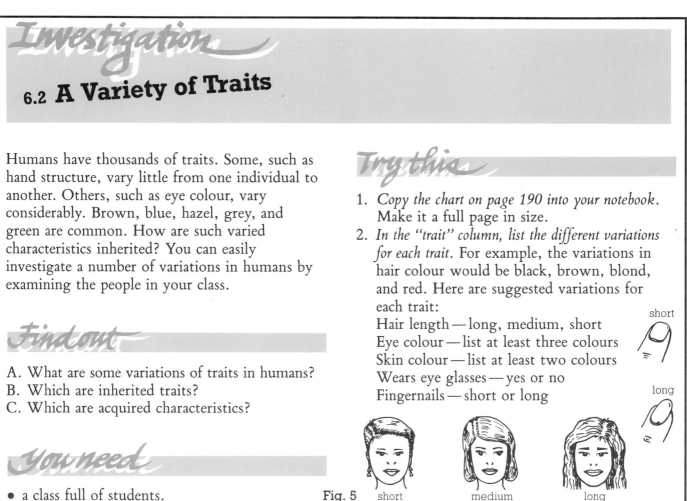

Fig. 5 short   medium   long

continued

3. Now observe each person in your classroom to examine the ten different traits. *For each variation of a trait that you identify, place a stroke in the "number" column.*

Trait	Variation	Number of each in class	Inherited?	Acquired?	Why do you think so?
hair colour	1. black 2. brown 3. blond 4. red	IIIIIi (11) IIIIIIII (16) III (3) I (1)			
hair length	1. 2. 3.				
eye colour	1. 2. 3. 4.				
skin colour	1. 2. 3. 4.				
wears eye glasses	1. 2.				
ear lobe (see figure 6a)	1. 2.				
tongue-roller (see figure 6b)	1. 2.				
fingernails	1. 2.				
left- or right-handed	1. 2.				
native language	1. 2. 3. 4.				

4. When all traits of all the people in your class have been examined and the variations counted, calculate the total for each variation. *Do some variations appear more frequently than others?*

a) Ear lobe — attached vs free
   The ear lobes of some people are completely attached to the side of the face. On others, the bottom of the ear lobe is not attached, or is free from the side of the face.

Fig. 6a

free ear lobes   attached ear lobes

b) Tongue roller — roller vs non-roller
   Some people can roll their tongue. Others can't.

Fig. 6b

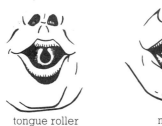

tongue roller   non-roller

5. *Decide whether each trait is inherited or acquired and check the appropriate column in your chart. (If you are uncertain, place a question mark in the column which you feel is most likely correct.)*

6. *In the last column, tell briefly why you think the traits are inherited or acquired.*

1. Which traits do you think are acquired?
2. Explain how any acquired trait could be changed by the person's environment or actions (behaviour).
3. Which traits do you think are inherited?
4. Which variations appear most frequently for:
   a) eye colour?
   b) ear lobe?
   c) tongue roller?

Now you know

You probably realize that some of the traits examined include things that can be changed. For example, people can remove their eyeglasses or cut their fingernails. People frequently learn a second language. Each of these characteristics is acquired in some manner.

Hair, eye, and skin colour, ear lobe type, tongue rolling, and left- or right-handedness are all traits inherited from your parents. Even if you wanted to do so, you could not permanently change them. You could dye your hair or wear tinted contact lenses, but that doesn't change your original natural colour. You could also lie in the sun to get a tan, but it would fade in time. The characteristics you inherited at conception are yours for life!

Some variations of inherited traits seem to be more common than others. In any large group of individuals selected at random in Canada, more people will have brown eyes than blue. More people can roll their tongues than can't. Free ear lobes are more common than attached ear lobes. Such odd relationships in variation numbers, or frequency of trait variations provide clues to understanding the inheritance of traits.

Investigation

6.3 A Question of Numbers

More than 100 years ago, a monk named Gregor Mendel cultivated a small garden in a monastery located in Austria. Here he experimented with the traits of pea plants. He made some interesting observations about the number relationship in inherited traits. You can do a similar investigation by examining some human traits, and counting the numbers of these traits as they occur in a large random sample population of people. The bigger the sample, the more representative your results will be; about 100 people would be good.

Find out

What is the special number relationship of some inherited traits?

You need

• a large random sample of people

Try this

1. *Copy the chart into your notebook.*
2. Divide the population so that each student in your class examines an equal number of people. Then share the results.
3. For each person examined, observe eye colour, ear type, and tongue type. (To simplify the task, consider green or hazel eye colour as brown, and grey eye colour as blue). *Place a stroke in the appropriate space in the chart, in the "your count" column.*
4. Obtain the results from the other members of the class. Your teacher may organize these data on the chalkboard. *Total the number of each variation, and place this total in the appropriate space in the chart.*
5. a) Now calculate the ratio for each pair of characteristics. Determine the characteristic with the smaller number. Divide this number by itself. The answer will be 1.

Trait	Variation	Your count	Total number of variation	Ratio of variations	Rounded off ratio
eye colour	blue	~~HHH~~ III			
	brown				
ear type	attached				
	free				
tongue type	cannot roll				
	can roll				

b) For each pair, divide the smaller number into the larger number. The answer will be greater than 1. These two calculated numbers, compared to each other, represent the ratio of one characteristic to the other in a pair. *Place this ratio in the "ratio of variations" column.*

6. In the last column, round off the larger number in the ratio to the nearest whole number. *How many brown-eyed people are there for each blue-eyed person? How many free ear lobes are there for each attached lobe? How many tongue rollers are there for each non-roller?*

What happened?

1. What ratio did you find for each trait?

Now you know

You already knew that some inherited variations occur more often than others. Now it is clear that the number relationship is not haphazard. In a large group of people for every blue-eyed person there are, on average, THREE brown-eyed people. For every person with attached ear lobes, there are THREE with free ear lobes. For every person who can't curl the tongue, there are THREE who can. This 3:1 ratio occurs for many other traits as well. It also occurs in other organisms, including the pea plants grown by Mendel.

Ratio of pea plant characteristics	
3	1
tall	dwarf
yellow seeds	green seeds
green pods	yellow pods
smooth pods	wrinkled pods
round seeds	wrinkled seeds

6.4 Pedigrees

Pedigree refers to the line of descent in a family. A **pedigree diagram** is a useful method of determining how traits are inherited. This technique is used to show which characteristics are present in each member of a family. Each person in the family is represented by a symbol, females by circles [O], and males by squares [□]. Traits are represented by different colours. Figure 7 shows a pedigree diagram for three generations of a family, and describes a condition of human eyes — normal vision vs. short-sighted vision. When a man

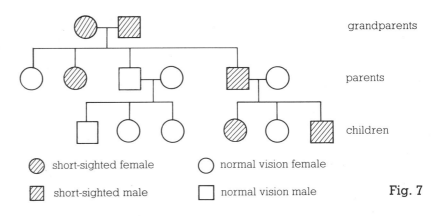

Fig. 7

grandparents

parents

children

⊘ short-sighted female ⃝ normal vision female
▨ short-sighted male ☐ normal vision male

and a woman are married, the circle and square which represent them are joined with a horizontal line. All their children are shown below them, connected by more lines. This pedigree includes three generations, but some pedigrees may include many more generations. If you examine the pedigree closely, some general conclusions may be drawn:

- For the offspring to be short-sighted at least one parent must be short-sighted.
- For the offspring to have normal vision, the parents may be any combination of vision. (Both may be short-sighted, both may have normal vision, or one may have normal vision while the other is short-sighted.)
- Two short-sighted parents produce both normal and short-sighted children.
- One short-sighted parent and one parent with normal vision produce both types of children.
- Two parents with normal vision produce only children with normal vision:

All this seems very complicated, but some simple conclusions are clear.

- Characteristics are passed on from parents to offspring. Short-sighted vision was passed on from the grandparents to one of their daughters and one of their sons. The son passed on short-sighted vision to two of his children.

194

- Some characteristics seem to be hidden in people. The grandparents did not have normal vision, but they were able to pass on normal vision to two of their children.
- Some characteristics seem to breed true. The man with normal vision and the woman with normal vision had children with normal vision only.

FEEDBACK

1. How are male and female individuals distinguished in a pedigree diagram?
2. How are two characteristics distinguished in a pedigree diagram?
3. A girl has blue eyes, brown hair, and normal vision. Where did she get these characteristics?
4. It is possible for two parents, both with brown eyes, to have children with blue eyes. How does this happen?

Investigation

6.5 A Family Pedigree

Some human disorders are inherited, or are influenced by heredity. Creating a family pedigree may be a useful aid for couples unsure about having children to determine if their children will inherit a disorder.

You can see how the technique works by preparing a family pedigree for an easily observed inherited trait, such as eye colour.

If you can't examine all your biological family members — aunts, uncles, grandfathers, grandmothers and cousins — another family member may remember their eye colour.

Find out

What eye colours appear in family members?

You need

- your family (or a friend's biological family)
- coloured pencil

continued

1. *Copy the pedigree diagram into your notebook.*

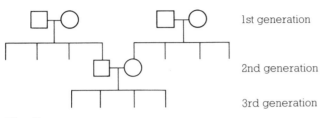

1st generation

2nd generation

3rd generation

Fig. 8

2. Each generation includes the following family members:
   a) 1st generation — both pairs of grandparents
   b) 2nd generation — your mother and father, and your uncles and aunts
   c) 3rd generation — you, your brothers and sisters, and your cousins.
   Add each person to your pedigree diagram, using the correct symbol for each sex.
3. Determine the eye colour of each person in your pedigree diagram. To simplify the task, classify each person as brown-eyed or blue-eyed. (Consider green or hazel eye colour as brown, and grey eye colour as blue.)
4. *Use the coloured pencil to colour each symbol which represents a brown-eyed person.*
5. Count the number of brown-eyed and blue-eyed people in your family pedigree diagram. *Do these numbers suggest a 3:1 ratio?*

1. Did everyone in your family pedigree have the same eye colour?

2. Does the 3:1 ratio for eye colour occur in your family pedigree?
3. Which eye colour seems to be hidden in some people?
4. Can you tell which of your parents gave you your eye colour? Remember, your parents may not have the same eye colour as you.

It is not very likely that every person in your family pedigree has blue eyes. It can happen, but very infrequently in Canada. If your family is Black, Asian, Inuit, or native Canadian it is probable that everyone in your family pedigree has brown eyes. If your family pedigree contains both brown-eyed and blue-eyed people, your family is probably white. Notice that each statement above is qualified by the word *probably*. Although eye colour seems to be closely associated with skin colour, exceptions can occur.

Not very many families exhibit the 3:1 ratio of brown eyes to blue eyes. In order for this ratio to appear, a very large number of white people must be examined. Few family pedigrees include large numbers of people.

By examining several pedigrees which include people with both eye colours, it should be possible to find two brown-eyed parents who have a blue-eyed child. The variation for blue eyes may be hidden in some people. If both parents have blue eyes, then all their children will have blue eyes. Very rarely, two blue-eyed parents have a brown-eyed child. This may be caused by a **mutation**. You really can't always tell which of your parents gave you your eye colour. There is more to eye colour than meets the eye. If you have brown eyes, and only one of your parents has brown eyes, that parent gave you your eye colour. But you will have to complete this chapter to find out why.

6.6 Pass It On

It is clear that all offspring receive their inherited traits from their parents. There must be some means by which these traits can be passed from both mother and father to the offspring. This is true of all living things. The path the traits follow is well understood.

During sexual reproduction, a sperm cell from the testes of the male parent swims to an egg cell formed in the ovaries of the female parent. The sperm cell fuses with the egg cell to produce a single cell called a zygote. The zygote then grows into a new individual.

The single connection between the offspring and its father is a sperm cell. Characteristics that are inherited from the father must be present in the microscopic sperm cell. Similarly, the connection between the offspring and its mother is an egg cell. Characteristics inherited from the mother must be present in the tiny egg cell.

FEEDBACK

1. Where are sperm cells produced? Egg cells?
2. How were your inherited characteristics passed to you from your parents?
3. How do you inherit characteristics from your grandparents?

Fig. 10

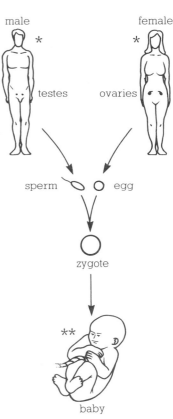

Fig. 9

6.7 Gregor Mendel

When Gregor Mendel conducted his famous experiments on pea plants, he focussed on traits such as plant height, pod colour, seed colour, and seed coat texture.

He noticed that pea plants grew either tall or dwarf. Unlike humans, pea plants didn't grow to intermediate heights. Knowing this, Mendel developed pea plant families in which a tall plant bred with another tall plant always produced seeds that grew into tall plants. A dwarf plant bred with another dwarf plant always produced seeds that grew into dwarf plants. Such exclusively tall or exclusively dwarf families were referred to as **pure for height**. It was easy to establish a family of plants that always grew dwarf. However, several attempts and selections were necessary before Mendel could establish a family of pure tall pea plants.

A surprise came when Mendel bred a pure tall plant with a pure dwarf plant. All the seeds grew into tall plants. Not one dwarf plant! These tall plants are called the **first filial generation** (F_1 generation).

Mendel used these new tall plants to repeat the experiment. An F_1 tall plant was bred with another F_1 tall plant. When the seeds grew, Mendel found both tall and dwarf plants. But there were more tall plants than dwarf plants. In fact, when Mendel counted them, there were about three tall plants for every dwarf plant. The special 3:1 ratio appeared! These plants were called the F_2 generation.

Mendel used his experiments to reach several conclusions. He knew that plants and animals inherited characteristics from their parents. Therefore, he believed that each new pea plant inherited its height from both parent plants. SOMETHING must be transferred from the male parents, and from the female parent, to the new plant. Mendel named these things **hereditary factors**. Here are some of his conclusions:

- Since pea plants can grow either tall or dwarf, THERE MUST BE BOTH TALL HEREDITARY AND DWARF HEREDITARY FACTORS.
- EACH PLANT HAS TWO HEREDITARY FACTORS FOR HEIGHT, ONE FROM EACH PARENT. The male plant contributes a height factor in the pollen (sperm) cell. Similarly, the female plant contributes a height factor in the egg cell. The seed thus has two height factors. As the seed grows into a new plant, the

Fig. 11 *Gregor Mendel*

Fig. 12 *Mendel could control the breeding of pea plants by removing the stamens, which produced sperm cells, from a pea plant flower. He then transferred the pollen from another flower (plant) to the pistil of the first plant which contained the egg cells. Thus, Mendel could control the parent plants which produced the seeds. He experimented with flower, pod, and seed colour, with the texture of seeds and pods, and with flower position.*

new plant also has two height factors. For example, pure tall plants must contain two tall factors, one from each parent. Pure dwarf plants must contain two dwarf factors, one from each parent.

- THE EGG CELLS AND THE SPERM CELLS (POLLEN) EACH CONTAIN ONLY ONE HEIGHT FACTOR. The combination of the egg and sperm thus produces two factors for height in the seed. Since a pure tall parent could only contribute a tall factor, and a pure dwarf parent could only contribute a dwarf factor, an F_1 plant must contain both a tall factor and a dwarf factor.

- THE TALL FACTOR MUST BE DOMINANT OVER THE DWARF FACTOR. THE DWARF FACTOR IS RECESSIVE. The F_1 plants grew tall. This must be due to the tall factor they received. The dwarf factor they had received had no effect on height. You might say that the dwarf factor was hidden!

6.8 Solving the Puzzle

It's a Fact
Geneticists use small letters to indicate recessive characteristics such as t for dwarf. Capital letters are used for dominant characteristics, such as T for tall.

What must have happened during Mendel's experiments in order for his conclusion to be true?

Let's represent the tall factor for height by the capital letter $\boxed{\text{T}}$. Since each parent has two factors for height, the pure tall parent may be represented by two capital letters $\boxed{\text{TT}}$. The dwarf factor may be represented as a small letter $\boxed{\text{t}}$; the pure dwarf parent as $\boxed{\text{tt}}$.

As the egg and sperm cells are produced by the parent plants, the factors split apart.

Fig. 13

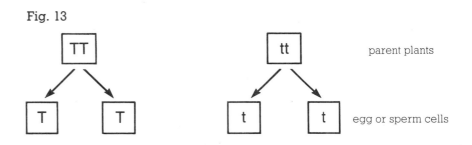

Thus, each egg and sperm contains only one factor for height.

When the egg and sperm form a seed, the seed has two factors for height, as shown.

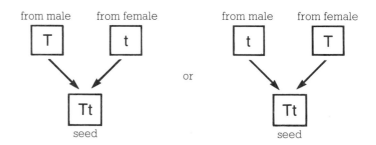

Fig. 14 *The seed now has two factors: one tall factor and one dwarf factor* $\boxed{\text{Tt}}$.

Because the tall factor is dominant, this seed grows into a tall plant. The dwarf factor is still present in the plant, but it seems to be hidden. These plants with both a tall and dwarf factor $\boxed{\text{Tt}}$, are called hybrid tall plants.

When these F₁, hybrid tall plants produce egg and sperm cells, they can contain either a dominant or a recessive factor for height.

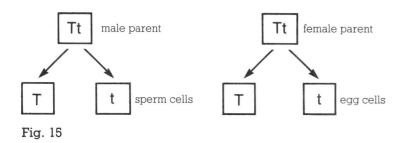

Fig. 15

Egg and sperm cells are usually produced in very large numbers. They join randomly to produce seeds. There are, however, only four different ways that the sperm and egg cells can combine.

	Egg		Sperm		Seed
1.	T	+	T	=	TT
2.	T	+	t	=	Tt
3.	t	+	T	=	tT
4.	t	+	t	=	tt

Examine the types of seeds produced. An old pattern becomes apparent for the third time!
- Seed 1 has only tall factors. It is pure tall, and the plant will grow TALL.
- Seed 2 has both a tall and a dwarf factor. It is hybrid tall and will grow TALL.
- Seed 3 also has a tall and dwarf factor. It too is hybrid tall and will grow TALL.
- Seed 4 has only dwarf factors. There is no dominant tall factor to make the plant tall. It will grow DWARF.

There are three possibilities for tall plants for every one for dwarf plants! Mendel's experiments and conclusions explain how the special 3:1 ratio appears in some cases.

Fig. 16 Dwarf and tall pea plants

201

6.9 Punnett Squares

The types of parents, and the predicted offspring, can be shown in a chart called a Punnett square. It's another way of showing the egg and sperm combinations. The F_1 generation and F_2 generation are shown in figures 17a and 17b.

Fig. 17a *F_1 generation*

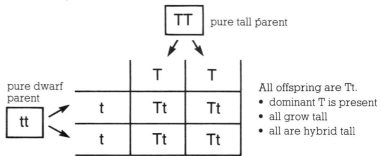

pure tall parent

pure dwarf parent

All offspring are Tt.
• dominant T is present
• all grow tall
• all are hybrid tall

Fig. 17b *F_2 generation*

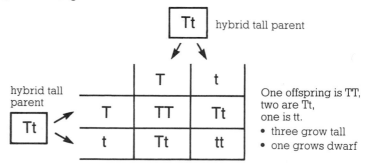

hybrid tall parent

hybrid tall parent

One offspring is TT, two are Tt, one is tt.
• three grow tall
• one grows dwarf

It is possible to describe the pea plants in two ways. In one way, the appearance of the plants is described. The physical appearance of the trait is the PHENOTYPE of the plants. The plants can be seen to grow TALL or DWARF.

It is also possible to describe the hereditary factors in the plants. This description is the GENOTYPE. The three genotypes may be PURE TALL TT, HYBRID TALL Tt, or PURE DWARF tt.

Many different traits are inherited in the same 3:1 pattern as height is inherited in pea plants. This pattern occurs in all organisms that reproduce sexually. The chart on page 203 lists several of these traits.

Inherited Variation	Dominant trait	Recessive trait
Seed colour in peas	yellow	green
Pod colour in peas	green	yellow
Wool colour in sheep	white	black
Skin surface in tomatoes	smooth	hairy, like a pea
Fur texture in dogs	wiry hair	smooth hair
Eye colour in humans	brown	blue
Extra finger in humans (polydactyly)	extra finger	
Hair texture in humans	curly	straight
Skin pigment in humans	pigment	albino
Blood type in humans	Type A, B, AB	Type O
Tongue-roller in humans	can roll	can't roll
Ear lobes in humans	free ear lobes	attached ear lobe

Fig. 18 *The length, colour, and texture of this dog's fur are examples of many inherited traits.*

FEEDBACK

1. How is a strain of pure tall pea plants different from a random selection of pea plants?
2. What height of plants grow from seeds produced by a pure tall and a pure dwarf plant?
3. What height of plants grow from seeds produced by two hybrid tall plants?
4. How many hereditary factors for height does each pea plant contain?
5. How many hereditary factors for height does an egg (or a sperm cell) of a pea plant contain?
6. Why is the dwarf factor called a recessive factor?
7. The Punnett square below shows a cross between a pure tall and a hybrid tall pea plant. Copy the Punnett square in your notebook and complete it to determine the type of plants that would grow from the resulting seeds.

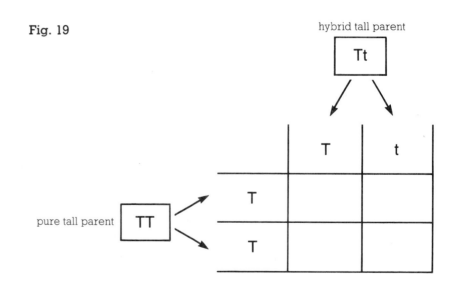

Fig. 19

hybrid tall parent

Tt

T   t

pure tall parent   TT

T

T

8. If a pure dwarf pea plant were crossed with a hybrid tall pea plant, to what height would the resulting seeds grow? Complete a Punnett square in your notebook to find out. Describe both the phenotypes and the genotypes produced.

Livestock Farmer

Do you like working outdoors? Do you enjoy working with animals? Do you feel an attachment to the land? Perhaps you would enjoy farming.

A farmer today really operates a small business. Many farms are passed from one generation to the next. Farming families have a large financial investment in land and equipment. Caring for livestock — beef cattle, dairy cattle, pigs, sheep — requires lengthy work days, every day of the week. The type of work varies. Cleaning stables and feeding stock is physically demanding. Maintaining financial and stock records is a behind-the-desk activity.

Most stock farmers maintain an organized breeding program. This process requires the ability to interpret animal pedigrees, and to apply this information to the breeding program. In this manner, a dairy farmer may breed cattle which produce more milk. Calves that grow into high milk production cows are in demand, and bulls that can sire such calves are valuable components of such a program. Many farmers utilize artificial insemination services as a means of utilizing the genes of several bulls in their breeding program.

In a similar fashion, farmers who raise animals for meat attempt to improve the rate of growth and the efficiency of weight gains in their beef cattle, pigs, or sheep.

Farmers generally begin their training as members of a farming family. They usually graduate from high school with several credits in science. Additional education may be obtained through agriculture courses offered at various colleges and universities.

A farmer enjoys working outdoors, sometimes in poor weather. Physical fitness and stamina are essential. The job demands a variety of skills and activities. Since considerable research is devoted to agriculture, farmers must be capable of learning new techniques and adapting to change.

Will this be you?

Fig. 20

6.10 Eye Colour Inheritance

The chart on page 203 shows that the variation for brown eyes in humans is dominant over blue eyes. There are three possible combinations of hereditary factors for eye colour, producing three genotypes and two phenotypes. These combinations are shown in the chart below. B represents the dominant brown eye factor, and b represents the recessive blue eye factor.

Combination of eye colour factors	Genotype	Phenotype
BB	pure brown eye	brown eye
Bb	hybrid brown eye	brown eye
bb	pure blue eye	blue eye

Using a Punnett square, you can predict the possible eye colour in the children of parents with various eye colours.

Find out

What eye colours might occur in the children of parents with various eye colours?

You need

• notepaper
• pen and ruler

Try this

1. Construct a Punnett square to determine the possible eye colours in children of two pure brown-eyed parents. BB × BB.
   What eye colour(s) can appear in the children of these parents?
2. Repeat step 1 for each of the following combinations of parents:
   a) two pure blue-eyed parents bb × bb
   b) two hybrid brown-eyed parents Bb × Bb
   c) a hybrid brown and a pure brown-eyed parent Bb × BB
   d) a hybrid brown and a pure blue-eyed parent Bb × bb.

Fig. 21 *What combination of hereditary factors might have produced this eye colour?*

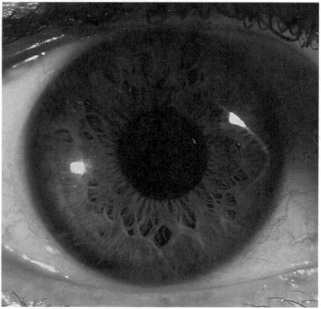

1. What are the possible genotypes of eye colour in the children of each pair of parents?
2. What are the possible phenotypes of eye colour in the children of each pair of parents?
3. Does the 3:1 ratio appear in the children of each pair of parents?
4. In step 2(d), the parents are of different genotypes. Does it matter which of the two genotypes is the mother, or the father? Why do you think so?

Now you know

From the Punnett square diagram, you can see that a great variety of eye colour combinations may appear in different families.

- If both parents are pure brown-eyed, all the children are pure brown-eyed too. No blue-eyed children are possible.
- If both parents are pure blue-eyed, all the children are pure blue-eyed too. No brown-eyed children are possible.
- When both parents are hybrid brown-eyed, both brown-eyed and blue-eyed children may appear in the family. On the average, but not always, there will be one pure blue-eyed child, one pure brown-eyed child, and two hybrid brown-eyed children. It is not possible, however, to observe which children are pure brown-eyed and which are hybrid brown-eyed. They all have brown eyes. It is not possible to predict what colour of eyes a child might have. During fusion of the egg and sperm, the hereditary factors join at random. It's similar to flipping coins — it is possible to turn up five heads in a row. Similarly, five blue-eyed children could appear in this family.

- The offspring of hybrid brown-eyed and pure brown-eyed parents are somewhat surprising. All their children have brown eyes. This is because the pure brown-eyed parent can only contribute a brown eye factor. Each child must receive at least one brown eye factor. Since the brown eye factor is dominant, all the children have brown eyes. Statistically, there is an equal chance that any child would be hybrid brown-eyed or pure brown-eyed. Although they are all the same phenotype, two different genotypes are possible.
- The hybrid brown-eyed and pure blue-eyed parents can produce yet a different combination of children. Half the children are pure blue-eyed. The other half are hybrid brown-eyed, because they inherit one blue eye factor from the blue-eyed parent and a brown eye factor from the other.

Fig. 22

6.11 Many Traits, Many Hereditary Factors

You have used a Punnett square to predict eye colour in families. You could also use them to predict other family traits in humans that are controlled by only one pair of hereditary factors. Some examples in humans are listed in the chart on page 203.

However, most traits seem to be influenced by more than one pair of hereditary factors. For example, the height of people is probably influenced by several pairs of hereditary factors.

Sometimes one factor is not dominant over the other factor. Instead, the factors blend. A white petunia bred with a red petunia produces seeds which grow into petunias with pink flowers.

Skin pigment in humans is influenced by two pairs of factors which also blend. This situation produces a broad range of skin colour in people.

6.12 Pedigree Puzzles

You are now able to predict the possible combinations of some hereditary traits, provided you know the genotype of the parents. For example, a person with blue eyes must be pure blue-eyed, and carry two recessive factors for blue eyes — bb. On the other hand, brown-eyed parents may be pure brown — BB, or hybrid brown — Bb. Sometimes you can use pedigree diagrams to determine the correct genotype(s) of parents, and of their children.

Examine the simple pedigree diagram below.

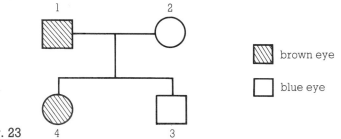

Fig. 23

brown eye

blue eye

The genotype of each person in this family can be predicted, including the brown-eyed people.

- Number 2, the mother: Since she has blue eyes, she must be pure blue eye — bb .
- Number 3, the son: Since he has blue eyes, he must also be pure blue eye — bb .
- Number 1, the father: Since he has brown eyes, he must have at least one brown eye factor — B . The second factor can't be determined by looking at his eye colour. It could be either brown — B, or blue — b. But note that his son is pure blue-eyed. The son has two b factors. He inherited one b factor from his mother. He must have inherited the second b factor from his father. The father must also have a b factor. Therefore, the father must be Bb , or hybrid brown-eyed.
- Number 4, the daughter: The daughter has brown eyes, and must have at least one B factor — B . She must have received this B factor from her father, since her mother is pure blue-eyed and has no B factor to pass on to her children. Mother can only pass on a b factor. Therefore the daughter must have a b factor inherited from her mother. The daughter must be Bb , or hybrid brown-eyed, like her father.

Analysing pedigree diagrams is like doing a puzzle. Examine the next pedigree diagram.

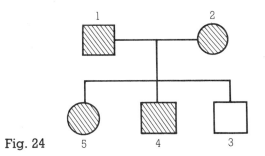

Fig. 24

- Number 3, a son: This son has blue eyes. He must be pure blue-eyed — bb . He inherited one b factor from his mother, and one b factor from his father.
- Number 1, father: Since his son (number 3) inherited a b factor from father, the father must have a b factor. But father is brown-eyed: he must also have a dominant B factor. Therefore, father is hybrid brown-eyed — Bb .

- Number 2, mother: Since her son (number 3) also inherited a b factor from his mother, the mother must have a b factor. But mother is brown-eyed: she must also have a B factor. Therefore, like father, mother is hybrid brown-eyed — Bb .
- Numbers 4 and 5, daughter and son: Since both have brown eyes, they must have a dominant B factor. What is the second factor? You can't tell. It could be another B factor from father or mother, or it could be a b factor from father or mother. In either case, the daughter and son would have brown eyes. At this stage it is not possible to determine the genotype of the daughter (number 5), or of the son (number 4). If they should marry and have children, it may be possible to determine their genotypes by examining their family pedigrees.

SUPERSLEUTH

Examine the pedigree you prepared in Investigation 6-5: A Family Pedigree. Can you determine the genotype of each person in your family pedigree?

Fig. 25 *The man on the right married the woman on the left, shown at two stages in her life. What inherited traits can you see in their small daughter?*

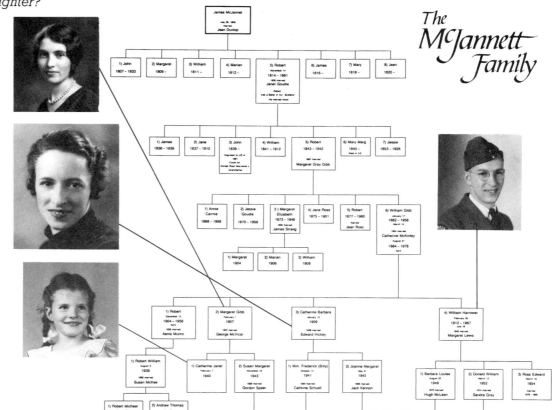

210

6.13 **It's a Dog's Life**

Knowing the characteristics that are likely to appear in each generation is important for people such as dog breeders. They want to make sure that puppies will be friendly and healthy. Dogs can inherit deafness, but it is a characteristic that can be avoided. Deafness in dogs is a recessive trait. Dogs may have pure normal hearing— DD , hybrid normal— Dd , or pure deaf— dd . D is the dominant normal hearing factor: d is the recessive deaf factor. How can a breeder determine if a parent dog that is not deaf is hybrid normal or pure normal? This is possible by breeding the dog in question with a deaf dog.

Fig. 26 *These pups from the same litter display the range of fur colour they inherited.*

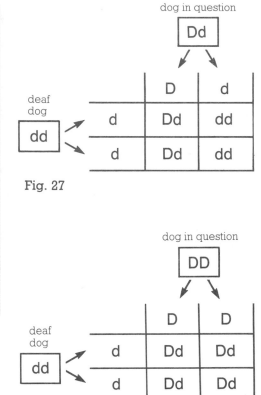

Fig. 27

Fig. 28

Figure 27 shows the types of puppies born if the dog in question is hybrid normal, and carries one d factor.

You can see that half the puppies, on the average, will be deaf.

On the other hand, figure 28 shows the type of puppies born if the dog in question has pure normal hearing.

211

In this case all the puppies are hybrid normal hearing, and none of the puppies are deaf.

If some of the puppies are deaf, the dog in question carries a d factor. It should not be used for breeding. If none of the puppies are deaf, the dog in question does not carry the d factor. It is pure normal hearing, and can be used for breeding. Thus, deafness can be eliminated from all the parent dogs used in a breeding program.

Breeders can improve plants and animals for specific purposes. Selective breeding has led to dairy cattle that produce more milk, chickens that lay more eggs, hogs that produce more meat, and wheat that forms more and larger grain.

Fig. 29 *A breeder may select certain birds in his flock and breed them in order to strengthen characteristics in the flock.*

FEEDBACK

1. Shorthorn cattle are raised for the production of beef. These cattle may have horns, or they may be hornless. The hornless condition is called POLLED. Some farmers prefer the polled form of shorthorns. The polled condition is due to a dominant factor — P. The horned condition is due to a recessive factor — p. How could a farmer determine if a polled bull shorthorn was pure polled PP, or hybrid polled Pp?

   To answer this question completely, you must realize that cows (female cattle) normally give birth to only one calf at a time.

2. Construct a Punnett square to determine the possible results in your answer to question 1.

Investigation

6.14 A Matter of Timing

If Mendel's ideas are true, it should be possible to find hereditary factors inside cells. However, when Mendel first announced his ideas between 1856 and 1863, no one could find hereditary factors. By 1900, microscopes made the study of cells much easier. They helped biologists to discover that when cells divide, many worm-like structures are found in the nucleus of cells. They are called **chromosomes**. Biologists began to see some similarities between Mendel's HEREDITARY FACTORS, and the CHROMOSOMES found in cells. You can see some of these similarities by examining some diagrams showing cells in various stages of division.

Find out

How do chromosomes behave during cell division?

You need

- Figures 30 and 31 on pages 214 and 215.

Try this

1. Examine the two sets of diagrams showing cell division on pages 214 and 215. *What kind of cells are produced by mitosis? What kind of cells are produced by meiosis?*
2. List the stages in mitosis and meiosis. *In what way is meiosis different from mitosis?*

3. *How many new cells have been produced at the end of mitosis? at the end of meiosis?*
4. Look at the chromosomes in prophase and metaphase of mitosis. *What seems to have happened to each chromosome?*
5. Now look at the chromosomes in meiosis. *When does this same process (step 4) seem to occur during meiosis?*

What happened?

1. During prophase I of meiosis, what happened to the chromosomes? Did this happen during prophase of mitosis?
2. In the process of mitosis, how many chromosomes are present in the original cell during prophase? How many chromosomes are present in the two new cells of telophase?
3. Now consider meiosis. How many chromosomes are present in the original cell during prophase I? How many are present in each of the four new cells of telophase II?

Now you know

Most of the cells in our bodies are called SOMATIC CELLS. Muscle cells, bone cells, nerve cells, skin cells, liver cells, kidney cells are all examples of somatic cells. All somatic cells divide by mitosis.

However, it is the SEX CELLS (the egg and sperm cells) that are important in the study of heredity. They are called **gametes**. Egg cells are female gametes: sperm cells are male gametes. They are both formed by meiosis.

Fig. 30 *Mitosis*

Most of the cells in your body divide by mitosis.
All cells, except egg cells and sperm cells are produced by mitosis.

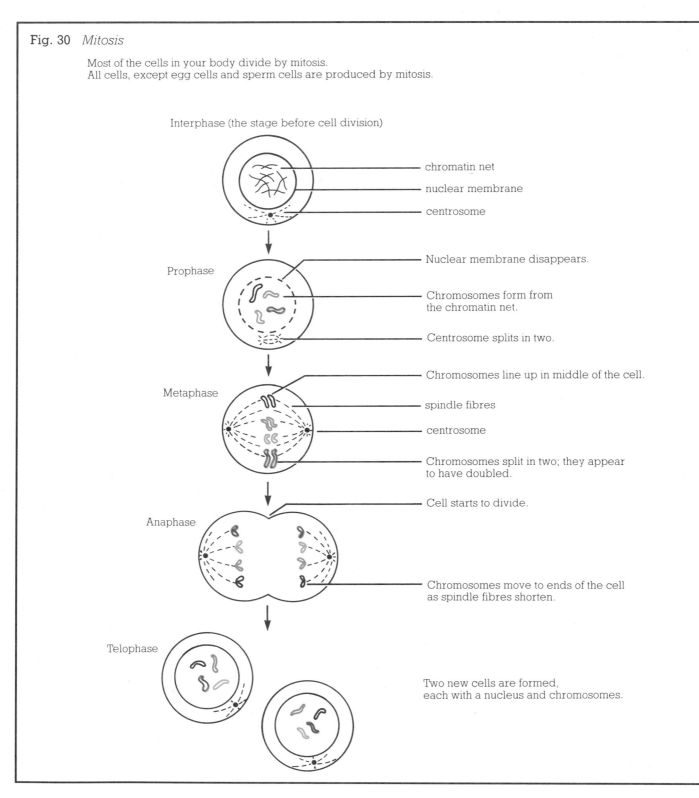

Interphase (the stage before cell division)

chromatin net

nuclear membrane

centrosome

Prophase

Nuclear membrane disappears.

Chromosomes form from
the chromatin net.

Centrosome splits in two.

Metaphase

Chromosomes line up in middle of the cell.

spindle fibres

centrosome

Chromosomes split in two; they appear
to have doubled.

Cell starts to divide.

Anaphase

Chromosomes move to ends of the cell
as spindle fibres shorten.

Telophase

Two new cells are formed,
each with a nucleus and chromosomes.

Fig. 31 *Meiosis*

Egg cells and sperm cells are formed by meiosis.
All other cells are produced by mitosis.

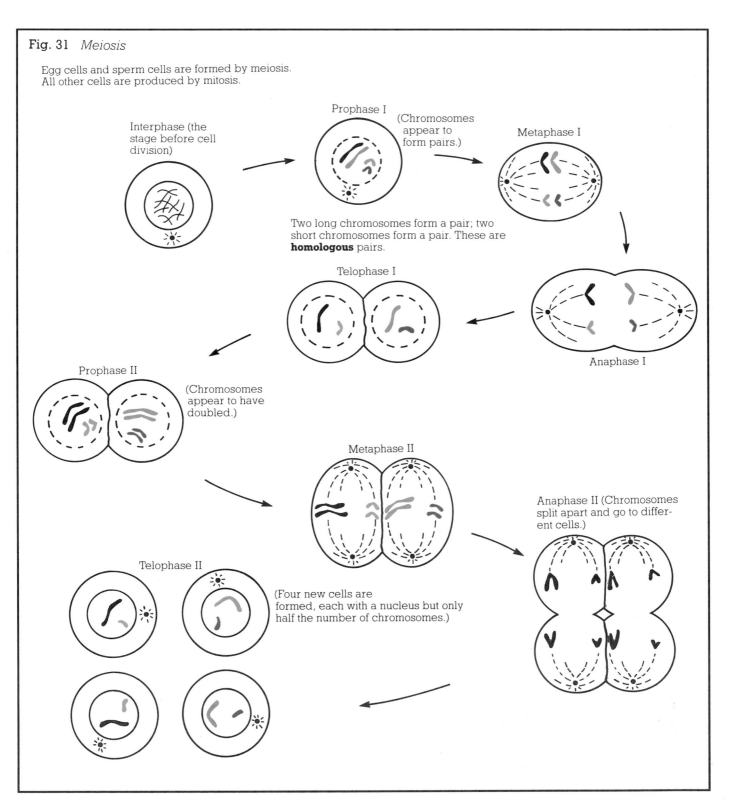

Interphase (the stage before cell division)

Prophase I
(Chromosomes appear to form pairs.)

Metaphase I

Two long chromosomes form a pair; two short chromosomes form a pair. These are **homologous** pairs.

Telophase I

Anaphase I

Prophase II
(Chromosomes appear to have doubled.)

Metaphase II

Anaphase II (Chromosomes split apart and go to different cells.)

Telophase II

(Four new cells are formed, each with a nucleus but only half the number of chromosomes.)

Before cell division begins, the cell is considered to be in interphase. The cell may be active in many ways, but it is not yet dividing. Once cells start to divide, they pass through a four-stage process: prophase, metaphase, anaphase and telophase. In the case of meiosis, the cell divides twice. As a result, mitosis produces two new cells while meiosis produces four new cells.

Between the stages of prophase and metaphase of mitosis, the chromosomes appear to have doubled in number, or to have duplicated themselves. This duplication is not seen until prophase II of meiosis. During prophase I of meiosis, the chromosomes seem to form pairs. In the diagram, the chromosomes are shown in different lengths. There are two chromosomes of each length, or of each type. The two long chromosomes form a pair, and the two short chromosomes form a pair. Each pair is an HOMOLOGOUS pair. Homologous means similar. The homologous chromosomes are similar to each other—like twins. Pairing does not occur in mitosis.

In anaphase II, the chromosomes split apart and go to different cells.

In humans, before meiosis takes place, the original cell has 46 chromosomes. Each gamete produced has only 23 chromosomes.

The number of chromosomes in somatic cells is called the DIPLOID number, or 2n number. There are two chromosomes of each type. In humans, the 2n number is 46. The number of chromosomes in the gametes is the haploid or 1n number. There is only one chromosome of each type. In humans, the 1n number is 23.

These observations can be summarized in the following table.

Characteristics	Somatic cells	Gametes
Number of new cells	2	4
Number of chromosomes in original cell	2n	2n
Number of chromosomes in new cells	2n	1n
Action of the homologous chromosomes	Homologous chromosomes don't form pairs.	Homologous chromosomes do form pairs, and split apart to go to different cells.

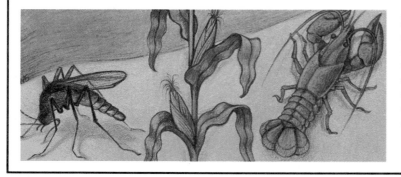

Fig. 32 *A human* **somatic** *cell, such as a skin cell, has 46 chromosomes. When it divides, the two new skin cells each have 46 chromosomes. Other organisms have different numbers of chromosomes. For example, mosquitoes have only six chromosomes, corn plants 20, and some crayfish 200.*

6.15 Gametogenesis and Fertilization

Two significant processes occur during sexual reproduction of humans.

- **Gametogenesis** is the process in the male and female parents that produces sperm cells and egg cells.
- **Fertilization** occurs in the female parent's body after sexual intercourse. During fertilization, the sperm and egg fuse to produce a zygote.

Sperm production occurs in the testes of a man in a process called **spermatogenesis**. After puberty, special cells in the testes divide by meiosis to produce sperm cells. Since the sperm cells are formed by meiosis, the sperm cells have 1n chromosomes.

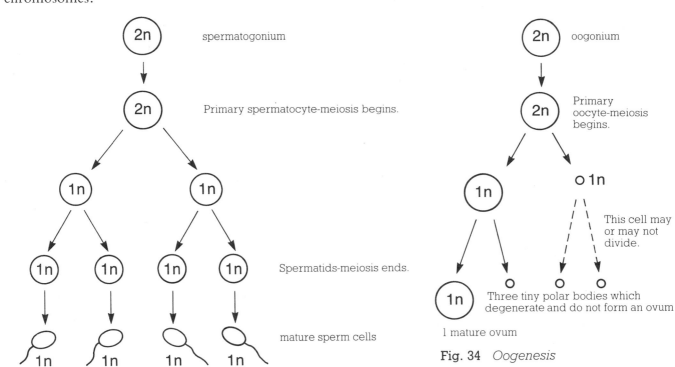

Fig. 33 *Spermatogenesis*

Fig. 34 *Oogenesis*

Oogenesis is a similar process that occurs in a woman's ovaries to produce eggs. Here, special cells divide by meiosis to produce eggs or ova, the resulting ova have 1n chromosomes. Only one of the four cells forms an ovum. The other three cells are very tiny, and do not develop into ova.

In the human female, one ovum is released from the ovaries every 28 days. After ovulation (release of the ovum), the ovum travels down the fallopian tube.

Fig. 35 *Male reproductive organs*

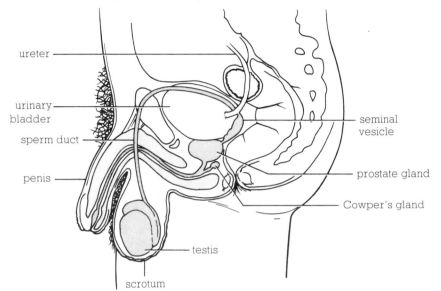

ureter

urinary bladder

sperm duct

penis

seminal vesicle

prostate gland

Cowper's gland

testis

scrotum

Fig. 36 *Female reproductive organs*

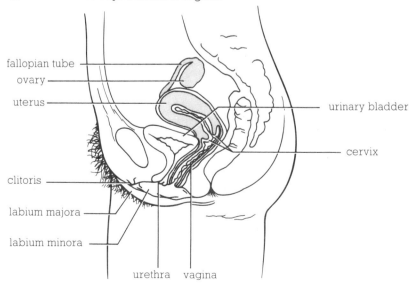

fallopian tube

ovary

uterus

urinary bladder

cervix

clitoris

labium majora

labium minora

urethra   vagina

After sexual intercourse, the sperm cells which were deposited in the vagina swim past the uterus and up the fallopian tube to the ovum. In the fallopian tube, one sperm cell fuses with the ovum. This is fertilization. When the sperm cell fuses with the ovum, the single cell formed is a **zygote**. The zygote continues down the fallopian tube to the uterus where it develops into a fetus.

The zygote receives 1n chromosomes from the sperm cell, and 1n chromosomes from the ovum. Consequently, the zygote contains 2n chromosomes. The zygote now divides by mitosis. Each new cell contains 2n chromosomes.

As the zygote divides and grows, a new fetus forms, with 2n chromosomes in all its cells. As this zygote develops into a baby by mitosis, each cell in the baby's body contains 46 chromosomes. In this manner, the number of chromosomes in the somatic cells of each species of organism remains constant.

FEEDBACK

1. Describe two ways in which the new cells produced by meiosis are different from the new cells produced by mitosis.
2. What two types of gametes must fuse to produce a zygote?
3. The somatic cells of a mouse contain 40 chromosomes. How many chromosomes are present in the sperm cells of a mouse?
4. The gametes of corn plants contain 10 chromosomes. How many chromosomes are present in leaf cells of corn plants?
5. What would happen during sexual reproduction if gametes were formed by mitosis?

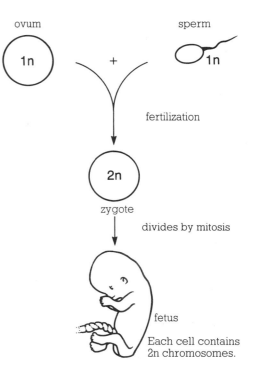

Fig. 37 *Fertilization*

It's a Fact
A zygote is a fertilized ovum, the cell produced when an egg and a sperm unite.
An embryo is the young organism in the stage between fertilization and the end of the eighth week.

6.16 **From Factors to Genes**

During the 1850s and 1860s, with little knowledge of cells, Mendel reached some surprising conclusions:

- Mendel stated that each parent contained two hereditary factors for each trait. The factors exist in pairs. Years later, geneticists realized that, during meiosis, homologous chromosomes form pairs during metaphase. The chromosomes appear as pairs.

- Mendel stated that during reproduction, the two hereditary factors separated. Each gamete contains only one factor for each trait. Again, geneticists built on Mendel's findings when they discovered that, during meiosis, the homologous chromosomes separate. Each gamete contains only one chromosome of each type.

- Mendel stated that for each trait, each parent contributed one hereditary factor to the new offspring. We now know that, during fertilization, the sperm cell and the egg cell each contribute one chromosome of each type to the zygote.

- Mendel stated that each new individual had two hereditary factors per trait. Later studies verified that, after sexual reproduction, each new individual has two homologous chromosomes of each type.

Mendel's research papers were generally ignored and collected dust on library shelves. However, in the early 1900s, biologists learned about chromosomes. They noted similarities between the behaviour of chromosomes and hereditary factors — perhaps the two were the same thing!

It appears initially that each type of chromosome represents the hereditary factor for each trait. However, there is a big problem with this idea. If it were true, the 23 pairs of homologous chromosomes in humans would be sufficient for only 23 traits. But there are several thousand different traits in humans. Clearly, there are not enough chromosomes for all the traits. So, biologists hypothesized that each chromosome consists of many tiny parts or segments. Each segment represents one hereditary factor. If this is true, each chromosome may contain several hundred segments, sufficient for all the human traits. Each segment is called a **gene**. The hereditary factors described by Mendel are really genes. Since there are two chromosomes of each type (homologous chromosomes), there are two genes of each type. Consider now the current picture:

- Cells of every individual contain genes which control inherited traits.
- Each chromosome is made up of many genes.
- There is a pair of genes for each trait, one on each of the homologous chromosomes.
- The genes separate with the chromosomes during gametogenesis, so that each gamete contains only one gene of each type.
- The genes form pairs again after fertilization when the sperm and egg fuse.
- The cells of each new individual contain a pair of genes for each trait.

FEEDBACK

1. Describe three ways in which the behaviour of chromosomes is similar to Mendel's hereditary factors.
2. What is the difference between a gene and a chromosome?

6.17 Punnett Squares and Genes

Since genes are the same thing as hereditary factors, you can use Punnett squares to predict the distribution of genes in the offspring of two parents. In humans, the characteristic for long eyelashes is controlled by a dominant gene (L), while the characteristic for short eyelashes is produced by a recessive gene (l). A mother with hybrid long eyelashes has a genotype that is hybrid long— L̲l̲ . Mother's phenotype is long eyelashes. The short eyelash father is a pure short genotype— l̲l̲ . His phenotype is short eyelashes. A Punnett square can be constructed as before, but now the letters can represent genes.

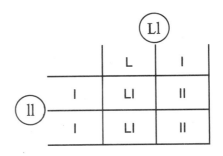

Fig. 38

Statistically, half the children will be hybrid long eyelash — $\boxed{Ll}$, and half will be pure short eyelash — $\boxed{ll}$. On the average, half the children will have long eyelashes, and half will have short eyelashes.

FEEDBACK

1. A couple are expecting their first child. They are curious to know what type of hair the child will have. Father has straight hair, which is a recessive trait. Mother carries two dominant genes for curly hair.
   a) Select a letter to represent the curly hair trait.
   b) Use this letter to show the genotype of the mother.
   c) What is her phenotype?
   d) Show the genotype of the father. How do you know?
   e) Complete a Punnett square to determine the genotypes of the offspring.
   f) For each genotype produced, describe the phenotype.
   g) On the average, what fraction of the children in this family will be pure curly-haired, hybrid curly-haired, and pure straight-haired?
   h) What hair type will their first child have?

6.18 Boy Meets Girl

It may not seem like it when you're looking for a date, but there are about the same number of girls as there are boys. Have you ever wondered why? The answer to the question lies in the chromosomes. You inherited your sex!

When the 23 pairs of chromosomes in human cells are examined with a microscope, 22 pairs appear similar. The 23rd pair is unusual. In males, the two chromosomes making up the pair are different. One chromosome is long, the other is short. The long chromosome is an X chromosome. The short one is a Y chromosome. In females, both chromosomes are long. Females have two X chromosomes.

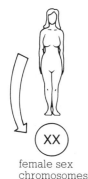
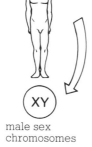

female sex chromosomes male sex chromosomes

Fig. 39

222

These are the chromosomes that determine the sex of an individual, and are called sex chromosomes. Males have XY sex chromosomes; females have XX sex chromosomes.

During oogenesis, women, who have two X chromosomes, always produce eggs with one X chromosome.

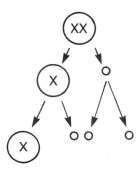

Fig. 40 *In oogenesis, there is no choice for the egg cell. It can only contain an X chromosome.*

During spermatogenesis, men who have an X and a Y chromosome produce two kinds of sperm. Half have an X chromosome and half have a Y chromosome.

During fertilization of the egg, there is a 50% chance that the egg will fuse with an X sperm. Similarly, there is a 50% chance it will fuse with a Y sperm. About half the babies born are girls, and about half are boys. This relationship is clearly seen in the Punnett square in figure 42.

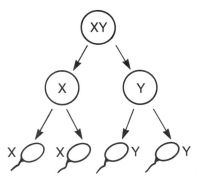

Fig. 41 *In spermatogenesis, half the sperm cells have an X chromosome; half have a Y chromosome.*

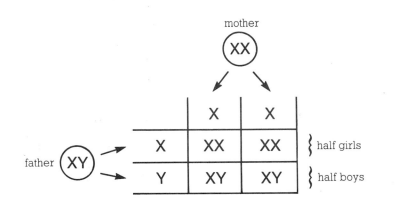

Fig. 42

223

FEEDBACK

1. How do the sex chromosomes of men differ from the sex chromosomes of women?
2. Which type of gamete, male or female, determines the sex of a baby? Explain why this is the case.

6.19 There's More to Sex Than Sex

The X and Y chromosomes provide a simple explanation for sex determination. However, this pair of chromosomes produces some unusual hereditary results. Certain characteristics occur more frequently in men than they do in women. The characteristics seem to be linked to the male sex! Colour-blindness, hemophilia (an inability to clot blood), and a form of muscular dystrophy are examples. They are known as **sex-linked characteristics**.

This odd situation is caused by the difference in size of the X and Y chromosomes. The larger X chromosome has room for more genes than does the smaller Y chromosome.

Fig. 43

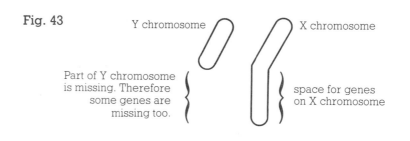

Y chromosome

X chromosome

Part of Y chromosome is missing. Therefore some genes are missing too.

space for genes on X chromosome

It is the missing part of the Y chromosome that causes some traits to appear in men more frequently than in women. Consider red-green colour-blindness as an example. In this condition, the colours red and green appear the same. Far more men than women suffer from red-green colour-blindness. Normal colour vision is dominant. The normal gene may be represented by the letter C. The recessive gene for red-green colour-blindness may be represented by c. This gene for colour-blindness is located on the extra portion of the X chromosome, so it is missing on the Y chromosome. Women have two genes for colour vision, while men have only one.

If a woman has a gene for colour-blindness (c) on one X chromosome, and a gene for normal vision (C) on the other X chromosome, she will have normal vision. She will, however, be a CARRIER of colour-blindness, since the recessive gene for colour-blindness (c) is present on one of the X chromosomes. On the average, half of her sons will inherit this colour-blind gene, and they will be colour-blind. Boys always inherit colour-blindness from their mother.

X normal colour vision

X red-green colour-blindness

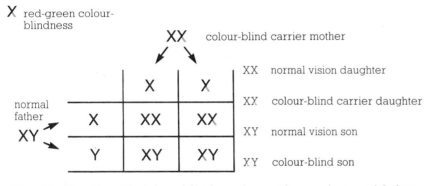

Fig. 44 *Family with colour-blind carrier mother and normal father*

On the other hand, if a man has a gene for colour-blindness (c) on the X chromosome, he will be colour-blind. It is not possible for him to have also a dominant gene for normal vision (C), since he does not have a second gene for colour vision. The smaller Y chromosome does not carry a gene for colour vision. Since the man passes on the Y chromosome to his sons, it is strange but true that none of this man's sons will inherit colour-blindness from him! However, all this man's daughters will carry colour-blindness. To be female, his daughters must inherit an X chromosome from him. It is the father's X chromosome that carries the colour-blind gene. (See figure 45.)

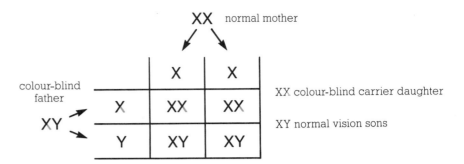

XX normal mother

colour-blind father

	X	X
X	XX	XX
Y	XY	XY

XY

XX colour-blind carrier daughter

XY normal vision sons

Fig. 45 *Family with normal mother and colour-blind father*

FEEDBACK

1. Hemophilia is a genetic disorder in which a person lacks the ability to clot blood. Injuries and cuts continue to bleed, and the person risks bleeding to death. Hemophilia is a recessive trait. It is also a sex-linked characteristic which occurs predominantly in human males. On which of the sex chromosomes would the hemophilia gene occur?
2. A small percentage of women are red-green colour-blind. What type of sex chromosomes would such a woman have?
3. Assume that a woman with red-green colour-blindness marries a man with normal vision. Construct a Punnett square to determine the possible colour vision characteristics of their sons and daughters.

Fig. 46 *If you have normal colour vision, you will see the number 29 in the figure on the left. People with red-green colour-blindness will see 70. Those with normal colour vision will see a 2 in the figure on the right, while those with colour-deficient vision will have a very hard time distinguishing anything.*

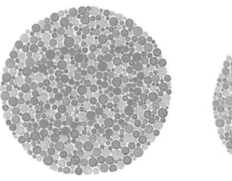

6.20 Predicting the Future: Amniocentesis

Amniocentesis is a technique designed to examine chromosomes of a developing embryo before it is born. Using this technique, the sex of the baby can be learned, and the possibility of some genetic defects may also be determined.

The **amnion** is a membrane that surrounds the developing embryo. It contains the amniotic fluid which bathes the growing embryo. During pregnancy, cells from the embryo are scattered into the amniotic fluid.

During the 16th week of pregnancy, a hypodermic needle may be inserted through the mother's abdomen and uterus into the amnion to obtain a small amount of amniotic fluid. This is done after tests are done to determine the location of the fetus.

Some of the fetal cells in the amniotic fluid are still alive, and can be placed on a substance where the cells grow and reproduce by mitosis. The resulting cluster of cells is a **tissue culture.**

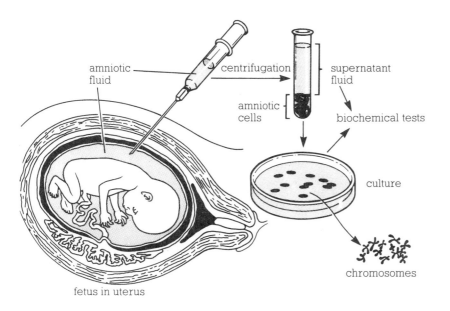

Fig. 47 *Amniocentesis*

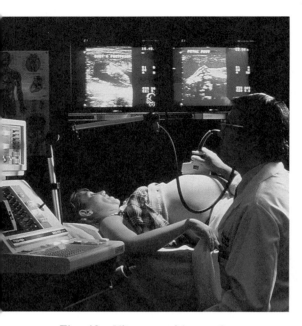

Fig. 48 *Ultrasound is another technique designed to check the progress of the developing embryo. Sound waves are bounced off the embryo, producing a picture.*

Cells from the tissue culture are stained so that the chromosomes can be examined with a microscope. The sex chromosomes show the sex of the embryo. Some genetic defects, if present, can also be determined. One such defect is Down syndrome. It is determined by the presence of an extra chromosome. Medical biologists refer to this as the number 21 chromosome. The abnormal chromosome may form after fertilization, and is not always present in the father's sperm or the mother's egg. Down syndrome seems to appear more frequently when the mother is over 35 years of age. It also appears more frequently if the parents have had an earlier child with a genetic defect.

Down syndrome is a genetic disorder that exhibits specific characteristics in people. These include mental retardation, a flattened face, and short thumbs and fingers. Amniocentesis allows the prospective parents of a genetically abnormal fetus to prepare for any necessary medical treatment.

FEEDBACK

1. At what stage of pregnancy is an amniocentesis test conducted?
2. How are cells from the embryo obtained for this test?
3. What evidence indicates that the embryo has Down syndrome?
4. What steps might prospective parents take to avoid giving birth to a child with Down syndrome?

SUPERSLEUTH

Several years ago, the drug thalidomide was given to pregnant women to reduce morning sickness. Unfortunately, this drug caused genetic mutations in the developing fetus, and produced severe changes in the babies. Other substances, and other factors in the lifestyles of expectant mothers may also alter the genes and influence the development of their babies. Use the library, or your local community health service, to learn more about the causes of these mutations.

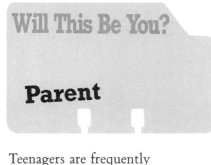

Will This Be You?

Parent

Teenagers are frequently struggling to become independent of their parents. During this time, conflicts often arise, and resolutions may be difficult. In some cases, there seems to be no solution to these difficulties. Neither parent nor adolescent is able to appreciate the other's point of view. Sometimes, conflicts escalate to the point where the teenager moves out of the home. Often, though, these conflicts can be resolved. Co-operation and patience on the part of parents helps. So does the fact that a son or daughter matures and perhaps develops a different viewpoint.

Parents can remember what it was like to be a teenager and this may help them understand their child's feelings and difficulties. Whether you have thought of it or not, you may well become a parent, too.

Most parents enjoy their children, and try to raise them to become healthy, confident, and capable people who can enjoy life. Different parents have different qualities, but most want the best for their children. They try to be fair and just, caring and responsible. A healthy sense of humour is a must for a parent.

At times, children can "try the patience of a saint," and humour helps keep things in perspective.

Young men and women rarely learn to become good parents through formal education. Some may attend Family Studies classes in secondary school, but most learn from their own parents, or from friends who are already parents. Before having children, many married couples wisely seek advice about the possible genetic characteristics of the children they may have. The best genetic advice for most couples is available from their family doctor, or from one of the many family counselling services.

Becoming a parent can be a wonderful and amazing experience. Will this be you?

Fig. 49 *Most parents want the best for their children.*

THIS CONCERNS YOU

Designer Genes

Research into the structure of genes and DNA (the cell's blueprint) has led to some amazing genetic achievements. (Genes are made of huge complex molecules called Deoxyribonucleic Acid–DNA.) It is now possible to splice a gene from one organism into the chromosome of a different organism. You have probably heard of this process as **genetic engineering**.

Most commonly, a gene from an organism is spliced into the **plasmid** of a bacterium. A plasmid is a structure, similar to chromosomes, found in bacteria. They are tiny circular structures made of DNA. Once the bacterium has this new gene, it can reproduce to produce millions of bacteria, all containing the new gene.

There are companies today which use this technique to produce useful substances, such as insulin. The gene which controls the production of insulin in a rat has been spliced into a bacterium. This bacterium reproduced to give billions of bacteria which produce insulin. The insulin is separated from the bacteria, purified, and used to treat people who have diabetes.

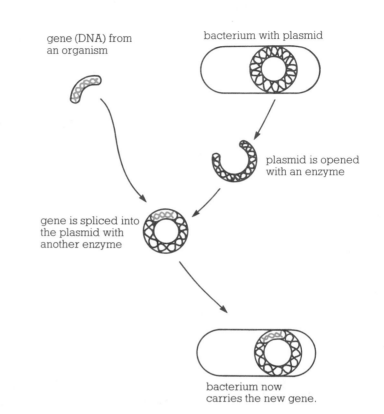

gene (DNA) from an organism

bacterium with plasmid

plasmid is opened with an enzyme

gene is spliced into the plasmid with another enzyme

bacterium now carries the new gene.

Fig. 50

One area of genetic engineering may help to feed an increasingly hungry world. Using genetic engineering techniques, biologists may be able to add a new set of genes to a crop plant. These genes could increase the yield of the crop or accelerate the growth and maturation of the plants. Such plants could then be grown in the northern regions of Canada where the growing season is short. Genes could also increase the plant's resistance to pests such as insects and weeds. Then the plants could be grown without the use of environmentally dangerous chemical pesticides.

Some people lack the human growth hormone (HGH), which is normally produced by the pituitary gland. Without this hormone, children do not grow to a normal height, and suffer from dwarfism. It is now possible to produce HGH from genetically engineered bacteria. Dwarf children given this HGH can then grow to a normal height.

Bacteria that digest and break down oil have been developed using these techniques. They may be useful in destroying oil in oceans from oil spills.

The potential also exists to create new organisms, alter existing ones, or to change the structure of the human organism. Perhaps in the future parents may be able to "order" children with specific traits: eye colour, hair colour, height, sex, certain talents.

But tomorrow's challenge is not only for biologists. You, your friends, and others like you will be influenced by the use of genetics and genetic engineering. As in any other field of science, the wise use of this knowledge depends on your concern. Being aware of the nature of genetics will enable you to share in many of the important decisions of the future.

1. Imagine that ten years from now parents really could "order" the traits of their children. What traits would you order? What would happen if all other parents ordered the same set of traits? Is this capability a good idea?
2. E. Coli is a usually harmless bacterium that lives in the intestine of humans. Suppose genetic engineers developed a strain of E. Coli that could convert cellulose into amino acids. Amino acids are essential for good nutrition. The cellulose needed by the bacteria could be supplied by plants such as trees which cannot now be eaten by people. Cellulose is also present in many vegetables that we eat. It provides essential fibre in our diet.

Suppose that a company in your community proposed to develop and use these bacteria to produce amino acids from cellulose.

a) List the advantages that would result from developing and using such a strain of bacteria.

b) What might happen if these bacteria escaped into forests and farms?

c) Assume that the people in the community voted to support the company's proposal, but with the condition that a committee be established to develop precautions and safety guidelines for the company. You have been assigned to that committee. Prepare a list of safety rules that you would recommend.
Briefly explain each rule.

Fig. 51 *This child's bones and muscles can't support him; he suffers from a form of dwarfism.*

6.21 Chapter Summary

- Many characteristics of living organisms are inherited.
- A pedigree diagram can be used to show the inheritance of a characteristic in all members of a family.
- Gregor Mendel was one of the first scientists to successfully investigate the science of genetics.
- Many traits are controlled by a pair of genes (hereditary factors).
- Some characteristics, or genes, are dominant, while others are recessive.
- For many traits, each individual inherits one gene from each parent.
- Punnett squares may be used to predict the possible characteristics of the offspring of two parents.
- Somatic cells are produced by mitosis. Sex cells are produced by meiosis.
- Somatic cells contain a diploid (2n) number of chromosomes. Sex cells contain a haploid (1n) number of chromosomes.
- Egg cells are produced in a female's ovaries. Sperm cells are produced in a male's testes.
- During fertilization, an egg cell and a sperm cell fuse to form a zygote.
- Female humans have two X chromosomes (XX). Male humans have one X and one Y chromosome (XY).
- Some genes for inherited characteristics are located on the X chromosome only. These are sex-linked characteristics.
- Genes are molecules of DNA which control the development of specific characteristics.
- Chromosomes consist of many genes.

6.22 Are You Ready to Go On?

Do not write in the text.

1. This chapter contains many words related to the science of heredity. How many of the scrambled words below can you unscramble? Write each unscrambled word in your notebook.

   a) geg   f) merps
   b) temseag   g) eeergdip
   c) sisoime   h) notepyeg
   d) ticamso   i) oooomhslug
   e) dtnioman   j) nottaium

2. a) Construct a Punnett square to determine the genotype of the possible offspring (children) of a pure blue-eyed mother and a hybrid brown-eyed father.
   b) What eye colour phenotypes can be born to these parents?

3. Decide if each statement is true or false. If it is true, copy the statement into your notebook. If it is false, rewrite the statement to make it true.
   a) A person can learn to roll their tongue.
   b) Inherited characteristics are passed on from parents to offspring.
   c) In order that a girl have blue eyes, at least one of her parents must have blue eyes.
   d) Sperm cells are produced in the ovary.
   e) The cells of pea plants each carry two genes for height.
   f) During meiosis, homologous chromosomes form pairs, and then split apart to go to different cells.
   g) Human males have two X chromosomes in their cells.
   h) A human sperm cell contains 23 chromosomes.
   i) Genes consist of molecules of DNA.

4. In sheep, white wool is dominant and black wool is recessive. A farmer who raises sheep

bred a black male sheep (ram) with a hybrid female sheep (ewe).
a) Select a letter to represent white wool.
b) Use this letter to show the genotype of the ram, and the ewe.
c) What colour of wool does the ewe have?
d) Complete a Punnett square to determine the genotype of the lambs.
e) On the average, what fraction of lambs from these parent sheep will have white wool?

5. Wire hair texture is a dominant characteristic in dogs. Smooth hair is recessive. Describe the steps that a dog breeder may take to learn if a dog which has wire hair is pure wire hair or hybrid wire hair.

6. Write each of the following sentences in your notebook. Fill in each blank with an appropriate word or number.
a) It is possible for parents both of whom have brown eyes to have children with _____ and _____ eyes.
b) When an egg cell is fertilized by a _____ cell, a _____ is produced.
c) Hereditary factors described by Mendel are really _____ which make up chromosomes.
d) In humans, blue eyes is a _____ characteristic.
e) Both egg and sperm cells are produced by a process called _____ .
f) A male gamete is an _____ cell.
g) A human muscle cell contains _____ chromosomes.
h) After sexual intercourse, _____ occurs in the female parent's body.
i) Colour blindness is a _____ characteristic which is found most frequently in _____ .
j) An X chromosome is _____ than a Y chromosome.

7. Choose the correct completion, then rewrite each of the following sentences in your notebook.
a) One characteristic which is inherited in humans is:
   i) body mass
   ii) eye colour
   iii) hair length
   iv) native language
b) Curly hair (C) in humans is a dominant characteristic. Straight hair (c) is recessive. A person who has Cc genes in his cells is:
   i) pure curly hair
   ii) hybrid curly hair
   iii) pure straight hair
   iv) hybrid straight hair
c) Somatic cells of the body are produced by:
   i) mitosis
   ii) meiosis
   iii) chromosomes
   iv) the ovary
d) Somatic cells of a mouse contain 40 chromosomes. An egg cell of a mouse contains:
   i) 20 chromosomes
   ii) 40 chromosomes
   iii) 80 chromosomes
   iv) no chromosomes
e) Hemophilia is a genetic disorder which:
   i) is sex-linked
   ii) has its gene located on the X chromosome
   iii) occurs most often in males
   iv) is all of the above

8. A white ram (white wool is dominant in sheep) is bred to three different ewes. The first ewe has black wool, and has a lamb with black wool. The second ewe has black wool also, but has a lamb with white wool. Finally, the third ewe has white wool and has a lamb with black wool. What is the genotype of each of the seven sheep?

Contents

Chapter Seven

Charge It

7.1 Living With Electricity

How did you first use electricity today? Did an electric alarm clock wake you up? Did you turn on any electric lights? Did you wash in electrically heated water? Did your breakfast come out of an electric refrigerator, possibly via the toaster, kettle, or oven? You probably used electricity in at least a dozen different ways before you even stepped inside school!

Fig. 1 *The girl in the photo on the opposite page seems to be getting a real charge out of demonstrating one effect of static electricity.*

Fig. 2 *Going out tonight? Thanks to electricity, you won't be in the dark.*

235

Electricity is probably near the top of everyone's list of ways that science has improved daily living. The photos below show some common uses.

In our homes, in business, and in industry, electrical energy has become so much a part of everything we do that it's difficult to even imagine life without it.

Yet, while electricity is extremely useful, it can also be very dangerous. People die each year as a result of electrical accidents. Some electrical accidents cause death by electrocution; others cause death by fire due to overloading of household electric circuits. How can we avoid electrical hazards? A good understanding of how electricity works can help us to avoid mistakes which might otherwise be fatal.

FEEDBACK

1. Many devices operate from electric batteries. Which of these devices do you own?
2. Name as many of the electrical appliances as you can that you used in the last twenty-four hours.
3. Which electric tools do you think should be in every home?
4. If you could own only five electrical appliances, which ones would you choose?
5. Describe two ways in which electricity can be dangerous.

Fig. 3

Fig. 4

Investigation

7.2 At a Standstill

You are familiar with **current electricity**. Current electricity moves through wires and circuits, such as those in your home. However, many years before current electricity was discovered, the ancient Greeks learned about **static electricity**. Static electricity does not move. The Greeks observed the effects of static electricity on a substance called amber and on pieces of straw.

If they rubbed the amber with some other substance, the amber would attract and pick up small pieces of straw. You have probably seen similar effects. After you comb your hair with a plastic comb, the comb may attract tiny pieces of paper.

The cartoon shows one of the common effects of static electricity. You can probably think of others.

You can do an experiment to discover more about the way static electricity works.

Find out

What effect does static electricity have on different objects?

You need

- ebonite rod
- glass rod
- piece of wool
- piece of silk
- retort stand
- ring clamp
- tiny pieces of paper (3)
- sheet of paper
- sawdust
- chalk dust
- pith ball attached to a thread

continued

1. Place the tiny pieces of paper, a small amount of sawdust, and a small amount of chalk dust in three separate piles on a sheet of paper on your desk.
2. Bring the ebonite rod near the pieces of paper, sawdust, and chalk dust. *What happens?* Try this with the glass rod. *What happens?*
3. Now briskly rub the ebonite rod a few times with the piece of wool to charge it.
4. Bring the rubbed ebonite rod near the small pieces of paper. *What happens to the pieces of paper this time?* Try this with the sawdust and chalk dust. *What happens?*
5. Now rub the glass rod with the piece of silk.
6. Repeat step 4, using the rubbed glass rod. *What happens to the paper, sawdust, and chalk dust?*
7. Attach the clamp to the retort stand, and tie the pith ball to the clamp. The pith ball should hang about 15 cm below the clamp.

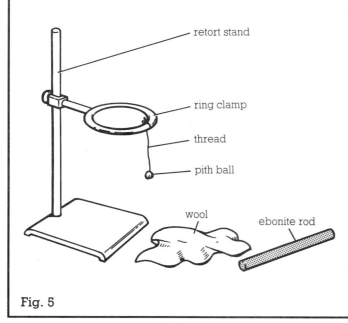

retort stand

ring clamp

thread

pith ball

wool

ebonite rod

Fig. 5

8. Charge the ebonite rod again by rubbing it with the piece of wool.
9. Bring the charged ebonite rod close to the pith ball so that the ball and rod touch. *What happens to the pith ball first? Then what happens to the pith ball?*
10. Now very quickly charge the glass rod by rubbing it with the piece of silk.
11. Bring the charged glass rod close to the same pith ball, but DON'T LET IT TOUCH THE PITH BALL. (If it does, repeat steps 8 to 11.)
12. Lift the retort stand so that the pith ball can touch the sawdust. *What happens to the sawdust?* (If nothing happens, repeat steps 8 and 9 before touching the sawdust with the pith ball.)

1. What effect did the charged rods have on pieces of paper, sawdust, and chalk dust?
2. a) Why did the pith ball attract the sawdust?
   b) How did the pith ball get this ability to attract the sawdust?
3. Why did the ebonite rod and the glass rod affect the pith ball differently?

You have discovered that the ebonite rod and glass rod could be charged with static electricity by rubbing the rods with some other material. In fact, any substance can be charged if it is rubbed with a different material (e.g., a plastic comb and hair, leather shoes and a rayon rug, a wool sweater and synthetic shirt.)

The charged object has the ability to attract uncharged objects. The charged rods could attract the paper, sawdust, and chalk dust. The easiest way to tell if an object is charged is to see if it attracts other things.

The pith ball was initially attracted by the ebonite rod too, but the pith ball itself attracted the sawdust. The pith ball must have been charged! How did that happen? You didn't rub it with anything, but you did touch it with the charged ebonite rod. The pith ball was charged by contact.

After the pith ball was charged, it moved away from the ebonite rod. In other words, the charged pith ball and the ebonite rod **repelled** each other.

Since the pith ball got its charge from the ebonite rod, the pith ball and the ebonite rod must have the same kind of charge. Since the charged pith ball and the charged ebonite rod repelled each other, the same kinds of charges must repel each other. On the other hand, the charged glass rod attacted the charged pith ball. The glass rod must have a different kind of charge. Different kinds of charges must attract each other.

The charge on the ebonite rod is called a **negative** charge. The charge on the glass rod is **positive**. The following points summarize what happened:

- Negative charges repel other negative charges.
- Negative charges attract positive charges.
- Positive charges attract negative charges.
- Positive charges repel other positive charges.
- Both positive and negative charges attract uncharged objects.

7.3 **Static Electricity in Action**

Static electricity can produce some interesting effects. Lightning is a dramatic result of static electricity. You've probably rubbed a party balloon on a wool sweater and made the balloon stick to a wall!

Fig. 6

239

Static electricity has some useful applications as well. Some air purifiers use static electricity. A small fan in the air purifier blows air from a room past a screen. The screen is charged with static electricity, which attracts dust particles from the air. The same principle can be used in the smokestacks of factories to reduce air pollution.

FEEDBACK

1. Describe two ways that objects can be charged with static electricity.
2. What effects do positive and negative charges have on each other?
3. What is an easy way to tell if an object is charged?
4. A piece of plastic is repelled by a positively charged glass rod. What kind of charge must be on the plastic?
5. A piece of acetate attracts a piece of vinyl and also attracts a pith ball. The piece of vinyl attracts the pith ball too.
   a) If the acetate is positively charged, what charge is on the vinyl?
   b) What charge is on the pith ball?
6. a) Describe one use of static electricity that you have been reading about.
   b) Describe one other use of static electricity.

Fig. 7 *Electrostatic precipitators can reduce the smoke emissions and pollution from smokestacks.*

7.4 **Shuffling the Electrons**

According to atomic theory, all atoms contain both positive and negative particles. The negative particles are called **electrons**. The positive particles are **protons**. Each atom of a certain element has the same number of electrons and protons. The negative charge of each electron cancels the positive charge of a proton. Therefore, each atom normally has no charge. It is **neutral**.

Since all substances are made up of atoms, therefore all substances contain an equal number of protons and electrons. If a substance gains some extra electrons, it becomes negatively charged. If another substance loses these electrons, it becomes positively charged. This transfer of electrons happens when two different substances are rubbed together. When ebonite is rubbed with wool, electrons move from the wool to the ebonite. The ebonite then has more electrons, so it is negatively charged. The wool has lost some of its electrons, so it now has fewer electrons than protons and is positively charged.

It's a Fact
The Greeks used amber for ornamental purposes, just as gems and gold are used. Their word for amber was "electron."

Fig. 8

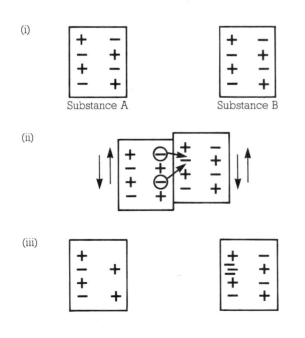

(i) Both substance A and substance B have an equal number of protons (+) and electrons (−).

Substance A   Substance B

(ii) Substance A and substance B are rubbed together. Electrons move from A to B.

(iii) Substance B has more electrons than protons. It is negatively charged.

Substance A has more protons than electrons. It is positively charged.

The negative electrons on the ebonite rod all repel one another, but they have no place to go. If the ebonite touches a pith ball, some of the extra electrons move to the pith ball. Now the pith ball has extra electrons and is charged negatively too.

Once the electrons are on the ebonite rod, or on the pith ball, they don't move from place to place the way current electricity does. The charge stays in one place. That is why it is called static electricity.

FEEDBACK

1. Why are atoms normally neutral?
2. Explain how ebonite becomes negatively charged.
3. How does a glass rod become positively charged when rubbed with silk?
4. Explain how a pith ball can become negatively charged.

Investigation

7.5 Electrons in Motion

If electrons could be made to move around a circuit, there would be current electricity. Remember, the electrons repel one another and would move away from one another if they could. In the next investigation, you'll discover the conditions that allow electrons to move.

Find out

Under what conditions can electrons move in a substance?

You need

- ebonite rod
- piece of wool
- retort stand
- ring clamp
- two pith balls, each attached to a thread
- piece of copper wire
- piece of aluminum wire
- plastic ruler
- wooden stick (wood splint)

1. Attach the clamp to the retort stand.
2. Tie one of the pith balls to the clamp. The pith ball should hang about 15 cm below the clamp. (See figure 9.)
3. Lift the second pith ball by the thread, and hold it very close to the pith ball tied to the clamp. *Do they attract each other? Do they repel each other? Does either of the pith balls have an electric charge? How do you know?*
4. Charge the ebonite rod by rubbing it with the wool. Then charge the hanging pith ball by contact. Electrons will move from the rod to the pith ball, giving it a negative charge.
5. Again, lift the second pith ball by the thread and hold it very close to the pith ball on the clamp. *What happens?* You can use this method to see if the pith ball on the clamp has a charge.

6. Pick up the copper wire and touch the hanging pith ball with it.
7. Now repeat step 5. *What happens? Does the pith ball still have a charge?*
8. Repeat step 4 to charge the hanging pith ball again.
9. Try steps 6 and 7 using the aluminum wire, the wooden stick, and the plastic ruler. Don't forget to charge the hanging pith ball each time. *What happens in each case?*

1. a) Which items allowed the charge to leave the pith ball when you touched it?
   b) In what way are these items the same?
2. a) Which items left the charge on the pith ball when you touched it?
   b) How are these items the same?
3. What kind of substance allowed the charge to escape the pith ball?
4. How do you think the charge got out of the pith ball?

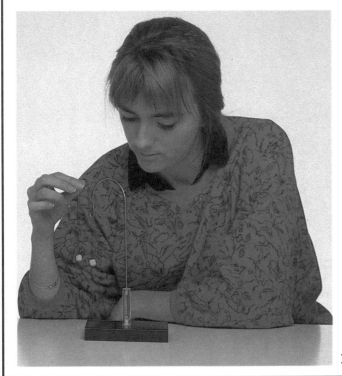

Fig. 9

continued

Can you see a pattern? The charge was able to escape the pith ball when it was touched by the metal wires. This means that the electrons were able to move through the metal wires. That makes metals good **conductors** of electricity. A conductor is anything that conducts, or transmits, something (in this case, electricity) well. The electrons could not move through the wood and the plastic. The charge stayed on the pith ball when touched with these items. Substances that do not conduct electricity are called **insulators**.

When you touched the charged pith ball with the metal wires, the electrons moved into your body. Your body is also a good conductor of electricity. In this experiment, the pith ball had only a small number of extra electrons. If there had been a larger number of electrons, you might have felt a shock. If a very large number of electrons moved through your body for several seconds, you could be killed! The moving electrons in current electricity can cause burns or even stop your heart.

Investigation

7.6 Electric Chemistry

The current electricity that we use is produced by electric companies. Since electricity is a form of energy, the electric companies must use some other kind of energy to produce the electrical energy. This may be the energy in a waterfall, heat energy from burning fossil fuels, or nuclear energy in radioactive elements. In each case, the energy is used to turn generators which convert this energy into electrical energy. The electrical energy is conducted to where it is needed by means of metal wires, such as those on tall metal towers, or those on poles along the roads.

It is also possible to produce electrical energy from chemical energy. You have already used devices that do this. Perhaps you will recognize them as you do this activity.

Fig. 10 *The metal wires supported by these towers carry current electricity.*

Find out

How can electrical energy be produced from chemical energy?

You need

- 250 mL beakers (4)
- labelling materials
- voltmeter
- two wires with connecting clips
- distilled water
- salt solution
- dilute sulfuric acid
- dilute hydrochloric acid
- copper strip
- zinc strip
- lead strip
- carbon rod
- safety goggles

SAFETY ALERT

Wear safety goggles. Keep chemicals off your skin: acid is corrosive.

Try this

1. Prepare a chart in your notebook like the one shown below:

2. Label each beaker with the name of one liquid: distilled water, hydrochloric acid, sulfuric acid, salt solution.
3. Half fill each beaker with the correct liquid.
4. Attach one wire to the positive terminal of the voltmeter.
5. Attach the other end of this wire to the carbon rod.
6. Attach the second wire to the negative terminal of the voltmeter.
7. Attach the other end of this wire to the zinc strip.
8. Hold the carbon rod in one hand and the zinc strip in the other hand. Place them both in the beaker of distilled water. Do not let the carbon and zinc touch each other. *What happens to the voltmeter? Record your result in the table.*

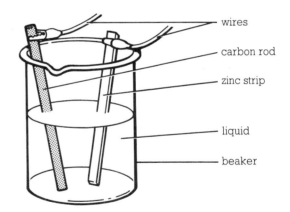

Fig. 11

Pair combination	Potential difference (in volts) from meter			
	Distilled water	Hydrochloric acid	Sulfuric acid	Salt solution
carbon and zinc				
zinc and copper				

continued

9. Now dip the carbon and zinc in the beaker of hydrochloric acid. Remember, do not let the carbon and zinc touch each other. *What happens to the voltmeter? Record your results.*

10. Remove the carbon and zinc from the hydrochloric acid, and rinse them with tap water.

11. Repeat steps 9 and 10 using the sulfuric acid and then the salt solution. *Record the results each time.*

12. Now try a different pair of materials, perhaps zinc and copper. Dip the pair in each of the four liquids. Rinse the materials with tap water after testing each liquid. *Record the four readings from the meter.* If the meter needle moves in the wrong direction, switch the wires on the meter.

13. Try as many pair combinations as you can. *Which liquid and pair combination gives you the highest reading on the voltmeter?*

14. Try using two strips of the same metal. *What happens?*

What happened?

1. What conditions were necessary in order to obtain a reading on the voltmeter?

2. Which combination of materials and liquid gave you the highest reading on the voltmeter?

3. What must happen between the metal strips and the chemical in the liquid?

4. Where did the electrical energy come from?

5. Why was there no electrical energy when the liquid used was water?

Now you know

When the metal strips were placed in the chemical solution, chemical reactions took place in some cases, producing electrical energy. On one strip, the chemical reaction added extra electrons to the metal. The metal strip became negatively charged. On the other strip, the chemical reaction removed electrons. This metal strip became positively charged. In the first example, the carbon rod became positive and the zinc became negative.

When the zinc strip was connected by wires to the voltmeter, and the voltmeter to the carbon rod, electrons moved through the wires and voltmeter. The negative electrons were repelled from the negative zinc, and the electrons were attracted to the positive carbon.

You produced an **electric current**—moving electrons—through the wires and the voltmeter. The **voltmeter** is simply a device used to measure the amount of energy the electrons have. It measures **potential difference** (or **voltage**) in units called **volts** (V). The more electrical energy each electron has, the higher the potential difference and the greater the number of volts.

7.7 Cells and Batteries

What could you call the electrical device you made in the beaker with metal strips and a chemical solution? If you called it a battery, you would be very close. It is really called a **voltaic cell**. It is named after Alessandro Volta who first produced current electricity over 150 years ago. A **battery** is several connected voltaic cells.

A voltaic cell consists of two different materials, often metals, usually called **plates** (or **electrodes**). The liquid is a chemical solution called an **electrolyte**. The plates and electrolyte are placed in a leakproof container so that the electrolyte will not spill. The two plates are attached to a positive and a negative terminal on the outside of the container.

Fig. 12 *Alessandro Volta*

Fig. 13 *Inside the dry cell, you can see the black carbon rod. The grey powder contains the electrolyte. The zinc case also acts as a plate. The top of the case is sealed so that the electrolyte will not leak.*

Voltaic cells and batteries are widely used in everyday life. Cells of different potential differences can be made by changing the material in the plates and the chemical in the electrolyte. Batteries of different potential difference can be made by connecting different numbers of voltaic cells together. A modern twelve-volt car battery is made up of six voltaic cells.

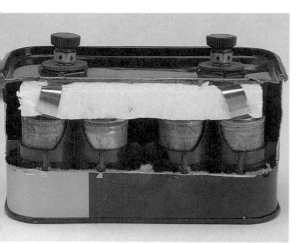

Fig. 14 *Here you can see six dry cells that make up the battery.*

Fig. 15 *Car batteries consist of six cells each with a potential difference of 2 V. The total potential difference is 12 V.*

It's a Fact
The electrolyte in a car battery is sulfuric acid—dangerous stuff if you spill it on yourself.

Fig. 17

Fig. 16

The old truck in the photograph uses a six-volt battery containing only three voltaic cells. Consequently, the six-volt battery provides less power than a twelve-volt battery. The truck, using this old type of battery, is difficult to start in cold weather. You have used different types of voltaic cells in flashlights, radios, tape players, calculators, cameras, and wristwatches. Large batteries may be used to operate instruments in remote or inaccessible areas. Navigation markers at sea and weather monitoring instruments in northern Canada are good examples.

Fig. 18a, b, c *Many different cells are available for different purposes. Do you recognize some of these?*

FEEDBACK

1. What unit is used for measuring potential difference?
2. What kind of meter is used to measure potential difference?
3. Name three important parts of a voltaic cell.
4. How is a battery different from a voltaic cell?
5. Describe five or six common uses of batteries or voltaic cells.
6. What hazard is associated with handling car batteries?

SUPERSLEUTH

1. You can make a voltaic cell from a lemon! Use nails or screws of different metals as electrodes. Just push them into the lemon. What is the potential difference of your lemon cell? Can it be used to light a flashlight bulb? What substance in the lemon acts as the electrolyte?
2. If you have a tooth with a metal filling, you may have experienced a sharp pain when you accidentally chewed on a piece of metal foil from a wrapper. What could have produced this pain? (Hint: The fluids in your mouth are slightly acidic.)

It's a Fact
The wires in your home carry a maximum of 15 A. The current in a flashlight is less then 1 A, while some high tension wires can carry up to 5000 A.

Fig. 19 *Some electrical devices include meters. This battery charger contains an ammeter.*

7.8 Measuring Electricity

Voltaic cells and batteries use chemical energy to push the electrons through metal wires. You have already measured the size of this push, or potential difference, using a voltmeter.

The potential difference pushes the electrons through the wires, much as water pressure pushes water through pipes. This flow of electrons can also be measured. It is called the **electric current** and is measured in **amperes** (A). An **ammeter** is used to measure electric current.

Fig. 20 *Ammeters measure current in amperes. The symbol for amperes is A. Voltmeters measure potential difference in volts. The symbol for volts is V.*

FEEDBACK

1. Describe the difference between potential difference and electric current.
2. What kind of meter is used to measure electric current?
3. How much electric current (in amperes) can the wires in your home safely carry?
4. a) How many different fuses are in your car? your stove?
   b) At how many amperes are they set to burn out?

"I would like 20 000 W of electricity delivered to my house today." That is the order that several thousand families make to their electric company each day. And the electric company does deliver! Once this electricity is delivered to the homes through transmission wires, it must be distributed to different parts of the house through the wires in the house circuit.

It is the job of an electrician to install and repair these electric circuits and related equipment in houses, apartment buildings, stores, factories, schools, and other buildings. An electrician installs the components (e.g., wires, switches, outlets, lights, motors, fuse boxes) of an electric circuit. Users can then turn electric lamps on and off conveniently, plug appliances into electric receptacles easily, and use all electrical equipment safely.

Electricians must be able to read and understand drawings and specifications in order to install electrical systems according to a master plan. Part of this job requires measuring electricity with voltmeters, ammeters, and ohmmeters.

Fig. 21 *Electricians do a variety of interesting but hazardous jobs both indoors and out of doors.*

The safety hazards of electricity are a constant concern. Electricians must adopt very safe work habits and be aware of safety standards for the electric circuits that are installed. The use of certain safety equipment is part of this occupation. Work may be either indoors or outdoors.

Electricians are people who can handle hand and power tools with skill. Some students have the opportunity to take electricity classes at school. After completing grade ten at a secondary school, they enter an extensive apprenticeship program. Part of this program requires twenty-four weeks of full-time attendance at a trade school (or equivalent). After successful completion of the apprenticeship program, electricians are certified to work on construction, maintenance, domestic, or rural applications. Will this be you?

Investigation

7.9 Magnets and Electricity

Many common electrical devices also utilize magnets. Electric motors in fans, cassette players, turntables, record player pickup cartridges, automobile starter switches, electric bells, and radio speakers all contain magnets. There is a very close connection between electricity and magnetism.

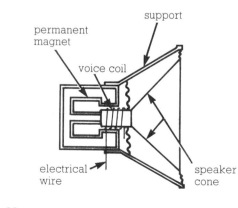

Fig. 22 *A tiny magnet is located inside the record player pickup cartridge.*

Find out

What are some of the effects of magnets on various materials?

You need

- bar magnet
- rulers (2)
- small pieces of metal: iron, nickel, lead, and copper
- piece of cardboard (5 cm × 5 cm)
- piece of glass (5 cm × 5 cm)
- piece of aluminum foil (5 cm × 5 cm)
- sheet of notepaper
- iron filings in a "salt shaker"
- small compass
- hollow cardboard tube (toilet paper core)
- insulated copper wire—2 m long
- milliammeter

Fig. 23

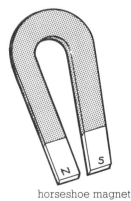

bar magnet   horseshoe magnet

Fig. 24

1. Bring the bar magnet close to each of the four pieces of metal. *Which metals are attracted by the magnet?*
2. Select a piece of metal that was attracted by the magnet. Place the piece of cardboard over the metal. *Does the magnet attract the metal through the cardboard?*
3. Repeat step 2 using the piece of glass and then the piece of foil. *Does the magnet attract the metal through these materials?*
4. Place the bar magnet flat on your desk. On each side of the magnet, place a ruler. See figure 25. Now cover the magnet and rulers with the sheet of notepaper.

Fig. 25

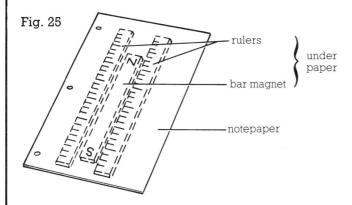

5. Sprinkle a few of the iron filings on the surface of the sheet of paper. Gently tap the sheet of paper. *What happens to the iron filings?*
6. Carefully lift the paper away from the magnet, and pour the iron filings back into the container.
7. Place the compass flat on your desk. Place one end of the magnet near the compass (about 10 cm away). *What happens?* Place the other end of the magnet near the compass. *What happens this time?*

8. Slowly move one end of the magnet in a circle around the compass. *What happens?*
9. Wrap the length of insulated copper wire around the cardboard tube to form a coil. See figure 26.
10. Attach the two ends of the wire to the **milliammeter**. A milliammeter measures electric current in **milliamperes** (mA). (1 A = 1000 mA)

Fig. 26

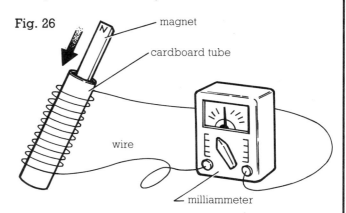

11. Now slide the magnet in and out of the coil several times. *What happens to the milliammeter? What must be present in the wire of the coil? Does anything happen when the magnet remains stationary inside the coil?*

1. Did the magnet attract all metals? Which metals did the magnet attract?
2. What effect did the cardboard, glass, and foil have on the magnet's ability to attract the metal?
3. Must the magnet be in contact with the metals in order to attract them?
4. a) Describe the pattern of the iron filings that were sprinkled on the paper covering the bar magnet.
   b) Can you explain why the pattern formed like that?

continued

5. When you brought the magnet near the compass, what effect did the magnet have on the compass?
6. What effect did the moving magnet have on the wire coil and the milliammeter?
7. What effect did the stationary magnet have on the wire coil and the milliammeter?

Now you know

The metals iron and nickel are normally attracted by magnets, even through some substances like cardboard, glass, and aluminum foil.

The pattern of iron filings indicates that the magnet's influence extends into the space surrounding it. This space is called the **magnetic field of force**. The field is strongest near the magnet.

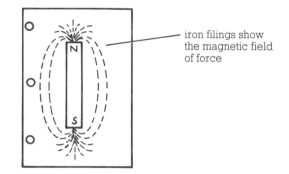

Fig. 27

iron filings show the magnetic field of force

Problems can occur with electronic equipment when a magnet is close by. Some serious accidents involving electronic robots out of control have been blamed on unexpected and unwanted magnetic fields of force. Information on a cassette tape or computer disk can be destroyed by magnetic fields.

When you brought the magnet near the compass, one end of the compass needle was attracted to the magnet.
The needle of the compass is really a tiny magnet. If you used the south pole of the magnet, it attracted the north pole of the compass needle, and vice versa. Opposite poles attract. Like poles repel.

Perhaps most amazing of all is the effect of a moving magnet in a wire coil. When the wire coil was near the moving magnet, the coil was in a moving magnetic field of force. The moving magnetic field of force produced a current in the wire of the coil. As you pushed the magnet into the coil, the meter needle moved one way. When you pulled the magnet out of the coil, the needle moved the other way. This is because the electric current in the wire moved one way and then the other way. This unusual behaviour of the wire and the magnet was first discovered by an English scientist, Michael Faraday, on December 25, 1821. Faraday's discovery led to many of today's electrical devices such as generators, magnetic tape player heads, phonograph pickup cartridges, and microphones. What a gift for the world!

SUPERSLEUTH

Inside a cassette tape is a plastic tape coated with a layer of magnetic particles arranged in a certain way. Think of these magnetic particles as thousands of tiny magnets. As these tiny magnets on the tape move past the tape head in the player, tiny electric currents are produced in the tape head. These electric currents are then amplified by the player and sent to the speaker to produce the sound. What happens when a tape is brought near a strong magnet?

Select a tape you no longer wish to keep. Make sure it plays normally. Move a strong magnet over the tape a few centimetres from it a few times. Now play the tape again. What happens to the sound? Try to explain why this happens.

Investigation

7.10 Wired for Field Forces

If a moving magnetic field of force can generate an electric current in a wire, can an electric current in a wire produce a magnetic field of force? If so, the wire and its magnetic field of force should be affected by a nearby magnet.

Find out

Is a wire that carries an electric current affected by a magnet?

You need

- horseshoe magnet
- 2 pieces of insulated copper wire (50 cm and 15 cm)
- switch
- 6 V battery

Try this

1. Connect one end of the longer copper wire to one battery terminal. Connect one end of the shorter wire to the other battery terminal.
2. Connect the other end of each wire to the terminals of the switch. Keep the switch open (see figure 28).
3. Place the horseshoe magnet on its side so that one pole lies on the desk and the other pole is directly above it.

4. Now arrange the long wire so that a part of it is between the poles of the magnet. Your equipment should look like figure 28. *Does anything happen to the wire?*

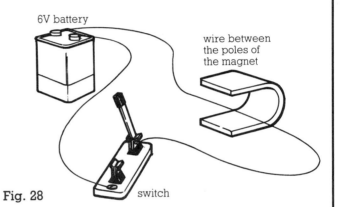

6V battery

wire between the poles of the magnet

Fig. 28   switch

5. Now close and then immediately open the switch. *What happens to the wire?* Try it again.
6. Reverse the wire connections at the battery.
7. Repeat step 5. *What happens to the wire?*

What happened?

1. When a wire was placed in a magnetic field of force and a current passed through the wire, what happened to the wire?
2. When the battery terminals were reversed so that the current flowed in the opposite direction, what happened to the wire?
3. Did anything happen to the wire when no current passed through it?

continued

When no current flowed through the wire, there was no noticeable effect of the magnet on the wire. But as soon as a current passed through the wire, the wire moved. When the current moved in the wire one way, the wire moved in one direction. When the current moved the other way, the wire moved in the opposite direction. The explanation is that, when an electric current flows through a wire, it produces a magnetic field of force around the wire. The wire's magnetic field of force is affected by the magnetic field of force of a magnet. The wire and the magnet move with respect to each other.

As a current flows through the wire, the wire moves with respect to the magnet. Depending on the direction of the current and on the position of the magnet's poles, the wire may move away from or towards the magnet. This magnetic field of force can react with other magnets. This is the principle on which electric motors, electric bells, radio speakers, and electromagnets work.

An electromagnet is easy to build. You can make one and compare it to a regular magnet. Try to measure its strength and identify which factors affect its strength.

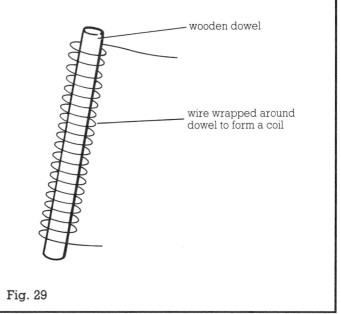

wooden dowel

wire wrapped around dowel to form a coil

Fig. 29

7.11 Generators and Motors

You have seen that an electric current is produced in a wire coil when the coil is near a moving magnet or a magnetic field of force. Remember, as you moved the magnet in and out of the wire coil, the electric current changed direction. As long as you kept moving the magnet, you kept producing an electric current. This closely resembles how an electric generator works. However, in a generator, the wire coil moves and the magnet(s) is(are) stationary. Figure 30 shows a simple electric generator. As the coil rotates between the magnets, an electric current is produced in the coil. The two ends of the wire coil are connected to a commutator. The commutator allows the coil to rotate without twisting or tangling the ends of the wire.

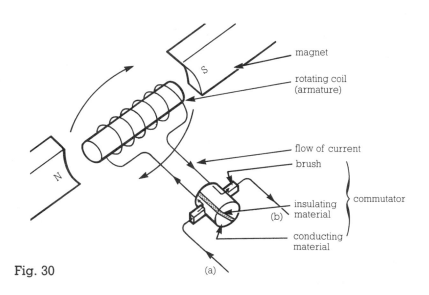

Fig. 30

Fig. 31 *This photo and the one below show electric motors being used in equipment you are probably familiar with.*

In Investigation 7.9, you discovered that when a coil and a magnet move with respect to each other, a current is produced in the coil. However, you discovered in Investigation 7.10 that the reverse is also true. When you make a current go through a wire, the wire moves with respect to the magnet. This is how an electric motor works. An electric motor is designed very much like a generator. The motor consists of a wire coil placed between magnets. When an electric current flows through the wire coil, the coil rotates between the magnets. The coil is attached to a rod, which may then rotate a device, such as a circular saw.

Kinetic energy is the energy in something that is moving. As you can see, a generator converts kinetic energy to electrical energy. An electric motor does just the reverse, converting electrical energy to kinetic energy.

Fig. 32

FEEDBACK

1. How can an electric current be produced in a wire coil?
2. What are the differences between an electric motor and an electric generator?
3. In what way are motors and generators similar?

7.12 Direct Current and Alternating Current

Voltaic cells and batteries produce a type of electric current called **direct current**, or dc. The current flows in one direction only. As you know, batteries have a negative terminal and a positive terminal. When connected in a circuit, the electrons, and therefore the current, always flow away from the negative terminal toward the positive terminal.

Direct current has many uses. The electric circuits in automobiles use direct current. Battery operated calculators, portable radios, personal cassette players, and flashlights all use direct current. These batteries and cells are a convenient, portable source of electrical energy. Since they supply only direct current, portable electrical devices must be designed to use direct current.

On the other hand, generators are capable of producing greater amounts of electrical energy much more economically. Most generators produce an electric current called **alternating current**, or ac. In this case, the electrons flow through the wire one way then change direction and flow the opposite way.

Fig. 33a   6 V   battery   light bulb   current   Fig. 33b   generator   current   light bulb

The electric current used in Canadian homes, factories, schools, farms, and stores is alternating current. This electric current changes its direction sixty times each second. We call this current 60 cycle ac or 60 Hz ac.

FEEDBACK

1. a) What kind of current is produced by batteries?
   b) What kind of current flows through your school's wiring?
2. Describe the difference between direct current and alternating current.
3. Some countries in Europe use 50 cycle ac or 60 Hz. How is this different from the current used in Canada?

Telecommunications-equipment installer

One of the earliest forms of telecommunication used smoke signals. Build a smoky fire and you were in business. Today telecommunications may use satellites and sophisticated computers to transmit electronic signals around the world.

Telecommunications is the transmission of information over long distances. A television program produced in Vancouver, British Columbia, may be transmitted to St. John's, Newfoundland, in less time than it takes to read this sentence. Long-distance phone calls are a familiar form of telecommunications. Businesses may rely on telecommunication from a computer in one city to another computer in a second city thousands of kilometres away.

A telecommunications-equipment installer installs, tests, and maintains a variety of equipment necessary to operate a national and international system of communication. The installer works indoors, using both hand and power tools to arrange and repair electrical equipment in the system. Once installed or repaired, the electric circuits must be tested using voltmeters, ammeters, or ohmmeters. Working with electricity, telecommunication-equipment installers must be very safety-conscious.

Since telecommunication equipment is constantly improving, this occupation requires people who like to learn about new things. They must be able to handle and manipulate the many parts of electrical equipment. Equipment installers are usually interested in following written instructions and working with details, and can visualize the operation of the telecommunication system.

People interested in this job usually include physics and mathematics in their school timetable. After secondary school, a two- or three-year community college program in electronics is recommended.
Up to six months of on-the-job training under the supervision of an experienced installer is necessary. In addition, the job requires frequent in-service training to keep up-to-date with new equipment.

Will this be you?

Fig. 34 *A telecommunications equipment installer routinely handles components such as these.*

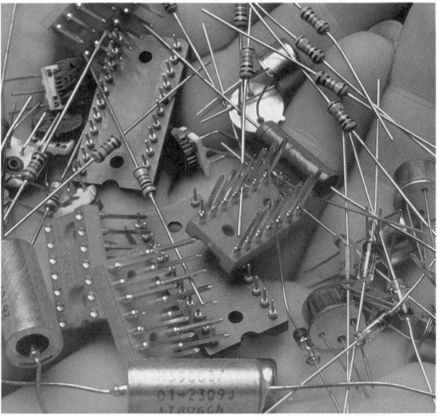

Fig. 35a

7.13 Electric Circuits

In order for electrical devices to be used, they must be connected to a source of electrical energy. This may be a battery. In your home, the electrical outlets supply the electrical energy. The outlets are connected by wires to generators that may be many kilometres away.

An electrical device, such as a light bulb, is connected to the source of electricity by wires, to form an electric circuit. In the simplest circuit, all the parts are connected to form a single loop or path for the electric current.

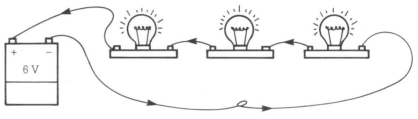

Fig. 36

This kind of circuit is called a **series circuit** and is sometimes drawn as a schematic diagram, with each part represented by a symbol. Series circuits are not very common,

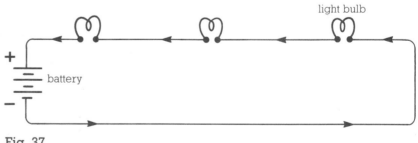

Fig. 37

but they are used to connect some Christmas tree lights. They may also form part of burglar alarm systems and radio and TV circuits.

Fig. 35b *If one bulb in this series circuit is out, the current is broken, and the entire string of lights goes out.*

The second kind of circuit, a **parallel circuit**, is more complicated. Parallel circuits are designed so that each component has a separate path for the current. Figure 38a shows a parallel circuit. It, too, can be drawn as a schematic diagram (figure 38b). Parallel circuits are used in most buildings.

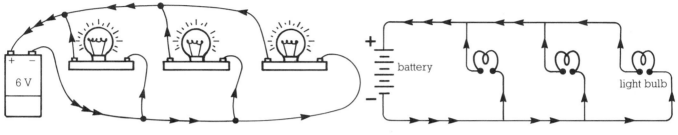

Fig. 38a   Fig. 38b

7.14 A Series Circuit

Investigation

You can easily construct each type of circuit to see how the electric current behaves in each type.

Find out

How does an electric current flow through a series circuit?

You need

- 6 V battery
- flashlight bulbs (3)
- bulb sockets (3)
- connector wires (6) with clips
- voltmeter
- ammeter

Try this

1. Copy the chart in your notebook and complete it as you do this activity.
2. Connect the battery, three sockets, and four connector wires to form a circuit as shown in figures 36 or 37 on page 260.
3. Place a bulb in one of the sockets. *Does it light up?*
4. Place the other two bulbs in the remaining sockets. *What happens?*
5. Loosen one of the bulbs. *What happens now? Can you explain why this happens?*

continued

Property	Variable	Observations
Light (on or off)	1 bulb	
	3 bulbs	
	1 bulb loosened	
Potential difference	battery	
	bulb 1	
	bulb 2	
	bulb 3	
	total	
Current	between bulb 1 and +ve terminal of battery	
	between bulbs 1 and 2	
	between bulbs 2 and 3	
	between bulb 3 and −ve terminal of battery	

6. Examine the voltmeter. Turn the knob to the 10 V scale. All electric meters must be adjusted to the suitable scale whenever they are used to measure electricity. The scale must be greater than the maximum expected measurement. In this case, the scale must be greater than the 6 V provided by the battery.

7. Without changing the circuit, connect the voltmeter to the terminals of the battery. THIS MUST BE DONE IN A CERTAIN WAY. Use a connector wire to connect the positive (red) terminal of the meter to the positive terminal of the battery. Connect the negative (black) terminal of the meter to the negative terminal of the battery. *What is the total potential difference (voltage) supplied by the battery? Record your measurement.* This is the total energy supplied by the battery.

8. Now measure the potential difference across the first bulb. To do this, disconnect the voltmeter from the battery. The light bulb should still be on. Connect the positive (red) terminal of the meter to the side of the bulb socket closer to the positive terminal of the battery. Connect the negative (black) terminal of the meter to the other side of the bulb socket. See figure 39. Measure the potential difference across the bulb. *Record the measurement.*

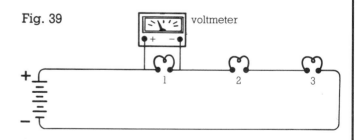

Fig. 39

9. Repeat step 7 for each of the other two bulbs. *Record the potential difference each time.*

10. Add the potential differences for the three bulbs. *How does the total compare with the potential difference of the battery?*

11. Remove the voltmeter from the circuit.

12. Now you can use an ammeter to measure the current in the circuit. Find the positive (red) terminal that is labelled 1.0 A on the ammeter.

13. Remove the connector wire in the circuit from the positive terminal of the battery. Connect this wire to the negative (black) terminal of the ammeter. Use another connector wire to connect the positive (red) terminal of the ammeter to the positive terminal of the battery. See figure 40. The bulbs should be on. Measure the current flowing through this part of the series circuit. *Record your result.*

Fig. 40

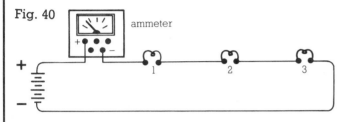

14. Next measure the current flowing between the first and second bulb. Remove the meter from the circuit, and connect the first bulb to the positive terminal of the battery again. The bulbs should be on.

15. Reconnect the ammeter between the first and second bulbs. See figure 41. The bulbs should be on. Measure the current flowing in this part of the circuit. *Record your result.*

16. Now measure the current between the second and third bulbs. *Record your result.*

Fig. 41

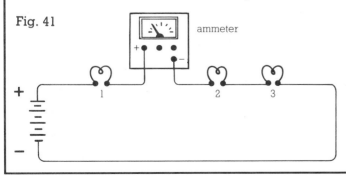

17. Finally, measure the current between the third bulb and the negative terminal of the battery. The negative terminal of the battery must be connected to the negative terminal of the ammeter. The third bulb must be connected to the positive terminal of the ammeter. *Record your result.*

What happened?

1. a) When you removed one bulb from the circuit, what happened to the other bulbs?
   b) Why did this happen?
2. How does the potential difference across all three bulbs compare with the potential difference of the battery?
3. How does the current in one part of a series circuit compare with the current in other parts of the circuit?

Now you know

In a series circuit, all the light bulbs went out if one bulb was removed from the circuit because the path of the electric current was broken. When the bulb was screwed in again, the circuit was complete and the current could flow again.

The battery provided the energy to make the electrons flow and produce a current. The total potential difference, measured by the voltmeter, was about 6 V. The potential difference across each bulb was less than 6 V. However, when all three values were added, they totalled approximately 6 V. In a series circuit, the potential difference of the battery is divided up among the different components.

On the other hand, the current in a series circuit is the same everywhere in the circuit. The same amount of current that leaves the battery at the negative terminal enters the battery at the positive terminal.

Generation of Electricity

Throughout North America, a complex network of transmission wires carries electricity to millions of buildings such as factories, offices, stores, farms, schools, and movie theatres. A branch of this network provides electrical energy to your home as well. You use the energy to operate all of the electrical appliances that you own. Virtually all this electrical energy is produced by generators. In order for a generator to produce electrical energy, the generator needs some other kind of energy. Several types of energy are used today in electrical generating stations.

Fossil fuels, such as coal and oil, are burned to heat water and produce steam. The steam causes a turbine to rotate. The turbines are attached to generators which rotate to produce electrical energy.

At nuclear generating stations, radioactive substances are used to produce heat. Otherwise, nuclear generating stations function much as fossil fuel stations do.

One of the first methods of producing electrical energy used hydro energy. This is the energy from falling water. The falling

Fig. 42

water causes the turbines and generators to rotate. The kinetic energy of the falling water is converted to electrical energy.

Unfortunately, there are damaging side effects to the generation of electrical energy. Fossil fuels contribute to air pollution. Nuclear generating stations produce radioactive wastes. Both types of generating stations produce hot water which is often dumped into lakes or rivers. This hot water is a form of heat pollution which can drastically affect the living organisms in the lakes and rivers.

In order to use falling water in hydro generating stations, dams usually have to be built which alter the natural flow of water in rivers. Fast-moving rivers are changed into slow-moving lakes. Forested land is flooded by the water collecting behind the dam. The natural habitat of many plants and animals is destroyed.

Some sources of energy used to produce electrical energy will eventually be used up. Fossil fuels have been estimated to last for no more than three hundred years. These are non-renewable sources of energy. Once they are used up, fossil fuel generating stations will be useless. Radioactive materials are also non-renewable. But it is expected that nuclear energy from radioactive materials will be available for a very long time. Hydro energy, on the other hand, is renewable. As water keeps falling from a dam, rainfall keeps filling up the lake behind the dam. As long as rain keeps filling the

dam, there will be enough water falling from the dam to operate the turbines and generators.

Some fuels are running out of supply. Others produce hazardous wastes as by-products. Some damage the environment in other ways. Consequently, society is searching for alternative sources of energy to produce electricity. Ideally, such sources should be renewable, not hazardous, and should not damage the environment. That is a tall order!

Think about it

1. Conservation of electrical energy is one method of reducing the problems associated with the generation of electricity. Suppose a law were passed that allowed each person to use only 13 500 kJ of electrical energy. How would you use your share? Look at the chart. Select the appliances from the chart that you would want in your home.

Home appliance	Energy Consumption
electric kettle	1400 kJ
stove	9000 kJ
refrigerator	2700 kJ
dishwasher	2500 kJ
TV set	1600 kJ
radio	30 kJ
vacuum cleaner	800 kJ
electric fan	240 kJ

2. Hydro electricity depends on rainfall to renew its source of energy. Rainfall is part of the water cycle. Use your library to learn more about the water cycle and what kind of energy keeps the water cycle going.

3. A small community is considering an alternative source of energy for producing electrical energy. The choices include tidal, geothermal, wind, and solar energy. You have been employed by a research company to investigate these sources of energy. For one of these alternate sources of energy, prepare a report describing:
   a) the process of producing energy from this source.
   b) the practicability of using this source at the present time. If it is being used now, describe where and how.
   c) the advantages of this source of energy.
   d) the disadvantages of this source of energy.

7.15 A Parallel Circuit

Now look at a parallel circuit to see how it differs from a series circuit.

Find out

A. What is the potential difference at various points in a circuit?
B. What is the current at various points in a circuit?

You need

- 6 V battery
- flashlight bulbs (3)
- bulb sockets (3)
- connector wires (8) with clips
- 6 bare wires (6 cm each)
- voltmeter
- ammeter

Part A:
Measuring the potential difference

1. Copy the chart below into your notebook and complete it as you do this activity.
2. Attach a short bare wire to each side of the three bulb sockets. See figure 43.

short bare wire

bulb socket

Fig. 43

Measuring the potential difference		Observations
Lightbulb (on or off):	in socket 1	
	in socket 2	
	in all 3 sockets	
	in only 2 sockets	
Potential difference:	of battery	
	of first bulb	
	of second bulb	
	of third bulb	

DO NOT WRITE IN THE TEXTBOOK

3. Attach one connector wire to each terminal of the battery.
4. Connect the other end of each connector wire to one of the bare wires attached to a socket.
5. Now connect two more connector wires to the bare wires of the socket. Connect the other end of these connector wires to a second socket.
6. Repeat step 4 to connect the second socket to the third socket. Your circuit should look like figure 44.

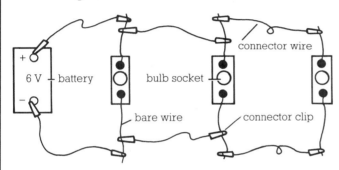

Fig. 44 *Top view of parallel circuit*

7. Screw a bulb into the first socket. *What happens?*
8. Take the bulb out of the first socket and screw it into the second socket. *What happens?*
9. Screw bulbs into the other two sockets. *What happens now?* (Two things will happen.)
10. Unscrew one of the bulbs. *What happens to the other bulbs?*
11. Use the following procedure to measure the potential difference across different parts of the circuit:
    - Turn the knob of the voltmeter to the 10 V scale.
    - Use a connector wire to link the positive terminal of the voltmeter to the positive terminal of the battery.

- With a second connector wire, connect the negative terminal of the voltmeter to the negative terminal of the battery. *What is the potential difference of the battery? Record your result.*
12. Remove the voltmeter from the battery. The bulbs should still be on.
13. Measure the potential difference across the first bulb. To do this, connect the positive terminal of the meter to the side of the socket connected to the positive (red) terminal of the battery. Connect the negative (black) side of the meter to the negative side of the socket. See figure 45.

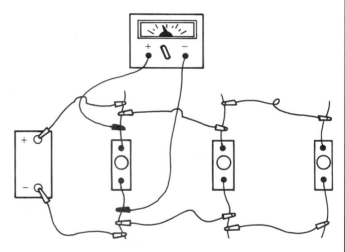

Fig. 45 *Voltmeter connected to circuit*

What is the potential difference across the first bulb? Record your result.
14. Remove the meter from the circuit. The bulbs should still be on.
15. Repeat steps 12 and 13 to measure the potential difference across the second and third bulbs. *Record the result for each bulb.*
16. *How does the potential difference across each bulb compare with the potential difference of the battery?*

continued

Part B:
Measuring the current

1. Copy the chart below into your notebook and complete it as you do this activity.

Current flow	Current (in amperes)
Out of battery	
Through bulb 1	
Through bulb 2	
Through bulb 3	
Total current through all 3 bulbs	

2. Use the following procedure to measure the current in different places in the circuit:
- Disconnect the connector wire from the negative terminal of the battery.
- Connect this end of the wire to the positive terminal, labelled 1.0 A on the ammeter.
- Use another connector wire to connect the negative terminal of the battery to the negative terminal of the ammeter. See figure 46.

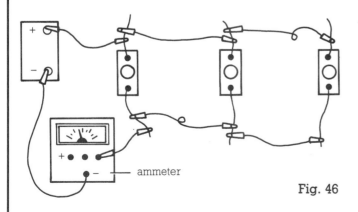

Fig. 46

- Measure the current flowing out of the battery. *Record your result.*

3. Remove the ammeter from the circuit. Re-connect the circuit as in figure 44.
4. Now disconnect the two connector wires from the bare wire on the negative side of the first bulb. Join these two connector wires together.
5. Use another connector wire to connect these two wires to the negative terminal of the ammeter.
6. Use another connector wire to connect the positive terminal of the ammeter to the bare wire of the first bulb socket. See figure 47.

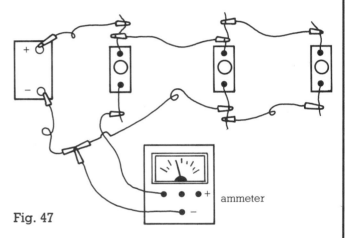

Fig. 47

Read the current flowing through the first bulb. *Record your result.*

7. Repeat steps 2, 3, 4, and 5 for the second and then the third bulb. *Record your result for each bulb.*
8. Add the current readings for the three bulbs. *How does the total current compare with the current leaving the negative terminal of the battery?*

1. When you removed one bulb from the parallel circuit, why didn't the other bulbs go out as they did in the series circuit?

2. How did the potential difference across each of the bulbs compare with the potential difference of the battery?
3. How did the current in one part of the parallel circuit compare with the current in other parts of the circuit?

Now you know

Although parallel circuits are more complex, they have an important advantage over series circuits. When one bulb in a parallel circuit is removed, the current still flows through the wires to the other bulbs, so they stay on.

The potential difference provided by the battery in your investigation was 6 V. Each bulb in the parallel circuit had the same potential difference because each bulb had a direct connection to the battery.

The current, however, behaved differently. The current that left the negative terminal of the battery was split up as it flowed through the circuit. Some of the current went through the first bulb, some through the second bulb, and some through the third bulb. The total of these three currents added up to the current that left the negative terminal of the battery. When the electrons flowed back to the battery, the current was the same as when it left the battery. The same number of electrons that leave the negative terminal of the battery return to the battery at the positive terminal.

7.16 Household Circuits

The wiring in your home consists of parallel circuits. You can turn one light off but leave all the other lights on. If a light bulb in one part of your home burns out, the other bulbs on the same circuit are not affected. Clearly, parallel circuits have a distinct advantage.

7.17 How Many Amperes Are Showing?

As you know, electrical energy is useful in many ways. One way is that it can easily be converted into other forms of energy. All the electrical appliances in your home are designed to convert electrical energy to some other kind of energy. A stove converts electrical energy to heat energy. A radio converts electrical energy to sound energy. Other appliances convert electrical energy to light or kinetic energy. However, appliances must be used with care. Using too many appliances on the same circuit at the same time, for example, can be dangerous. You may have already noticed that a high current in a wire can cause the wire to get hot and may start a fire. Most home circuits are designed to carry a maximum of 15 A. You can probably predict what would happen if a home circuit carried more than 15 A.

Find out

Which appliances can be used together on one 15 A circuit?

You need

- Several electrical appliances, such as:

heater	TV set
fan	radio
toaster	tape player
iron	vacuum cleaner
hair dryer	blender

Try this

1. Copy the chart into your notebook. Provide one row for each appliance available.

Appliance	Potential difference (in volts)	Power (in watts)	$\dfrac{\text{watts}}{\text{volts}}$ = amperes	Current (in amperes)
toaster	115 V	1050 W	$\dfrac{1050}{115} = 9.1$ A	9.1 A

Power is the rate at which an electrical appliance uses electric energy. It is measured in **watts**.

2. Locate the data plate on each appliance.
3. Copy the data for the potential difference (volts) and the power (watts) onto the chart with the name of each appliance.
4. *Calculate the current by dividing the power (watts) by the potential difference (volts).* The toaster on the chart uses 9.1 A.
5. In order to use the appliances safely, the total current must not exceed 15 A.
   a) *Do any of the appliances use 15 A?*
   b) *Could the fan and radio be used on the same circuit at the same time?*
   c) *Could a person iron a shirt and watch a television program at the same time? Why do you think so?*
6. *Make a list of as many appliances as possible that could be used together on the same circuit.*
7. *What would happen to a 15 A fuse if the circuit were used to operate an electric heater, toaster, and iron at the same time?*
8. *What might happen in question 7 if the 15 A fuse were replaced with a 30 A fuse?*

Now you know

Appliances vary considerably with respect to the current that flows through them. Many electric heaters need 15 A of current and cannot be used with other appliances on the same circuit. Some, like the toaster and iron, need close to 10 A each. Together they would cause a 15 A fuse to melt. So would the iron and TV set together. (Most people would say that the fuse would blow.)

On the other hand, the radio and fan together need less then 15 A and could operate on the same circuit. If someone were foolish enough to replace a 15 A fuse with a 30 A fuse to allow more appliances to operate on the same circuit, the appliances would continue to operate, but the home wiring would overheat and could cause a fire! The fuses and circuit breakers in most of the circuits in the average home must never exceed 15 A.

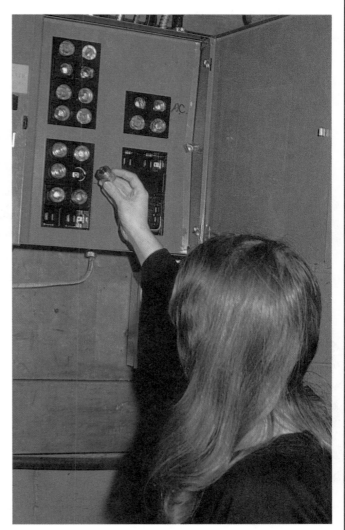

Fig. 48 *Fuses rated at 15 A are designed to melt when the current through them exceeds 15 A. When they melt, they can no longer carry an electric current. Some homes use* **circuit breakers** *instead of fuses. These are simply switches that turn off when they get too hot.*

7.18 **Electricity and Home Safety**

Did you know that your heartbeat is actually electrical in nature? The heart automatically produces electrical impulses which make it beat. When household alternating current passes through a person's body, that person becomes part of the circuit. The alternating current interferes with the electrical impulses that tell the heart to beat and makes the heart vibrate rapidly instead. The vibrating heart can't pump blood, and death may result. To avoid becoming part of an electric circuit, never touch bare electrical wires. Loose or frayed wires on an appliance are also a hazard. All electrical appliances and components must be in excellent condition.

Fig. 50

Fig. 49

Fig. 51

The risk of electrocution is even greater when a person is standing in water which can be an excellent conductor of electricity. The person then may become part of an electric circuit. This is particularly true if the person is standing on the ground or in a basement or is touching metal pipes attached to the ground.

Since faulty electrical appliances or components are a hazard, they must be kept in good repair. However, they must first be disconnected from the source of electrical energy. Appliances should simply be unplugged from the electrical outlet. If someone is repairing a part of a household circuit, such as a wall switch, the fuse should be removed or the circuit breaker turned off. Then it is safe to work on the circuit because the current can't flow. Of course other circuits in the house can still carry a current, and they are still dangerous.

Electrical fires are the other hazard associated with electricity. They too may be caused by faulty circuits and appliances. Another cause of electrical fires is an overloaded circuit which can cause the wires to overheat. Use of 15 A fuses or circuit breakers and your knowledge of the safe use of electrical appliances are the best protection against overloaded circuits and danger from electricity.

FEEDBACK

1. Describe two ways in which electricity can be dangerous.
2. Why can a person be killed when an electric current (ac) passes through his or her body?
3. How can one avoid electrocution? Describe three ways.
4. What safety precautions must one take when repairing electrical appliances or electric circuits?
5. Explain how electrical fires are caused. What type of fire extinguisher should be used on electric fires?

7.19 Chapter Summary

- Electricity is one of the most useful forms of energy.
- There are two types of electrical charges: positive charges and negative charges.
- Like charges repel each other, unlike charges attract each other.
- Current electricity usually consists of negative electrons flowing through metal conductors.
- Voltaic cells convert chemical energy to electric energy. Batteries consist of two or more voltaic cells.
- Magnets have the ability to attract certain metals.
- Like poles of magnets repel each other, unlike poles attract each other.
- Moving magnetic fields can produce an electric current in conductors.
- Electric currents can produce magnetic fields.
- Generators and motors operate on the principles of magnetism and electricity.
- Electric currents may be direct current (dc) or alternating current (ac).
- Electric circuits may be arranged in series or in parallel.
- Household circuits are arranged in parallel.
- The maximum safe current in most household circuits is 15 amperes.
- Like other forms of energy, electric energy is measured in watts.
- The generation of electric energy from other energy sources causes environmental problems.

7.20 Are You Ready to Go On?
Do not write in the text.

1. Describe the difference between static electricity and current electricity.

2. When a glass rod is rubbed with silk, both the glass rod and the silk become charged.
   a) What charge forms on the glass rod?
   b) What charge forms on the silk?
   c) Explain how the two substances become charged.

3. This chapter contains many new words relating to science. How many of the scrambled words below can you unscramble? Write each unscrambled word in your notebook.
   a) yretbta
   b) uiiccrt
   c) elop
   d) atngeevi
   e) ragehc
   f) tgamen
   g) atwt
   h) uccnotdro
   i) tyeectleor
   j) otvl

4. Decide if each statement is true or false. If it is true, copy the statement in your notebook. If it is false, rewrite the statement to make it true.
   a) An electric charge can be produced by rubbing two similar substances together.
   b) Protons are positively charged.
   c) Voltaic cells convert heat energy to electric energy.
   d) An ammeter can be used to measure potential difference.
   e) Electric current is measured in amperes.
   f) A generator converts kinetic energy to electric energy.
   g) If one light bulb in a parallel circuit is removed from the circuit, all the other bulbs in the circuit will go out.
   h) The current in one part of a series circuit is 3.0 amperes. In another part of the same circuit, the current will be only 2.0 amperes.
   i) Electric energy is measured in watts.

5. Construct a schematic diagram of a parallel circuit which contains a battery and four light bulbs. Label each part of your circuit diagram.

6. Write each of the following sentences in your notebook. Fill in each blank with an appropriate word.
   a) Electrons have a _____ charge.
   b) When a charged ebonite rod comes in contact with a pith ball, the pith ball may be charged by _____ .
   c) _____ are able to flow through conductors.
   d) Magnets are surrounded by a _____ _____ .
   e) A motor is a device for converting electric energy into _____ energy.
   f) The potential difference across one bulb in a parallel circuit is 1.5 volts. The potential difference across a second bulb in the same circuit will be _____ volts.
   g) Household circuits are _____ circuits.
   h) Household circuits are protected from high currents and overheating by _____ and _____ _____ .
   i) If an electric current from a household circuit should flow through a person's body, it may cause the person's _____ to vibrate rapidly and then stop.
   j) When a battery is connected to an electric circuit, electrons flow through the wires from the _____ terminal of the battery to the _____ terminal of the battery.

7. List five devices that use
   a) batteries   b) ac electricity

8. Choose the number of the correct answer. Then copy the complete statement into your notebook.
   a) A negatively charged object will ATTRACT another object that is:
      i) negatively charged ii) positively charged
      iii) neutral   iv) two of the above
   b) A negatively charged object will REPEL another object that is:
      i) negatively charged
      ii) positively charged
      iii) neutral
      iv) two of the above
   c) The electrolyte in a car battery is:
      i) tap water
      ii) a strong acid
      iii) a dilute solution of salt
      iv) a black powder containing carbon and zinc.
   d) A magnet is capable of attracting:
      i) small pieces of paper   ii) plastic
      iii) wood   iv) iron
   e) An electric current can be produced by:
      i) a voltaic cell
      ii) a magnet moving in a wire coil
      iii) a generator
      iv) all of the above
   f) While a person is watching television, and ironing clothes at the same time, a 15 ampere fuse in the electric circuit blows. This person should:
      i) replace the fuse with another 15 ampere fuse and continue watching TV and ironing.
      ii) replace the fuse with a 30 ampere fuse and continue watching TV and ironing.
      iii) turn off the TV, replace the fuse with another 15 ampere fuse, and continue ironing.
      iv) be certain that both the TV and the iron are plugged into the same receptacle, replace the fuse with another 15 ampere fuse, and continue watching TV and ironing.

9. a) Describe three environmental hazards that are associated with the generation of electric energy.
   b) Suggest some ways in which these hazards may be reduced.

Contents

Chapter Eight
We're Into Saving Energy and Resources

8.1 Using Our Resources

Take a look around you and consider all the resources that have been used to create your environment. A **resource** is anything that humans can use to make a product or useful energy. **Renewable resources** are those that can be replaced by nature. Plant products, such as wood, or animal products, such as wool, are renewable resources. Resources such as metal ores and fossil fuels are **non-renewable** because they either cannot be replaced once they have been used or take many millions of years to replace.

Our modern society has developed an incredible ability to obtain resources and to change them into things and energy. Nearly all of the things you have and the activities you do are directly connected to Earth's resources.

In this chapter, you will consider some ways that we use resources. You will become aware of serious problems that face those who live in our home — the planet Earth — as a result. You will learn about alternatives to our use of resources.

It's a Fact
We're Into Saving Energy and Resources, and that makes us a WISER society.

Fig. 2 *Your classroom probably contains concrete made from sand, cement, and water; floor tiles or a rug made from oil; window glass made from sand; light fixtures and chalkboards made from metals; furniture and shelving made from wood; clothing made from plant and animal products; light produced by using the energy in oil, gas, coal, uranium, or falling water.*

FEEDBACK

1. What is meant by the term "resource"? Give some examples of resources that you use each day.
2. What is the difference between renewable and non-renewable resources?
3. What good has come from our use of resources?

Fig. 1 *The Niagara River, which flows into Niagara Falls, provides water for several power plants in Canada and the U.S.A., having a total capacity of about 4 200 000 kW.*

Activity

8.2 Going Broke With Double Jeopardy

Your science teacher has offered you a job cleaning up a storage room. You can choose to be paid $4.00/hour for each of five hours that you work. Alternatively, you could accept a payment of $1.00 for the first hour of work, but then have the payment doubled every hour for the next four hours.

The first offer sounds fair, giving you: $5 \times \$4.00 = \$20.00$. But think carefully about the second offer. If you accepted it, you would receive: $\$1.00 + (2 \times \$1.00) + (2 \times \$2.00) + (2 \times \$4.00) + (2 \times \$8.00) = \$31.00$, a much better deal! Now consider the following situation and answer the questions to see a different effect that is produced by doubling something every so often.

1. Put 127 items, such as pennies, nails, poker chips, or toothpicks, on a piece of paper. These 127 items represent resources, and the paper represents your home today. Of course, you need to maintain and operate your home, and to feed and clothe the people in it. Thus you must use up some of these resources to keep living the way you are.

2. Suppose something happens that requires the use of more resources each day. Perhaps friends and relatives, and then their friends and relatives, move in. Perhaps your home needs more and more repairs. To survive now, you must double the use of your resources as each day passes. Your wealth is 127 items at the start, and you again use one resource item the first day. On the second day, you double your use to two items, then to four on the third day, etc. *Make a copy of the chart on page 279.* As you use up your resources each day, remove the items from your "home." *Complete the chart to show how much of your wealth is left after each day.*

Fig. 3 *Good work brings good rewards—but which reward is better?*

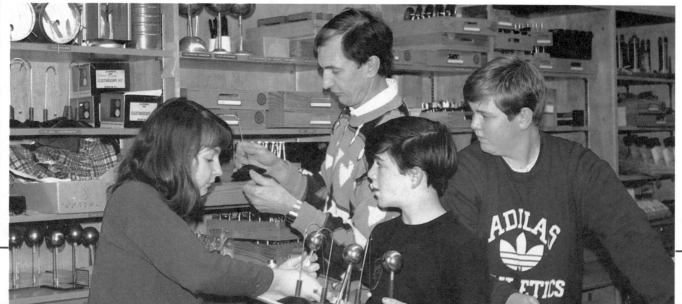

Number of days that pass	START	1	2	3	4	5	6	7	8	9	10	11
Number of resources used that day	—	1	2									
Resources left at end of that day	127	126	124									

Think about it

1. Suppose that you must use up one resource each day to survive. How many days would pass before all your wealth was gone?
2. Now consider the effect if the use doubles each day. On what day have you used up all of your resources and your wealth?
3. On what day have you used up half of your resources? If, on this day, you recognize that your resources are quickly being used up, how much time do you have to take some action before you go broke?
4. How does this compare to the length of time it took to use up all your wealth at the rate of one item a day? Suggest a meaning for the title of this activity.
5. Just as you run out of resources you discover another 128 items in your home. Add this new wealth to the chart, in the appropriate box. How many more days could you now survive, assuming that your use still doubles every day?
6. Suppose the doubling occurred every month, instead of every day, and only one resource item was used in the first month. Would this outcome change your answer to question 3?
7. What is the effect of repeated doubling of resource use on the time that these resources can last?

It's a Fact
When something changes by doubling at regular intervals, the result is called *exponential growth*. Human population and the use of some resources, such as fossil fuels, are growing approximately exponentially.

8.3 Energy and Energy Systems

Energy comes in many easily recognizable forms, such as light, sound, heat, elastic, kinetic, or gravitational. You may also know something about chemical, electrical, magnetic, and perhaps even nuclear energy. All forms of energy have one thing in common: each has the ability to do work on something. This work always involves exerting a force that causes something to move.

Fig. 4 *What is a foot doing among all these forms of energy? A foot is like energy—it's so familiar, you take it for granted until something goes wrong. But energy, like your feet, is necessary for getting around and making things happen.*

Memory Jog
Recall that kinetic energy is the energy something has because of its motion. Gravitational energy is a kind of potential energy something has because it could fall down. Elastic energy occurs when something is stretched or bent, but can spring back into shape.

It's a Fact
Machines and engines are devices that convert some form of energy into useful work.

Doing work always requires a change in energy. A useful way to think about changes in energy is by thinking about energy systems. Every system has an INPUT of energy to make it go. Some PROCESS occurs in the system to cause changes. Then there is some OUTPUT from the system. Usually there are two kinds of outputs: the INTENDED OUTPUT (energy) that is the purpose for which the system exists and the WASTE OUTPUT.

The automobile is one example of an energy system. The energy input is the chemical energy of gasoline. Oxygen is a necessary input. Processes occur inside the engine to change this chemical energy into the intended output, the kinetic

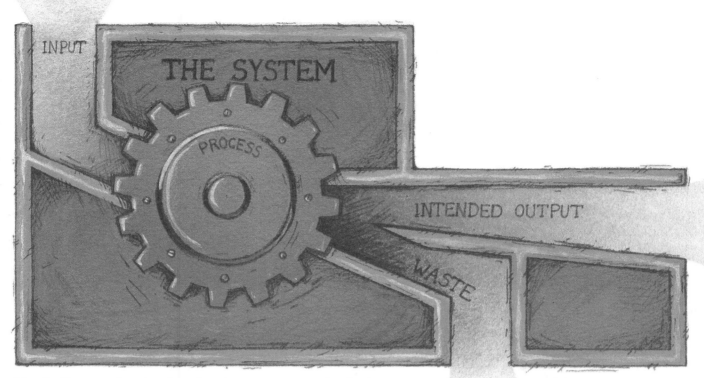

Fig. 5 *Every system involves inputs, processes, and outputs.*

energy of the moving car. Waste outputs are heat and exhaust gases. (See figure 6a) Your body is an energy system also. Chemical energy is stored in your body when you eat and digest your input of food. Oxygen from the air is also an input. When you walk up the stairs at school, oxygen from the air helps many processes in your muscles, lungs, heart, and liver to occur to change the stored energy into the intended output—the increased gravitational potential energy of your body. Heat energy from your body is a waste output. Waste matter in the form of carbon dioxide and water vapour in breath, plus feces and urine, is produced.

As you read this chapter, think about the world around you as a group of systems of inputs, processes, and outputs. You will become aware that any input to one system must have been an output from some other system. For example, the gasoline input for a car is one output of an oil refinery. You will also gain insights into how outputs from one system become inputs to other systems. The waste heat put out by

Do You Recall?
A system is a group of parts that work together for some purpose.

your body as you climb the school stairs is one input to the heating system of the school building. Systems can overlap, intertwine, work together, interfere with each other, grow larger and larger, or get more and more complicated. However, each one always involves energy as part of its input, process, and output.

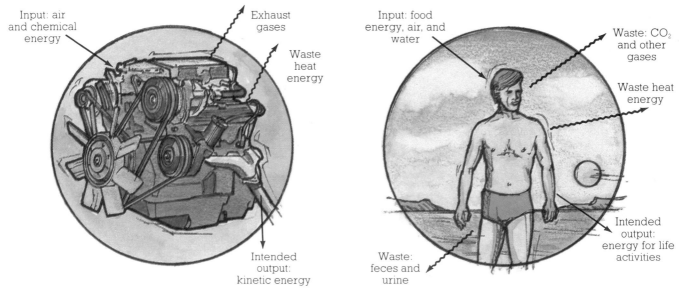

Fig. 6a *A gasoline engine*

Fig. 6b *The human body*

FEEDBACK

1. What do all forms of energy have in common?
2. Consider all the events happening around you and inside you right now. List the forms of energy involved.
3. a) What is involved when work is done?
   b) What is usually a waste product when work is done?
4. a) What is a system?
   b) What three words are useful when thinking about a system?
   c) What is the role of energy in a system?
5. You have decided to bake a cake. Use the concept of an energy system to describe the stove that you would use.
6. You should have identified at least two outputs in question 5.
7. Identify one system for which each of these is an input.

8.4 Learning to Think Energetically and Systematically

At the beginning of this chapter, you saw that you were surrounded—surrounded by friends, the resources used to create your environment. Now get to know some more friends—the energy systems that also surround you.

What are some energy systems that are commonly used? What are the inputs, processes, and outputs for each one?

About ten of these items will be enough for the whole class.

- electric kettle
- electric toaster
- goldfish in bowl
- electric or battery-powered fan
- flashlight
- radiometer
- gerbil or hamster on a treadmill
- solar cell (on a motor or in a calculator)
- wind up toy
- tape deck
- electric lamp
- Bunsen burner heating water
- television

SAFETY ALERT!
Use normal safety precautions around any electrical device.

1. *Make a chart like the one below.* Leave three lines for each of the ten energy systems that you will be observing.
2. Several energy systems are operating at different work stations around the room. Your teacher will tell you how much time to spend at each station.
3. *Record the number of the station in the chart. Write a name that describes this energy system. Observe it operating briefly, then record the energy form(s) that is/are the input(s). Write a short description of the process that is occurring. Think carefully about all the outputs, then record these under either the "Intended" or "Waste" column in the chart.*
4. At the signal from your teacher, go to the next work station. Repeat step 3.

Station number	Name of energy system	Inputs	Processes	Outputs	
				Intended	Waste
1.					
2.					

DO NOT WRITE IN THE TEXTBOOK

1. Which energy system do you think was the simplest? Why do you think so?
2. Which energy system do you think was the most complicated? Why do you think so?
3. What form of energy was an input the most often? Is this true also for energy systems in your home?
4. What form of energy was often a waste output? Where does this waste output go eventually?
5. What made each energy system unique, that is, different from the others?

Now you know

You encounter and use dozens of energy systems every day. Each one can be described in terms of the inputs, the processes that occur in the system, and the outputs. Electricity is the most common energy input. Electrical energy can be changed by simple processes into useful heat, light, or motion. Heat is a common waste output from many systems.

Some systems, such as an electric kettle, are quite simple. There is one input (electricity), a simple process (an element heats up), and one intended output, (hot water, plus waste heat to air). Other systems, such as living organisms, are very complicated since several inputs — food, air, water — are required. Also, many interrelated processes occur inside the organ systems, and many outputs are produced. The processes that occur in a system are what make it unique. For example, both the kettle and the toaster use electrical energy as the input. Both have heat as the energy output, but you certainly don't toast your bread in the kettle!

8.5 Energy Efficiency

When energy is changed from one form to another in a system, some energy is always wasted. For example, an incandescent light bulb changes only 2% of the electrical energy input into the intended output, light. The rest of the electrical energy is "wasted" as heat. A car engine changes about 25% of the chemical energy in gasoline into the intended output, the kinetic energy of the moving car. An electrical heater changes about 99% of the energy input into the intended output, heat.

Fig. 7a *The electric light bulb system*
Components: electrical energy and the light bulb

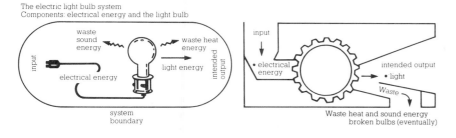

Fig. 7b *The automobile transportation system*
Components: chemical energy of gasoline and the automobile

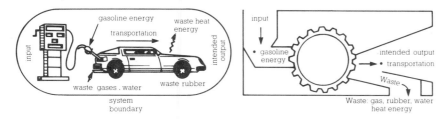

Efficiency is the measure of how well an energy system changes the energy input into the intended energy output. Efficiency is expressed as a percent, and is calculated as shown below:

$$\text{efficiency} = \frac{\text{intended output energy}}{\text{energy input}} \times 100\%$$

The actual measurement of efficiency for a system is difficult. Many kinds of systems have been studied, efficiencies of some familiar systems are shown below.

Approximate efficiencies of some systems	
electric kettle: 99%	car engine: 26%
electric motor: 90%	thermal generator of electricity: 25%
furnace in home: 70–90%	fluorescent light: 20%
wind generator of electricity: 60%	solar cell: 12%
diesel engine: 36%	incandescent light: 2%

Most energy resources, such as electricity, gasoline, heating oil, and natural gas, have to be purchased. Ideally, you would obtain one dollar's worth of useful energy for every dollar of energy that you buy. This never happens, as suggested by the efficiencies shown in the table above. Some energy is always wasted. When you have a limited amount of money to spend, or only a limited amount of energy resources that can be purchased, you try to waste as little as possible.

Think back to activity 8.2. If the items in that activity were energy resources and this energy were used at about 50% efficiency, then you would have to consume double the number of energy resources each day to survive. This means that you would run out of energy resources even more quickly.

It makes sense for every energy system to have the maximum output at minimum cost. To make maximum use of the Earth's resources, the efficiency of all processes in energy systems should be as large as possible.

FEEDBACK

1. Why do energy systems not have efficiency of 100%?
2. Define efficiency.
3. a) Steam engines, such as the ones that pulled trains several decades ago in Canada, have an efficiency of about 9%. What does this 9% mean in terms of energy inputs and outputs?

   b) Most modern trains in North America are pulled by locomotives with diesel engines. Use the table on page 286 to decide how much more efficient a diesel engine is than a steam engine.
4. Why is efficiency an important quantity?
5. Why should the efficiency of an energy system be as great as possible?

SUPERSLEUTH

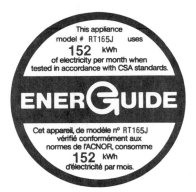

Every major electrical appliance must display a sticker giving the efficiency of the appliance. Usually the efficiency is described in terms of the number of energy units required to operate the appliance over a given period of time.

1. Choose a major appliance you might consider purchasing. Find and record the efficiency ratings of that appliance from three different manufacturers.
2. Should you choose an appliance with a large or a small number?
3. What other factors would you consider before actually purchasing your appliance?

Fig. 8 *Some solar radiation is reflected back into space by clouds, water, and the atmosphere.*

8.6 Inside Or Outside — Where's All the Energy?

Before reading this section, look at the scale below and decide where you fit into it.

1	2	3	4	5
I'm not interested in energy resources, and I don't care what happens to them.	There will always be enough energy to do all the things I want.	There will always be enough energy for the important things I need.	Energy costs and availability might limit the things I can do and have.	There could be real energy problems within my lifetime.

Our entire planet can be thought of as one large energy system. There are only two kinds of energy inputs to Earth — solar radiation from the sun and gravitational potential energy of tides caused by the moon. There are no spaceships bringing oil or gas; there are no electric power lines from other planets; there is no nuclear fuel from nearby stars. Light and tides are all we get from outside the Earth.

These two kinds of energy inputs directly or indirectly cause most of the natural processes on Earth. About one third of the solar radiation is reflected back into space by clouds, water, and the atmosphere. The Earth can be seen by astronauts because of this reflected light. (See figure 52, page 333.) Less than 0.1% of the light is absorbed by green plants and algae during the process of photosynthesis. Still, this small fraction of solar energy provides all our food and wood. About two-thirds of the solar radiation is absorbed as heat by land and water. Some of this heat evaporates water, creating the water cycle. A small amount of the heat creates the movement of air (winds) and water (ocean currents and waves). The rest of the heat simply warms the land and water. The second kind of energy input is a result of the force of gravity from the moon lifting water in oceans upwards, creating the tides. Although tides in some parts of the world raise water levels more than fifteen metres, tidal energy is less than 0.002% of the input of solar energy. (See figure 9.)

All of the energy that Earth receives from outside
eventually escapes back into space as an output of heat. For
example, when plants and animals die and decompose, heat is
released to the air. Friction of water falling through the air and
of waves tumbling against a shore warms the air. All the heat
that is added to air eventually radiates into space. If this didn't
happen, the temperatures on the Earth would get hotter and
hotter.

Fig. 9 *The sun and moon provide the Earth with its only energy
from outside.*

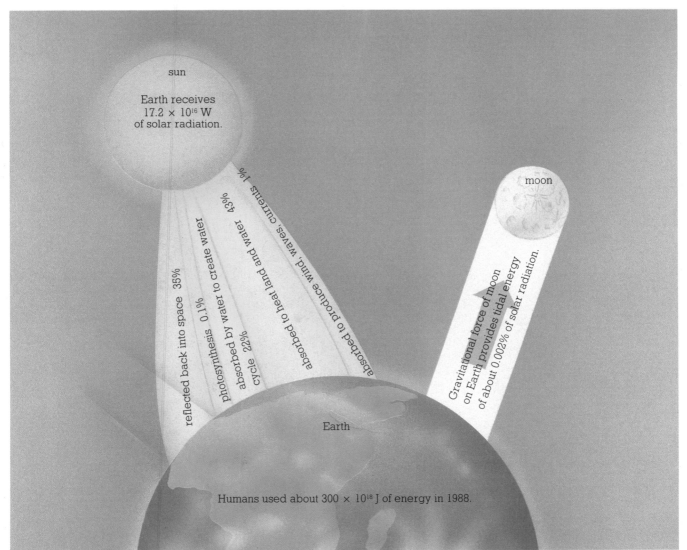

Because solar and tidal energies are continually reaching the Earth, they are classified as renewable energy sources. Many scientists believe that fossil fuels were created from plants that had used renewable solar radiation, but they are classified as non-renewable energy sources because the processes that made them required millions of years. Canadians started using the fossil fuels — oil, coal, and natural gas — as energy resources only 130 years ago. They now supply about three-quarters of the energy needs in Canada. But if our present pattern of use continues, Canada's, and the world's, oil and natural gas reserves will probably be used up in the next 50 to 200 years. Once a fossil fuel is burned, it is gone for a very long time. Consider this: humans have existed for about one million years, but in less than 300 years we will have used up all of the Earth's non-renewable oil and natural gas.

Fig. 10 *There is enough coal left in the world for about 200 more years, at present rate of use.*

Like oil and natural gas, non-renewable energy sources such as coal, nuclear fuels such as uranium, and heat from the Earth's interior cannot be replaced from outside the Earth either.

"Inside" energy — that which is stored on or in the Earth — is limited and is likely to become more and more expensive, just like rare coins, stamps, and cars, or people with unusual abilities. In 1973 those nations that depended heavily on the use of oil for energy experienced an "energy crisis." At that time a group of oil-supplying nations decided to greatly increase the price of oil. Countries that needed to import it had little choice but to pay the skyrocketing prices. The costs of gasoline, heating oil, food, and manufactured goods increased. People were greatly affected, and started to think seriously about supplies of energy resources. Governments analysed the availability of energy in all forms and the demands for this energy. Figure 11 shows a graph made in 1976 to predict the energy in Canada. Notice that energy demand exceeds the supply from Canadian sources. Thus Canada must import extra energy, mostly in the form of oil, and we are vulnerable to changes in oil prices.

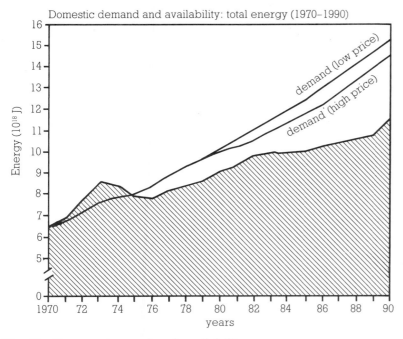

Fig. 11 *Energy demand and availability.*

Fig. 12 *Without some kind of energy input, any kind of transportation is impossible.*

However, the real "energy crisis" is not the cost of energy; it is the fact that the supply of useful energy on our whole planet has a definite limit. Without some kind of energy inputs, all the processes that we rely upon, such as home heating, transportation, manufacturing of goods, are impossible. If these processes are to continue, we must increase our use of renewable sources of energy (solar and tidal energies) and reduce our use of non-renewable resources. We want to make the energy wealth of our home, the Earth, last as long as possible.

FEEDBACK

1. a) What two major energy inputs come to Earth from outside?
   b) Name some natural processes that these energy inputs cause.
   c) What is the final output from the Earth energy system?
   d) Why does the Earth not become hotter or colder?
2. a) What kinds of energy resources come from inside Earth itself?
   b) Why are these kinds of energy called "non-renewable"?

3. a) What are some ways that Canadians use oil and natural gas?
   b) How much of Canada's energy need is met by oil and gas?
   c) At present rates of use, about how much longer will oil and natural gas in Canada last?
4. a) What is the "real" energy crisis?
   b) If no changes are made, what will be some likely effects of this energy crisis?
5. a) Has your position on the scale at the beginning of section 8.6 changed? In what way?
   b) Write a sentence or two to describe your feelings.
6. Where could we get energy that is needed? Explain.

SUPERSLEUTH

1. Look back at your data from activity 8.2. Make a "demand" graph by plotting the number of resources used each day against the days. Is the graph straight or curved? Look at figure 11. Are the "demand" lines straight or do they curve? What does this suggest about the rate at which we are using our resources?
2. Look at figure 11. Give some reasons for the differences between the "high price" and "low price" demand lines. (Think of how you react to costs.)

8.7 A Hot Time With Solar Radiation

Remember the last time you leaned against a sun-drenched wall on a cool day and felt the warmth of the sun soaking into your body? You were enjoying the effects of solar radiation. Suppose all this solar radiation coming to the Earth could be trapped and stored for later use. In just eight minutes, enough energy would be available to supply the energy needs of all of Canada for a year (about eight billion billion joules of energy). In this investigation you will learn one simple way that renewable energy from outside the Earth—sunlight—can be collected, stored, and distributed.

Find out

A. How can you collect energy from the sun?
B. How can you use solar energy to heat water?

You need

- shallow box (about 24 cm × 30 cm)
- 4 m to 6 m of black tubing
- pinch clamp or clothespin
- graduated cylinder (100 mL)
- acetate sheet or foodwrap (about 28 cm × 32 cm)
- black cloth, paper, or paint
- thermometer
- styrofoam cup
- 2 water containers (about 1 L)
- tape

Try this

A. Building a solar collector
1. Cover the insides of the shallow box with the black paper, cloth, or paint.
2. Coil or loop the black tubing so that it lies flat inside the box. Punch two holes in one side of the box, then push about 30 cm of each end of the tubing through these holes. See figure 13.

Fig. 13 *A model of a solar collector*

3. Cover the top of the box with a clear covering, then tape it in place. You now have a model of a solar collector that could be placed on the roof of a house to trap the energy in solar radiation.

B. Using a solar collector

1. *Copy the chart below into your notebook.*

Time (min)	Temperature of water (°C)
start	
2	
4	
6	

2. Place your solar collector where strong light (preferably sunlight) can fall on it.
3. When your collector is operating, water will flow in one end and out the other. Set up the collector so that light hits the front at a right angle. The container that supplies water must be raised above the bucket that collects the water. See figure 13.

4. During this step, block the light from the collector. Prepare to siphon water from the supply container by following the steps in the skills box.
5. Before letting light fall on the solar collector, measure the temperature of the water in the supply container. *Record this starting temperature in your chart.* Let light fall on the collector as you start timing.
6. Use the graduated cylinder to measure 100 mL of water from a tap into the styrofoam cup. Mark the 100 mL level on the cup, then empty the cup.
7. After light has shone on the collector for 2 min, drain 100 mL of water from the collector into the styrofoam cup. Close the clamp. *Measure and record the temperature of the water.* This is the water that would flow through the heating pipes in a home.
8. Repeat step 7 every 2 min, until the temperature of the water remains constant.
9. *Make a graph that shows the water temperature versus the time that light shone on the collector.*

Lab skill

How to Siphon Safely   Fig. 14

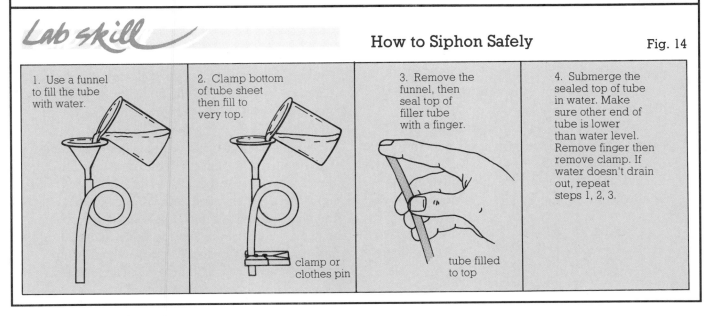

1. Use a funnel to fill the tube with water.

2. Clamp bottom of tube sheet then fill to very top.

clamp or clothes pin

3. Remove the funnel, then seal top of filler tube with a finger.

tube filled to top

4. Submerge the sealed top of tube in water. Make sure other end of tube is lower than water level. Remove finger then remove clamp. If water doesn't drain out, repeat steps 1, 2, 3.

10. If you have time, repeat steps 5, 7 and 8 after making one change in the collector, such as:
   a) laying the solar collector flat instead of facing the sun as in step 2.
   b) removing the clear covering.
   c) lining the box with white paper.
   d) using clear or white tubing instead of black.
   e) insulating the outside of the box with styrofoam sheet, etc.
   f) sealing all air leaks in the solar collector.
   g) adding extra tubing to the original piece in the box.

Fig. 15

What happened?

1. Why is the device you made called a "solar collector"?
2. By how much did your solar collector change the temperature of the water? Record the names of three other groups and the changes in temperature that they obtained.
3. How long did it take for the water to reach its highest temperature?
4. Describe a solar collector in terms of an energy system.
5. How did you construct your solar collector to make it efficient?
6. Read the list of some changes that could be made in a solar collector (step 10). Select those changes that you predict would produce hotter water than you got. Explain why you made each selection.
7. Look at figures 15 and 16. Explain why these houses could be thought of as solar collectors.

Now you know

Water, or air, that flows through the tubing of a solar collector is heated by the sun. To obtain as much solar heating as possible:
a) the surfaces inside the collector are black to absorb the light
b) a long piece of tubing is used to expose as much surface as possible
c) a clear cover on the collector and airtight sealing keeps hot air inside the collector
d) the collector is aimed to face the sun as directly as possible.

The efficiency of a solar collector can also be increased by insulating the collector so that the hot air and water lose very little heat to the air outside it.

A solar collector is a simple energy system. The input is light energy from the sun. Through the process of absorption by a black surface, this light energy is changed to heat and transferred to the water in the tubing. The output is hot water that can be distributed to radiators in a building and thus warm the air. Windows facing south and dark surfaces inside help to make an effective solar collector to help heat a home.

8.8 Energy Alternatives— They're Our Choice

The previous investigation showed you how easy it is to make use of our most plentiful, renewable energy source — sunlight. Just by opening drapes or blinds on the sunny side of your home during the day, you can let in sunlight that will warm your home. You have then started to use an alternative energy source, solar radiation. Such simple actions already result in our meeting about 12% of our energy needs by solar heating of buildings. This means, of course, that less fossil fuel is being burned to heat these buildings.

Fig. 16 *This solar house and the one in figure 15 have dark-coloured floors and well-insulated walls and roofs.*

It's a Fact
Nuclear energy and geothermal energy from heat in the Earth's core are alternative sources of energy, but they are not renewable.

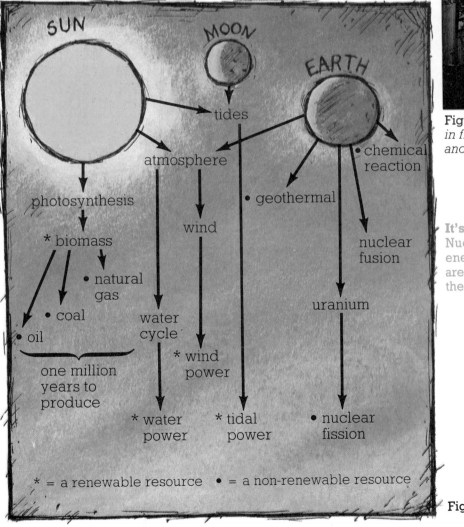

SUN MOON EARTH

tides

atmosphere

• chemical reaction

photosynthesis

• geothermal

* biomass

wind

nuclear fusion

• natural gas

• coal

water cycle

uranium

• oil

* wind power

one million years to produce

* water power

* tidal power

• nuclear fission

* = a renewable resource   • = a non-renewable resource

Fig. 17 *Sources of energy*

Fig. 18a *Sources of energy in Canada now*

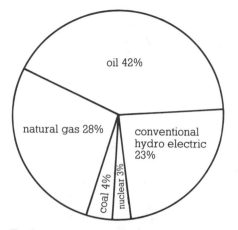

Total energy use now in Canada is equivalent to 1300 million barrels of oil each year.

Fig. 18b *Possible sources of energy in 2000.*

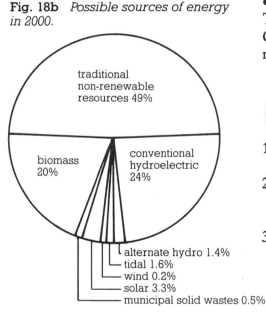

Predicted energy needs for year 2000 are about 1500 million barrels of oil each year.

Alternative energy sources are those that can replace "traditional" fuels such as oil, coal, and natural gas. Ideally, alternative energy sources should be renewable: they should depend upon energy from the sun or gravitational energy from the moon. Experts predict that additional energy from these renewable sources could reasonably provide about 50% of Canada's energy needs by the year 2000. About one quarter of our energy needs are already met by renewable energy — the hydroelectric energy generated by falling water.

There are alternatives to non-renewable fossil fuels. But these alternatives require planning and commitment. For example, we can't suddenly decide that, starting tomorrow, oil and natural gas should not be used. Too many processes in cars, home heating systems, and industries are designed to use only these fuels. However, if we don't begin reducing our use of non-renewable resources, it is only a matter of time until they are gone. We can cut down our use in two general ways:
● use alternative forms of energy from renewable sources
● reduce the amount of energy we use (conservation).
The next section describes some energy alternatives for Canadians. Later sections will deal with conservation of resources.

FEEDBACK

1. Give two reasons why we should be concerned about our non-renewable sources of energy.
2. a) What is meant by the term "alternative energy sources"?
   b) Are all alternative energy sources renewable? Explain.
3. a) From figure 18a, what percentage of Canada's energy now comes from non-renewable sources? How much comes from renewable sources?
   b) How much of Canada's energy could come from renewable resources by 2000?
   c) What advantages would the "energy mix" shown for the year 2000 have over our present energy mix?

precipitation

transpiration
from plants

surface
well

river

water
table

artesian
well

surface
well

ground
water

surface
stratum

evaporation

to
lake
or
reservoir

dam

transmission
tower

screen

powerhouse

Fig. 19 *The energy that
turns the electric generator
comes from the kinetic
energy in falling water,
"hydro." Heat from sunlight
evaporates water to lift it up
again.*

transformer

generator

penstock

turbine

spillway

hydro generating station

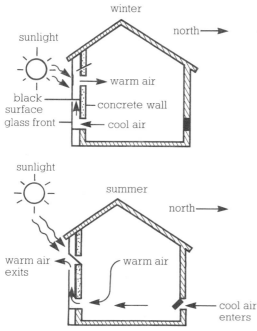

Fig. 20 *A Trombe Wall is a type of passive system that will help both to heat and to cool a home.*

8.9 Energy Forever From Renewable Sources

A. Solar Energy for Heating

Light from the sun — solar energy — arrives in different amounts at different times of the day and year. Thus a good solar energy system must trap large amounts of solar radiation and store the heat that it produces. There are two kinds of solar energy systems. In a **passive solar system**, a building is constructed to allow the maximum amount of sunlight to enter through windows, then to be absorbed by surfaces inside the building. Such a building is also well insulated to keep heat in and cold air out. In an **active solar system**, solar collectors heat liquid or air. This hot liquid or air is pumped to an insulated area to be stored until it is needed for distribution inside the building. You have already made a model of an active solar system in investigation 8.7. An active system can provide hot water for showers, washing, swimming pools, and so on.

Coniferous trees on north exposure minimize winter winds.

High roof vents allow escape of warm air in summer.

Banked earth reduces home's northern exposure.

Recessed windows and overhangs admit sun in winter but limit it in summer.

Low level vents let air from shaded ground areas and cool night air enter house in summer.

Fig. 21 *In a passive solar system, large amounts of sunlight are allowed to enter a building.*

Since about one third of the energy consumed in Canada is used for heating buildings, passive or active solar systems could be excellent alternatives to fossil fuels. The only environmental impacts from large-scale use of solar heating might be caused by consumption of extra materials to build solar collectors, or from use of large land areas for centralized collectors to heat large buildings or small communities. Perhaps new laws will be required to guarantee homeowners access to sunlight.

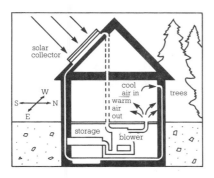

Fig. 22 *An active system uses solar collectors to trap the energy of sunlight.*

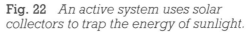
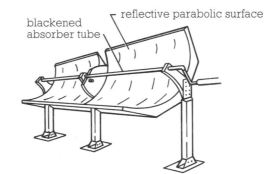

Fig. 23 *Details of a focussing collector*

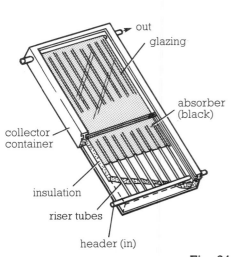
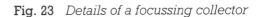

Fig. 24 *Details of a flat plate solar collector*

1. a) In figure 21, what features would help to increase the amount of solar radiation entering the house?
   b) What features help to keep heat in the house?
   c) What features would help keep it cool in summer?
   d) Why can a home not be totally heated by a passive system?
2. a) What advantages does an active system, such as the one shown in figure 22, have over a passive system?
   b) In what direction should a solar collector face?
   c) Some solar-heated homes are built with the solar collectors attached to a vertical wall. Show in a sketch the role that snow plays in such a system.
3. Referring to figure 24, describe how a flat plate solar collector works.

B. Solar Energy for Electricity

Our homes require heat only in cool weather but they require electricity at all times. **Solar cells** are used to change solar energy into electricity. Many electronic pocket calculators are powered by solar cells. Of course, any solar cell provides electricity only when exposed to light. Thus a home using only solar cells for electricity would need some kind of battery storage system to make electricity available at night.

In addition to the need for expensive storage systems, such as batteries, solar cells have other disadvantages. They are still very expensive, although the costs of manufacturing them are decreasing. Also, the present solar cells are only about 12% efficient, and the batteries used to store electrical energy have efficiency problems as well. However, it is likely that these problems can be solved.

Electricity can be produced by reflecting sunlight so that it is concentrated into a small area. Water passing through this area gains so much heat that it boils and changes into steam. This steam is under pressure and can turn a turbine connected to a generator, which produces the electricity. Solar-powered stations that can each provide energy for 15 000 homes have already been constructed.

Fig. 25 *Hundreds of satellites get all their electrical energy from panels of solar cells.*

Fig. 26 *A solar car*

Fig. 27 *A solar collector*

1. a) Why are solar cells not used now to provide electricity for homes?
   b) Sketch a house to show where solar cells could be placed.
   c) Describe a solar cell in terms of an energy system. Don't forget the waste outputs.
2. a) Use figure 28 to explain one way that solar energy could be used to produce electricity.
   b) Describe this energy system in terms of inputs and outputs.

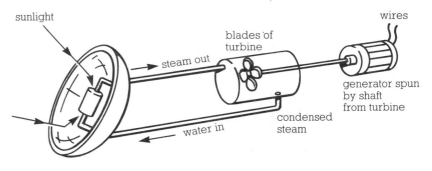

Fig. 28

C. Alternate Hydropower

"Hydro" is a short, simple way of referring to electrical energy produced from the energy of moving water. This water could come from a waterfall, such as Niagara Falls, from water trapped by artificial dams, or from a fast-moving river. During the 1960s, as generation of electricity became more and more controlled by large power utilities, hundreds of small hydro generating stations were abandoned because they were uneconomical. Now, with greatly increased energy costs and the possible shortage of fossil fuels, alternate hydropower (from sites with smaller amounts of moving water) has become

It's a Fact
China produces about 30% of its total hydroelectricity from 90 000 small generators.

attractive again. Also, small dams and rivers can produce significant amounts of electricity since turbines and generators are now more efficient.

In Canada small-scale hydro stations could eventually provide enough electrical energy to save about 180 million barrels of oil each year. However, water collecting behind new dams at these small stations could create some problems by flooding wildlife habitats and farm land.

Fig. 29 *A small hydroelectric generating station like the one shown here could provide electricity for about 300 homes.*

Think about it

1. a) What is alternative hydropower?
   b) Why is it not used more?
2. a) Refer back to figure 18b. About how many barrels of oil a year could alternate hydropower save by the year 2000?
   b) Use figures 18a and 18b to calculate the percentage increase in Canada's energy use from now to 2000.

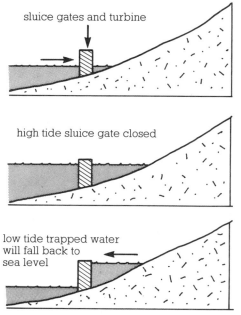

Fig. 30 *Generators in tidal power stations would be turned by the water flowing in as tides rise and by water flowing out as tides ebb.*

D. Tidal Energy

A tremendous amount of gravitational potential energy is stored by tidal action. A large-scale project costing about ten billion dollars has been proposed to build a huge dam across part of the Bay of Fundy on Canada's east coast. There, the difference between high and low tides is about 16 m. The water would flow through turbines in openings in the dam. The spinning turbines would be connected to generators that would produce the electrical energy. These generators could operate at least seven hours out of every twelve. The rise and fall of the tides would make the difference between water levels on the two sides of the dam large enough for the water to fall and gain speed.

Tidal energy is another kind of renewable, alternate energy that could be put to work in Canada. Tidal energy results when gravitational force exerted by the moon causes water in large bodies of water to "bulge" away from the Earth. As the Earth spins, the bulge of water moves around the Earth, making levels on some shores rise and on other shores drop. These are the tides. The tides could produce enough energy to save Canada the equivalent of 25 000 000 barrels of oil each

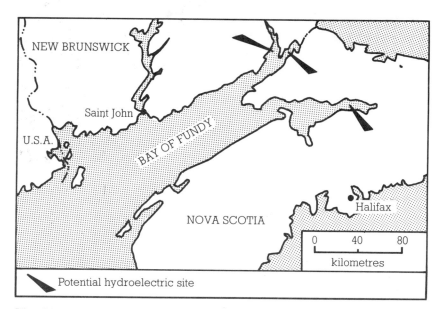

Fig. 31 *Use an atlas to name the bays where dams for tidal power stations could be built.*

year. As well producing electricity this way would create no air pollution. However, there are concerns about the high construction costs, and about environmental effects such as changes in nutrients in the water or changes in ocean currents. These concerns have delayed decisions by governments to start construction of a dam.

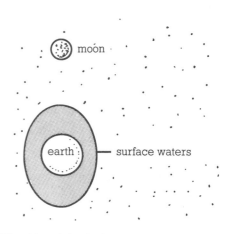

Fig. 32 *Tidal bulge. The moon pulls water away from Earth on the closest side and pulls Earth away from water on the far side.*

Think about it

1. Referring to figure 30, describe how tides can be used to produce electricity.
2. a) Why are tides being seriously considered as an alternative source of energy for Canada?
   b) What are some possible disadvantages to tidal energy?
3. "Individuals or small companies can themselves decide to use solar heating or alternative hydro, but only governments can decide to use tidal energy." Discuss why this statement is probably true.

SUPERSLEUTH

Tidal energy, like most other renewable forms of energy, can provide energy that is "free" since no one owns the sun or the moon. However, the initial costs of building devices to capture and change this energy must be paid. Calculate how many years of "free" tidal energy would be needed to make up for the building costs of a dam and tidal power stations, if the oil that is "saved" would have cost $30.00 per barrel.

E. Energy From the Wind

The kinetic energy of moving air — **wind energy** — has been used for more than a hundred years in Canada to pump water out of wells on farms. Wind is really one kind of solar energy, and is thus renewable. Winds are caused by sunlight heating different areas of land or water by different amounts, causing air currents between warm and cool areas.

Fig. 33 *Windmill*

307

Fig. 34 *A 230 kW, vertical axis wind turbine (much larger than the one shown here) on Magdalen Island in the St. Lawrence River was a joint experiment between the National Research Council of Canada and Hydro Québec.*

Many different systems have been designed to find reliable and efficient ways to change as much wind energy as possible into electrical energy. Every wind turbine system has the same problem—the wind doesn't always blow the strongest when the electricity is most needed. Using batteries to store the extra electricity produced when the wind is blowing hard is one solution to this problem. The charged-up batteries can then be used as the source of electricity when the wind dies down. A second solution involves feeding the extra electricity into the electrical system of a province or state. The owners of the wind turbine collect money for this electricity, then buy back the electricity that they need for themselves. A third solution uses wind energy to pump water up into a reservoir behind a dam. This stored water can then fall down to produce electricity, as it would at a regular hydro-generating station.

Wind generators of electricity can be built small enough to serve a single home, large enough to serve a community, or can be collected together on a wind farm to provide electricity for a city. Large-scale use of renewable wind energy is being planned for many places in the United States and Europe. There are disadvantages in addition to the problem of "storing" wind energy. Wind turbines can also take up much valuable land space, be unattractive, or create too much noise.

Fig. 35 *A wind turbine*

Fig. 36 *Energy of the wind can be stored by pumping water into a reservoir.*

reservoir

turbine generator

water level

pump

vertical axis

generator

Two of the many types of wind turbines. Can you make one?

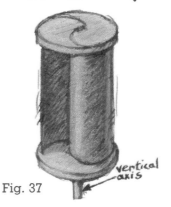

vertical axis

Fig. 37

1. Wind energy is not new to Canadians. Explain.
2. Identify two kinds of energy that wind can be changed into for storage.
3. What are some potential problems with wind power? For each of these problems suggest a possible solution.

SUPERSLEUTH

1. A wind farm sells about 5 000 000 kWh of energy each year. How much money could the owners of the wind farm make each year if they sold energy at $0.06/kWh?
2. a) A wind farm has 600 wind turbines. Each one produces 50 kWh every hour for a year. How many kWh of energy could be produced on this farm?
   b) What percent of the total possible energy in question 1 was actually sold?

F. Biomass Energy

Whenever you warm yourself in front of a wood fire you are using biomass energy. "Bio" refers to life, so **biomass energy** is chemical energy stored in plant and animal matter. Since all plants and animals ultimately depend upon solar radiation for their energy input, biomass energy is really one kind of renewable solar energy. In Canada our forests capture and store more than twice the total energy that we use each year. Burning wood already supplies about four percent of Canada's energy needs.

Some 200 000 Canadian homes now use wood as the main fuel for heating. This direct use of biomass is limited because firewood is expensive for city dwellers since forests are usually not nearby. Also, if most homes in a city burned wood, significant pollution problems would be created by all the smoke. Canada's forest industry is making more and more use of its own waste products, burning them to produce heating and electricity. In addition to branches and treetops that are usually left behind in the forest, about one-third of the wood hauled to the pulp, paper, and lumber mills ends up as waste. Wastes from the forestry industry now provide energy that is equivalent to over 50 000 000 barrels of oil each year.

It's a Fact
Wood provides about 13% of the world's energy, but forests are rapidly disappearing as populations increase. The Sahara Desert was once a huge forest.

But the chemical energy in biomass, such as wood, corn, water weeds, or manure, has uses other than direct burning. Efficient processes convert biomass into methane gas. This methane gas can also be converted into methanol, an alcohol that can replace gasoline as the fuel for automotive engines. It is possible that biomass from forests alone could produce enough methanol by 2005 to replace one half of the Canadian consumption of crude oil.

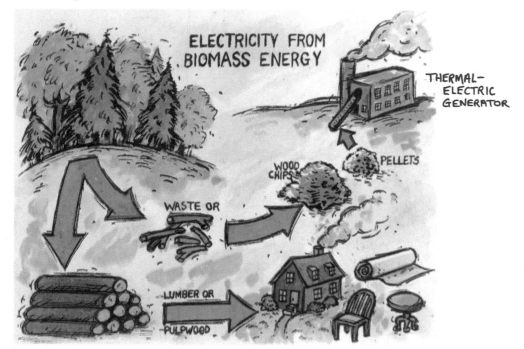

If the use of biomass as a source of energy is greatly increased, there could be significant environmental problems. Continual removal of all biomass from a forest could eventually deplete nutrients from the soil. Cutting down large areas of forest might change the local climate. Creation of tree plantations could use up valuable farmland or disrupt wildlife populations. Greatly increased burning of biomass would add pollutants, such as carbon dioxide and oxides of nitrogen, to the environment. They would increase the acid rain problem and possibly speed up changes in Earth's climate through the greenhouse effect. Still, biomass does have a great potential to satisfy our energy needs, although very careful thought must be given to avoid creating severe environmental problems.

Fig. 38 *This equipment grinds up trees for use as biomass energy.*

Think about it

1. a) What is biomass?
   b) Why is energy from biomass considered to be a
      renewable form of energy?
2. What are some ways that biomass can be used to provide
   energy?
3. What are some problems that could result from increased
   use of biomass for energy?

SUPERSLEUTH

In addition to the renewable sources of energy you have been reading about, there are also wave energy, ocean thermal energy, geothermal energy, municipal solid wastes, nuclear fission, and nuclear fusion which could all be developed as alternative sources of energy. Select any source of energy that interests you, then research it in the library. Present what you learn to your classmates in the form of a two- to four-page written report, a five- to ten-minute oral presentation, a physical model, a simple demonstration or experiment, a display poster, or a short video or audio tape.

Fig. 39 *Without energy from the wind, this person would be "sunk."*

8.10 Save the Energy and Solve the Crisis

There is a simple way that all the problems associated with our use of energy—problems such as future availability, costs, and environmental effects—can be greatly reduced: **energy conservation**. Energy conservation can be simply described as "making do with less." To be an energy conserver,

A. Examine how energy is being used around you.
B. Consider possible means to reduce each use of energy.
C. Take action to reduce the amount of energy that is used.

Conserving energy means less energy is used. Reducing energy use also reduces the amount of waste energy and matter that goes into our environment. Most importantly, conserving energy will prolong our energy supply since a barrel of oil that is saved today is a barrel of oil that can be used tomorrow. Saving energy increases our chances of developing efficient and inexpensive ways to make more use of renewable energy sources.

Someone who uses only a little energy daily can't be expected to conserve much. However "big spenders" should have many opportunities to save energy. Canadians use more energy in their homes than do residents of other industrialized countries. Thus Canadians, as "big spenders," have many

WHAT BRIGHT IDEAS DO YOU HAVE FOR SAVING ENERGY?

opportunities to save. People are recognizing these opportunities, and are acting to conserve energy. From 1970 to 1985 the average amount of energy used in each Ontario home has decreased by 23%. The next section will help YOU show how much WISER you are by becoming a CONSERVER.

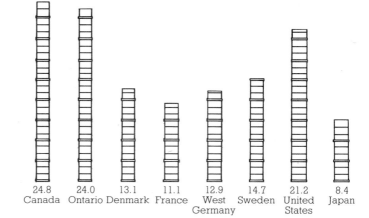

| 24.8 | 24.0 | 13.1 | 11.1 | 12.9 | 14.7 | 21.2 | 8.4 |
| Canada | Ontario | Denmark | France | West Germany | Sweden | United States | Japan |

Fig. 40 *A comparison of the average energy used by a single family home in different countries in 1982. The numbers show energy in terms of its equivalent in barrels of oil.*

FEEDBACK

1. a) State three problems associated with our high energy use.
   b) What is a partial solution to these problems?
2. a) What is meant by "energy conservation"?
   b) What three steps are involved in becoming an energy conserver?
3. What do you think is the best, immediate solution to the energy crisis?
4. Why do Canadians have many opportunities to save energy?

8.11 Conserving Energy at Home and on the Move

Figure 41 shows percentages of energy use. The amount of energy used for homes and transportation can be partly controlled by individuals such as yourself. This activity will help you examine ways you use energy directly, and decide upon some energy-conserving changes.

You need

- chart on page 316
- writing materials

1. Copy the chart on the following page into your notebook. For each action put a checkmark in the column that best describes how you would act.

NOTE: For some of the items you should consult with adults in your home.

Fig. 41 *How energy gets used in Canada (1985)*

Actions that conserve energy	I would take this action		
	Seldom (No) (0)	Some-times (1)	Always (Yes) (2)
A. HOME 1. During cold weather, the thermostat is set to 20°C or less. 2. On winter nights, the thermostat is lowered at least 2°C. 3. Air leaks around windows and doors are sealed. 4. Extra insulation has been added to the attic. 5. Window drapes are closed at night. 6. The furnace is serviced and adjusted annually. 7. On a sunny winter day, all the blinds or drapes on the south side of your home are opened. 8. During the winter, moisture is added to the air in your home by a humidifier.			
B. WATER HEATING 1. Showers are taken instead of baths. 2. Any dripping tap is reported and repaired as soon as possible. 3. The hot water tank is well insulated. Hot water pipes are insulated where possible. 4. Only a full load of dishes is washed in the sink or dishwasher. 5. Only a full load of dirty clothes is washed in the washer. 6. The thermostat on the hot water tank is turned down to 60°C (140°F).			
C. ELECTRICAL APPLIANCES 1. Lights are on only if someone is in the room. 2. Drapes and blinds on the south side of your home are closed on sunny summer days. 3. Lower-power light bulbs (40 W) are used in place of higher-power bulbs (60 W or 100 W) where possible. 4. Efforts are made to keep your home cool without using air conditioning. 5. Several items are cooked in the oven at once. 6. The refrigerator door is opened and shut as quickly and as seldom as possible. 7. Clothes are hung up to dry whenever possible instead of being placed in a clothes dryer.			
D. TRANSPORTATION 1. You walk or bike to your destination if the distance is less than one kilometre. 2. You prefer cross-country skiing and bicycling over snowmobiling and motorcycling. 3. You use public transportation and/or school buses to travel to school or around your community. 4. Your dream car will have to be fuel-efficient.			

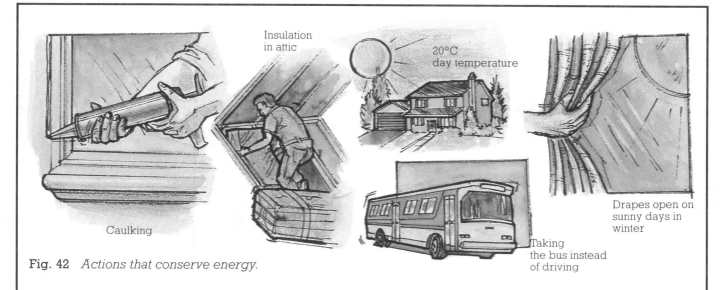

Fig. 42 *Actions that conserve energy.*

Think about it

1. a) Add the check marks in each column in the first section. Multiply the total for each column by the number at the top of the column.
   b) A "perfect" conserver would answer "always" or "yes" (honestly) for every action. Calculate the perfect score for each section. Then calculate your total score for the section as a percent of the perfect score.
2. a) Look at the "sometimes" and "seldom" responses that you made to some of the possible actions. Decide what you could reasonably do so that you could answer "always" or "yes" for most of the actions one year from now.
   b) Are there some conserving actions that are very difficult for you to take? Explain.
3. Suppose that it costs $900 to heat your home each year, either in direct costs to buy the energy or as part of the rent to the owner of the building who pays for the energy. Complete the table below to see how much money could be saved by certain actions that conserve energy.

Action	% saved	$ saved
a) Set the thermostat to 20°C or less, and lower the thermostat by 3°C at night. (Actions 1 and 2)	11%	
b) Seal air leaks. (Action 3)	5%	
c) Add insulation to the attic. (Action 4)	10%	
d) Clean and tune the furnace. (Action 6)	10%	
Total $ saved		

4. a) Look back through the chart that shows possible actions to conserve energy. Which actions could you take that would NOT cost any money?
   b) What are some reasons why people might not take these actions?
   c) How could more people be encouraged to take actions that would conserve energy?

317

5. Which means of transportation shown in the illustration is the most efficient? Which one is the least efficient?

Fig. 43 *A comparison of the distances that different types of transportation can move one person using one litre of fuel.*

airplane 60% full — 7.3 km

passenger train 23% full — 23.5 km

subway 33% full — 84.0 km

city bus 23% full — 21.1 km

urban automobile — 6.76 km

1 litre

bicycle (food equivalent) — 265 km

SUPERSLEUTH

1. Create a thirty-second radio commercial, a video, or a poster to encourage people to conserve energy. Present it to an audience, then ask for their reactions to both the message and the way it was presented.

2. The Toronto Transit Commission created the advertisement shown below to try to encourage car drivers to use public transportation more. Drivers are shown how to calculate the money they would save by using their car only half as much. Do the calculations. How would you answer the question asked at the end of the ad?

Fig. 44 **The TTC Advertisement**

EARN $100 A MINUTE DOING SIMPLE MATH.

Rethinking your car: the new TTC Test...

1985 NEW CAR OPERATING COSTS — METRO TORONTO

	8 cyl. Standard		6 cyl. Mid-size		4 cyl. Subcompact	
VARIABLE COSTS	km	mile	km	mile	km	mile
Fuel & Oil per km/mile	$.0758	$.1226	$.0623	$.1002	$.0435	$.0700
Maintenance per km/mile	.0112	.0180	.0099	.0160	.0083	.0134
Tires per km/mile	.0080	.0129	.0073	.0118	.0057	.0091
Variable Costs per km/mile	$.0950	$.1535	$.0795	$.1280	$.0575	$.0925
Multiply by km/miles per year:						
A. Metro average (24,000 km)	$ 2,280.00		$ 1,908.00		$ 1,380.00	
B. Or your km per year	$............		$............		$............	
Total Variable Costs per year:						
C. (enter line A or B)	$............		$............		$............	
ANNUAL FIXED COSTS						
D. Insurance (Metro average)	$ 726.00*		$ 726.00*		$ 726.00*	
Or your insurance costs per year	$............		$............		$............	
E. Licence & Registration	51.00		51.00		51.00	
F. Depreciation (annual average)	1,983.00		1,772.00		1,333.00	
G. Total Annual & Variable Costs: (add lines C, D, E & F)	$_____		$_____		$_____	
FINANCE COSTS						
H. 20% Down: Loan @ 12.5%/4 yrs.	$ 737.00		$ 695.00		$ 426.00	
Or your actual loan costs	$............		$............		$............	
I. Parking (estimate your annual parking costs)	$............		$............		$............	
TOTAL COST TO OWN AND OPERATE YOUR CAR FOR ONE YEAR (add lines G, H, and I)	$_____		$_____		$_____	

These figures are based on 1985 Metro Toronto costs and were prepared by Runzheimer and Company, Inc., with the exception of insurance rates, which were arrived at by averaging a survey of Toronto agents. Runzheimer and Company are transportation and living costs experts who supply industry, fleet operators and the Canadian Automobile Association with annual car cost information.

*Insurance costs are based on a married, over 25 driver, 4 years accident-free record with $100 deductible comprehensive, $250 deductible collision, and $500,000 inclusive 3rd party liability. Older cars cost less to insure — a five-year old car would cost less because of its low replacement value — a new luxury car could cost a lot more.

Here's what you can save:

ONE: you save half the "variable costs" shown in the chart (line C ÷ 2). $_____

TWO: you can save depreciation:

The Canadian Automobile Association says that cutting your driving in half should cut about 25% off your depreciation costs. Here are your likely depreciation savings if you only drive half the time:
Standard 8 cylinder/savings per year: $495.75
Standard 6 cylinder/savings per year: $443.00
Subcompact 4 cylinder/savings per year: $333.25 $_____

THREE: you can save half the parking costs (line I ÷ 2). $_____

Total car savings here: $_____

Now — subtract what TTC half the time costs a year: (based on 10 rides per week for 26 weeks — 8 tickets or tokens for $5.90) $ **191.75**

Here's what you save by leaving the car at home half the time and taking TTC... $_____

Ask the question: what are you denying yourself by driving all the time?

The Better Way.

Using the car less is one of the easiest ways to save money. You can invest it. Take a trip. Or save for a house. You'll have the savings...and the use of the car, when it makes most sense.

Activity

8.12 At Home With Use of Electrical Energy

Over 8% of the money in an average household is spent on energy to heat the air, produce hot water, operate electrical devices, and run the family's car or truck. In the previous activity you recognized some actions that you could take to conserve energy resources. These actions also save you money. In this activity you will keep a record for one week to show how much electricity is used by some devices in your home. You will then be able to calculate the cost of

using these appliances, and to decide if there are some changes you could make to conserve electrical energy.

You need

- chart
- writing materials
- 5 appliances

1. Copy the chart below into your notebook.

	Appliance	Power (W)	Amount of use each day (h)							Total for week (h)	Energy (kWh)	Cost at 6¢/kWh
			1	2	3	4	5	6	7			
E S S E N T I A L	1											
	2											
	3											
	4											
	5											
V E R Y N I C E	6											
	7											
	8											
	9											
	10											
N O T N E E D E D	11											
	12											
	13											
	14											
	15											

DO NOT WRITE IN THE TEXTBOOK

2. a) In the chart list five electrical devices that you consider to be absolutely essential to your home.
   b) List five devices that are not really essential but that you'd like in your home.
   c) Finally, name five appliances that you think you could easily stop using.
3. While at home, find the data plate on each appliance. It will be on the back or bottom, on a door, or on a door frame. From this data plate, record in your chart how much power the device uses.

4. During the next seven days keep a record of how much time each one of these devices is turned on. You will have to ask other members of the family to co-operate by recording the time, in minutes or hours, also.

Lab skill

Interpreting Information on Electrical Devices

Several pieces of information can be found on most electrical devices:

1. A stamp of approval from the Canadian Standards Association (CSA) to show that the device meets safety standards.
2. The power of the device in watts (W). This number describes the amount of energy (in joules) used each second. The larger the power rating, the more energy the device uses. To change from units of watts (W) to units of kilowatts (kW) divide by 1000.
3. The voltage (V) at which the device is designed to operate. High power appliances like ovens, clothes dryers, and hot water tanks operate at 220 V; most other electrical devices operate at 110 V.
4. The amount of electric charge flowing through the appliance per second—the current—in amperes (A).

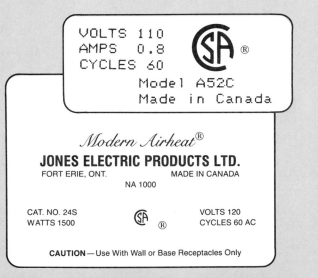

Fig. 45 *You can find information such as is shown here on most electrical devices.*

If the power is not listed on the device in watts, you can calculate the power by multiplying the voltage (V) by the current (A):

WATTS = VOLTS × AMPERES

Post your chart in some high-traffic area so that everyone can easily use it. If a device is used but the chart is not filled in by the user, then estimate the amount of time. The table below can help.

Average amount of use per week of some electrical appliances (estimates)

Appliance	Hours/Week
air conditioner	15–100
clock	168
clothes dryer	5
dishwasher	4
freezer	50
hair dryer	2
humidifier	25
iron	3
kettle	2
oil or gas burner	50
range	3
refrigerator	75
stereo system	50
television	40
vacuum cleaner	2
washing machine	4
water heater	25

5. After one week of record-keeping, calculate the total time, in hours (h) that each device was used.

6. To complete the "energy used" column, do the following calculation for each device:

$$\frac{\text{Power (W)} \times \text{Time (h)}}{1000}$$
= Energy used in kilowatt hours (kWh)

7. To find the weekly cost for each appliance, assume that each one kilowatt hour (1 kWh) costs $0.06 (or use the cost in your community).

Think about it

1. When you listed five appliances that are essential in your home, what kinds of factors did you consider? (i.e., do they provide entertainment? warmth? food? convenience? Do they have a unique function?)

2. What kinds of factors did you use to decide upon the five appliances that were not really needed in your home?

3. a) Which appliance cost the most to use each week? Was it an essential device?
   b) How much do the five most essential appliances cost to operate each week? How much would they cost for a year (assuming that the week you observed was an average week)?

4. a) For the five devices that you decided were not really needed in your home, how much did they cost to operate for the seven days? How much money could be saved in one year if you and your family stopped using them?
   b) If you could choose appliances for a home of your own, would you buy these appliances? Why, or why not?

5. a) Compare your list of five "essential" devices to the lists of three other students. Which devices appeared on everybody's list? Why are they essential?
   b) Again, compare your list to three other students' lists to identify some devices that most people think are not needed in a home. What would happen if everyone stopped buying these appliances?

6. Think of all the kinds of electrical devices that are in your home or the homes of your friends. Make a list of all the appliances you would be willing to do without to conserve energy.

A Recycling Worker?

Fig. 46 *Recycling workers are involved in all stages as cans and other wastes are recycled.*

Many communities have already established recycling projects for newspapers, metal cans, and glass containers. More and more are starting. Using the blue boxes is a sign of good citizenship and a symbol of the conserver society. People know that being a conserver will make our resources last longer. Recycling can reduce other problems such as pollution and waste disposal. Recycling is also creating many new jobs.

Materials that can be recycled are left outside in the distinctive blue boxes by a householder. These materials are then picked up separately from the regular garbage. Many people are required as drivers and helpers on the collection trucks. They sort the contents of the blue boxes into separate bins in the truck for paper, metal, and glass. When the bins are full, the trucks and workers return to the recycling depot and dump each bin into a separate area, then return back to their collection route. Many more jobs exist inside the depot. Some people drive machines called crawlers over the piles of cans to flatten them. This makes the metal easier and cheaper to ship to a processing plant. Many people work along conveyor belts to sort plastic or brown paper bags and cardboard from the newspapers. After the newspaper is compressed into bales, a forklift operator loads it into a transport truck. Of course each transport truck requires a driver to take it and its load of newsprint, metal, or glass to an industrial site for reprocessing back into usable products.

Recycling thus employs many people to collect, sort, and transport materials. Most of these people are employed by waste disposal companies and truck transport companies. More companies that specialize in processing recycled newsprint, metal, and glass are starting up. It is predicted that in the near future projects will start to recycle plastics. Soon corrugated cardboard from businesses may also be collected and recycled, since a city the size of Ottawa discards an incredible one hundred tonnes of cardboard containers each week.

Recycling workers in waste disposal companies generally have excellent fringe benefit packages and good wages. There are many opportunities to advance to supervisory roles. Training is usually on-the-job, although truck drivers and machine operators will normally have attended special courses and earned operating licences. Recycling offers a growing field for employment, and provides a valuable service to our society. Good, conscientious workers are needed. Will this be you?

8.13 Staying Out of Hot Water by Saving It

The hot water heater in an average home uses about 500 kWh of energy each month. The cost of this energy is about one dollar per day, a significant amount! In this activity you will calculate the energy saved by a) taking showers instead of baths and by b) repairing a dripping hot water tap.

You need

- centimetre ruler
- watch or clock
- 1 L container
- measuring cup

A. Shower or Bath?

1. Just before you shower next time, measure and record the depth of water that you would put into the tub if you were going to have a bath. (Use the drain hole as a reference level.)
2. Turn the shower on so that water flows at the rate it normally would while you have a shower. Place the 1 L container under the shower and record how long it takes to fill with water.
3. Now turn off the shower, plug the drain, and turn the water back on. Note the time. Take a normal shower and note what time you turn the water off. Keep the drain closed. Calculate the length of time of your shower.
4. After you dry off, note the time, then turn the shower on again to the same flow rate as when you had your shower (use cold water).

Measure how long the water runs until the tub is filled to the depth that it would be for a bath. Record this extra time. (Are your baths shallow, or your showers too long?)

Think about it

1. How many litres of hot water flowed during your shower? (Divide the time found in step 3 by the time required in step 2 for 1 L to flow.)
2. a) How much time would be required to run enough water for your bath using the shower head? (Add the times in steps 3 and 4).
   b) How many litres of water are used for a bath? Divide your answer to part a) by the time it takes for 1 L to flow.
3. a) Each litre of water for a shower or bath requires about 0.03 kWh of energy to heat it up to a comfortable temperature. Assuming that it costs $0.06 for each kWh of energy, calculate the cost of a shower and of a bath.
   b) How much is saved by each shower?
   c) Estimate the number of showers and baths taken in your home each week. Calculate how much would be saved if everybody had a shower instead of a bath each time.

B. Don't Have a Drip in Your Home

1. If you have a leaking tap in your home, use it for this part of the activity. If not, turn on a tap to create a slow, steady drip. Use the measuring cup to catch the water drops for exactly 15 min. Measure the volume of water collected in mL. Change this volume to litres (L) by dividing by 1000.

2. Calculate the volume of water that would be wasted if the drip continued for one whole year.

3. Assume that it is a hot water tap that is leaking. Use the information from ''Think About It'' question 3 in part A to calculate the cost of this leaking tap for one year. Is it worth fixing a leak quickly?

Think about it

1. Multiply the volume of water in the measuring cup by 4 to determine how much water would be wasted in 1 h.

8.14 Hidden Energy

In addition to the direct use of fossil fuels for light, heat, and transportation, we require an investment of ''hidden'' energy. For example, one small (40 g) bag of potato chips requires:

- 1.3 kJ of energy to plant, grow, fertilize, harvest, and store the potatoes.
- 0.2 kJ of energy to transport potatoes to the processor.
- 2.4 kJ of energy to peel, slice, cook, and package the potatoes.
- 1.2 kJ of energy for transporting, advertising, and storing the potato chips.
- 2.1 kJ of energy for storing and handling in the store.

This adds up to 7.2 kJ of energy, and brings you one bag of chips. When you eat this bag of chips, you receive 1.0 kJ of chemical energy, only one-seventh of the energy that was put into the bag! We are usually not aware of all the ways that energy is used to create the large numbers of products we use each day — the energy is ''hidden.''

Fig. 47 *Conserving energy is like putting money in the bank for future needs. Withdrawing fossil fuels too quickly will bankrupt us.*

Look back to figure 41. It shows that about half of the energy in Canada is consumed by mining (3%), industry (25%), and manufacturing (21%) in producing the many products our society demands. Consider the history of a steel stool or desk in your classroom:

- A mining company mined iron ore.
- The steel industry changed the iron ore into steel.
- A manufacturer shaped the steel into pipes and joined the pieces together.

Each of these activities consumes a large amount of energy. Energy was also required to transport the ore, steel, and finished products. All of this energy is usually provided by the burning of fossil fuels.

Thus one way we can conserve non-renewable fossil fuels again requires that we "make do with less." In this case "less" means that each consumer reduces the amounts of products and material that are used. Since every product contains "hidden" energy, reducing our consumption of products will reduce energy use.

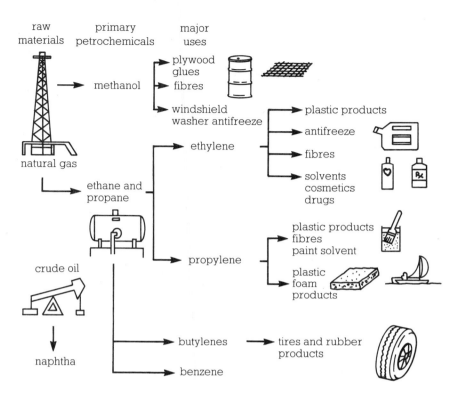

raw materials — primary petrochemicals — major uses

natural gas → methanol → plywood glues, fibres, windshield washer antifreeze

ethane and propane → ethylene → plastic products, antifreeze, fibres, solvents cosmetics drugs

crude oil → propylene → plastic products fibres paint solvent, plastic foam products

naphtha

butylenes → tires and rubber products

benzene

Fig. 48 *Perhaps fossil fuels such as oil and natural gas have too many other uses. Should they be burned at all?*

FEEDBACK

1. a) What does "WISER" stand for?
   b) Should you join the "WISER" crowd?
2. a) What is meant by the term "hidden energy"?
   b) Think carefully about an ordinary wooden pencil. List all the things that may have happened to "hide" energy in the pencil.
3. What can be done to reduce our consumption of "hidden" energy?

SUPERSLEUTH

Suppose that people decide to conserve by keeping their cars for two years longer than usual. Thus they reduce the number of new cars that are purchased. List as many effects as possible that such a decision could have on businesses, manufacturers, types of employment, and any other area you can think of.

It's a Fact
A bowl of cornflakes provides your body with only 1/25 of the energy that was required to produce that bowl of cereal.

It's a Fact
Each year an average Canadian eats 70 kg of grain directly and 850 kg of grain indirectly (through meat consumed). An Indian peasant eats 180 kg of grain per year. Much energy is "hidden" in meat.

It's a Fact
One-third of all trucks on the road carry food or food-related products.

8.15 Putting Hidden Energy Into Some Products

In this activity you will make two quite different products, baking powder biscuits and lime mortar (a type of cement). While you follow the steps in the recipes, consider all the energy that goes into the product—direct and hidden—as well as all the material resources required to create each product.

Part A: Baking Powder Biscuits

Your teacher may ask you to do this part at home; all of your family could enjoy this homework! As an alternative, your class might use the kitchen area of the Family Studies department.

You need

- 500 mL (2 cups) all-purpose flour
- 15 mL (3 teaspoons) baking powder
- 5 mL (1 teaspoon) salt
- 60 mL (¼ cup) shortening
- 180 mL (¾ cup) milk
- 30 cm wax paper
- mixing bowl, fork, rolling pin, baking sheet

1. Preheat the oven to 220°C (425°F)
2. Measure flour, baking powder, and salt into the bowl. Add the shortening, then use a fork to "cut" the shortening into the dry substances. You should end up with tiny lumps smaller than peas.
3. Stir in most of the milk. If the dough is not soft, puffy, and easy to flatten, then stir in a little more milk. (For "special" biscuits, add ⅓ cup of crisp bacon pieces, OR ½ cup of grated cheddar cheese, OR small amounts of your favorite spices.
4. Roll the dough into a ball on the wax paper. Knead (press and fold) the dough lightly about 20 times.
5. Roll the dough flat to a thickness of about 1–2 cm. Cut the dough into pieces about 3 cm square.
6. Place pieces on an ungreased baking sheet. Bake for 10–12 min, or until the biscuits are golden brown. Makes 16 biscuits. Serve hot.

Fig. 49 *Whose product is tastier—yours or your classmates'?*

Part B: Making Lime Mortar

A mortar is a mixture used to hold bricks or stones together. To make cement mortar requires a very high temperature. However, lime mortar can be made in the lab. It will require about three days to harden.

- large metal lid from a jar, or small tin can
- Bunsen burner
- tart-size aluminum plate
- glass stirring rod
- medicine dropper
- retort rod, iron ring, wire gauze
- safety goggles
- about 50 mL of powdered limestone
- about 150 mL of sand
- 2 small flat rocks (optional)

SAFETY ALERT!
Safety goggles must be worn.

1. Put the powdered limestone into the metal lid. Set up the retort rod, iron ring, and wire gauze. Put the metal lid on the wire gauze, then heat it strongly for about 20 min. Stir the limestone occasionally to allow gas to escape.
2. Allow the powder to cool down. Then use the dropper to add water drop by drop until the powder stops hissing. It is CRITICAL that you don't add too much water! You should end up with slaked lime which is still in powder form.
3. Add the slaked lime to the small metal plate. Estimate the volume of the slaked lime, then add three times this volume of sand. Mix thoroughly.

4. Add water DROP BY DROP, using the glass rod to stir, until you have produced a thick paste. This paste is the lime mortar.
5. Form the mortar into a shape, or cement the two small rocks together. Leave it for about three days until the mortar hardens. (Think of some ways that you can compare the hardness and strength of your lime mortar to that of your classmates.)

For each one of the products that you made:
1. Identify material resources that are required to make the product.
2. Identify the direct energy input(s).
3. Identify energy that is "wasted."
4. Identify as many ways as possible that "hidden" energy goes into the product.

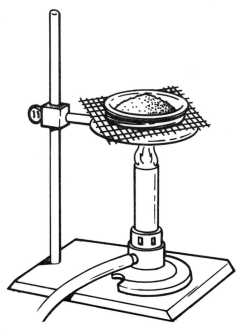

Fig. 50

8.16 A Society That Is Ready to Throw Away?

Aluminum cans, plastic and foil wrappers, wax paper, cardboard—these are some of the millions of containers and packing materials that are discarded every day by Canadians. All of this packaging contains both "hidden" energy from fossil fuels and material resources. The chart shows some of the inputs, processes, and outputs that occur to create one kind of packaging—aluminum cans.

There is an alternative to this waste. By recycling an aluminum can, we save about 95% of the energy input needed to produce a new can from raw materials. Since each resident of Ontario produces about 1.1 kg of garbage per day, 30% of which can be easily recycled, the potential saving in energy and resources is huge.

Members of a "WISER", conserving society would be solving other major problems besides the destruction of non-renewable resources. Problems such as acid rain, the greenhouse effect, toxic chemicals in the environment, storage of household garbage and industrial wastes, and the destruction of rain forests could all be partially solved if people used fewer products and recycled as much material as possible. Our high standard of living in Canada consumes both large amounts of energy and large quantities of material resources. If we become a **conserver society**, we will place even greater importance on saving non-renewable resources, on reducing waste, and on

It's a Fact
Paper products used by the largest fast food chain require trees from about 1000 km² of forest each year.

It's a Fact
Whenever a can is thrown away, the energy and matter that were inputs are wasted since they can't be used again. Recycling one tonne of aluminum saves about 68 000 kWh of electricity. This is enough energy for six Ontario homes for a year.

Energy input	Matter input	Processes	Intended output	Waste output
gasoline food for workers	machinery trucks buildings	mining of aluminum ore	aluminum ore	heat worn-out equipment
electricity	aluminum ore equipment buildings	processing of ore	pure aluminum	heat wastes from ore
electricity fuels	pure aluminum machinery	manufacturing of cans	aluminum cans	worn-out equipment heat

living in greater harmony with our environment. People in a conserver society would live by the "**Four R's**"

- REDUCE: Demands for energy and material goods are reduced as much as possible. Resources are not needed, and no waste is created if a product is not made!
- REUSE: Household goods are repaired instead of replaced, products are shared through rentals, second-hand products are purchased. Plastic bags are reused many times.
- RECYCLE: Materials such as glass, paper, metals, and plastics that have large amounts of hidden energy are sent back to be turned into new products.
- RECOVER: Energy in some materials that can't be recycled is partly recovered by using the material as fuel, or by using it in a compost pile.

FEEDBACK

1. What is one way that energy and material is wasted? Give some examples from your own experience of such waste.
2. a) What is an alternative to this waste?
   b) What kinds of materials can be recycled?
   c) What are the advantages of recycling?
3. What other problems could be partially solved by recycling.
4. What kinds of things are important in a conserver society?
5. a) What are the "Four R's" of a conserver society?
   b) For each "R," describe one thing you could do.

SUPERSLEUTH

Many communities and schools have excellent recycling programs. Find out what kinds of materials are recycled, what happens to the material and who pays for the recycling or makes money out of the program. Describe any differences between the school and community programs, if possible.

If your school or community have no recycling programs, find out why. Is any action planned for the near future? What is required to start a recycling program? Could a small business be set up to collect and sell soft drink cans for recycling?

Fig. 51 *Composting is one way of recovering energy.*

331

THIS CONCERNS YOU

Be Wiser, Be a Conserver

"You are forced to spend the rest of your life in the future!" We often wonder what this future will be like. Stock market investors, astrologers, bettors at a race track, and students studying for a test all try to predict the future, but nobody can do this with certainty. A wise person once said, "Our task is not to predict the future; our task is to shape the future."

You are learning that our country and our planet are facing many problems that could make the future less pleasant than the present. Some problems that are shaping our future occur because:

- industrial growth is using up more and more non-renewable resources, creating possible shortages;
- toxic chemicals from industrial processes are entering the land, air, and water, creating health hazards for many living things;
- the Greenhouse Effect, caused by increasing amounts of gases such as carbon dioxide in the air is changing our climate;
- large amounts of garbage and industrial wastes are using up valuable land and creating pollution;

- overpopulation in some regions is destroying forests, as people create new farmland for growing crops or for grazing cattle;
- farmland is overused or has too many chemicals put on it, and turns into desert;
- lack of trust among nations is causing governments to spend huge amounts of money on military activities, money that is then unavailable for other projects.

These problems have been created by people and can be solved by people. However they will not be solved unless people in industrialized nations like Canada work to create a CONSERVER SOCIETY. A conserver society could take different forms, each involving a different vision of the future. Each one of these futures could be shaped by the actions of individuals and governments, and would help to reduce the problems. Here are two possible futures:

FUTURE A: "Doing more with less." Economic growth occurs, with increases in living standards. However every effort is made to conserve energy and resources. Renewable energy sources are used as much as possible. Efficiency is stressed, and energy used is reduced by about 30%–40%. Products are built to last a long time. The cost of a product would include expenses involved in cleaning up any pollution that is caused by the product.

FUTURE B: "Doing less with less." There is a strong shift away from the Consumer Society. People don't buy as many material goods. There is less industrial and manufacturing activity. Much less energy is required. Lifestyles become simpler and more rural, with efforts made to live in harmony with the environment.

Both of these futures, and other "visions," would require that people change their behaviours and expectations. Each of these futures would require that much less fossil fuel is used. Consumption of non-renewable metals and plastics would be reduced through recycling. These futures would experience less pollution since fewer resources would be removed and processed, and less waste produced.

In recent years people have become used to seeing the Earth photographed from space by weather satellites or a space shuttle. From far away, our Earth looks like a huge spaceship on a lonely voyage through space. Like a spaceship, our planet carries with it all the materials that its passengers need to survive. Like a spaceship, the only "outside" energy can come from solar energy or gravity. As in a sealed spaceship, garbage and wastes must stay on board for the journey. Our only home is Spaceship Earth!

Even now many of the passengers —human and nonhuman, plant and animal—on Spaceship Earth are being threatened by the problems listed earlier. We humans are the

Fig. 52 *Our Earth is like a huge spaceship on a lonely voyage through space.*

captains of the spaceship, and have a responsibility to make sure that our spaceship is not damaged, and that all other passengers are comfortable and safe. Problems that we have created on this planet must be fixed. You have some knowledge about many of the problems, and have learned some ways that these problems could be solved, so you can help to shape the future.

Do you have the caring, courage, and commitment to act in ways that will ensure our Spaceship Earth continues on for a long, long time? This question concerns you, and everyone around you!

1. Science has an important part to play in helping to solve all but one of the problems that were listed. Which problems is

outside the help of science? Whose responsibility is it to solve this problem?

2. Many world problems can be considered from a systems view:
   "Inputs" involve use of resources;
   "Processes" are activities that humans have created;
   "Outputs" are wastes that are produced.
   a) Which items in the list are "input" problems?
   b) Which items in the list are "output" problems?
   c) How does the size of the human population affect both the inputs and outputs?

   (You may want to work in groups of 4–6 for the remaining questions. Each person should be prepared to discuss another group's answers to some of the questions)

3. a) Reread FUTURE A. Make a list of some things that could improve people's lifestyles, AND would also help to create Future A.
   b) Make a list of some things that happen in your school that don't fit the vision described in Future A.
   c) Brainstorm a list of as many ideas as possible that might help to change things in your school to create Future A.
4. a) Reread FUTURE B. Make a list of ways that life could be made simpler by doing with less.
   b) What evidence do you see in your school or community that shows we still live in a Consumer Society?
5. a) Reach a (group) decision about which future would be more desirable for a journey of hundreds or thousands of years on Spaceship Earth. Be prepared to defend your decision.
   b) List some reasons why many people might not want to change from a Consumer society to a Conserver Society.
6. Prepare a 30–60 s commercial in which you use the idea of "Spaceship Earth." In this commercial try to "sell" something—a product or an activity—that would help to solve one (or more) of the problems that was listed.

8.17 Chapter Summary

- Humans depend upon an incredible number of renewable and non-renewable resources.
- Non-renewable resources will eventually run out if they continue to be used up. This is the real energy crisis.
- Any energy system can be described in terms of INPUTS, PROCESSES, and OUTPUTS.
- High efficiency systems produce less waste.
- All renewable sources of energy depend upon outside sources—the sun and the moon.
- Solar energy from the sun can be changed into useful energy in passive solar systems, active solar systems, solar cells, hydro generating stations, as biomass, and as wind energy to make something move.
- The moon creates tides, whose potential energy can be changed into electricity.
- Increased use of alternative energy sources will make non-renewable fossil fuels last longer.
- The best, immediate solution to the energy crisis involves conservation of non-renewable resources.
- Every consumer product contains "hidden" energy.
- The "four R's" of the conserver society are REDUCE, REUSE, RECYCLE, and RECOVER.
- There are many simple and effective actions that individuals can take to conserve our resources.

8.18 Are You Ready to Go On?

Do not write in the textbook.

1. a) Give three examples each of renewable and non-renewable resources.
   b) What makes renewable resources different from non-renewable resources?
2. a) More people are "arriving" in our home, the Earth, than are "leaving." The human population is shown in the table over a long period of time. Make a graph that shows the population at each year. Join the points with a smooth line.

Year	1650	1700	1750	1800	1850	1900	1950	1970	1985
Population (billion)	.510	.625	.710	.910	1.130	1.600	2.510	3.575	4.800

   b) In what year was the number of people only one-half of what it is now?
   c) Extend the pattern shown by the line on the graph to predict the year in which the population will have doubled.
   d) Predict some effects of increased population on resource and energy use, and on pollution.
3. a) What can be done by anything that has energy?
   b) Name at least six forms of energy. Identify one situation in which each form would be present.
   c) What kind of energy is usually produced as waste. Where does it go?
4. a) Describe the following in terms of an energy system:
   i) hair dryer   ii) overhead projector
   b) A manufacturer claims that its hair dryer has an efficiency of 80%. What does this figure mean?
   c) What are some advantages of driving a car that has a high efficiency?

5. a) Why are solar and tidal energies called "outside" energy?
   b) What is the "real" energy crisis? Why is outside energy so very important to the solving of this crisis?
   c) Give several examples of non-renewable energy sources, and some ways that Canadians use these sources.

6. Draw and label a simple solar collector. How could it be made as efficient as possible?

7. a) What is the major advantage of using alternative energy sources?
   b) In section 8.9, six sources of alternative energy are discussed. Define each. Give your opinion of how important each kind of alternative energy could be to Canadians. State a possible problem that could be caused by using each one more.

8. a) How can energy conservation help to solve the energy crisis?
   b) What simple steps are needed to become a conserver?

9. Several activities in the chapter help you identify ways that you and other members of your home can conserve energy. Describe at least three ways that you will act to reduce your use of:
   a) fossil fuels for heating and transportation;
   b) use of electricity in your home;
   c) "hidden" energy.

10. What are some ways that energy has been "hidden" in a can of vegetable soup?

11. a) What are the "FOUR R's" of the Conserver Society?
    b) Why would a society that practised the Four R's help to solve both the energy crisis and the problem of resource shortages?

12. True or false?
    a) A system is a group of parts that can work independent of each other.
    b) A furnace that is 70% efficient wastes 30% of the energy input.
    c) Heat is the most common form of energy waste from a system.
    d) The human population's increasing size is helping to solve the energy crisis.
    e) Most buildings can easily make use of passive solar heating.
    f) Energy conservation is the best, immediate solution to our problems with resources.

13. Read the paragraph. Then copy it into your notes, filling in each blank with the word that best completes the meaning of the paragraph:

    Our planet, _____ , will eventually run out of _____ resources such as _____ , _____ , and _____ since the supply of these is limited. Thus, we should start making more use of "outside" energy sources that come from the _____ and _____ . The more important one provides the _____ energy that causes _____ in the atmosphere and _____ on the water, and also creates the _____ cycle.

14. In your notebook copy the column on the left, then write beside each term the word(s) from the right hand column that is(are) the best match.

a) hydro energy	A. 4 R's
b) nuclear energy	B. sunlight
c) fossil fuel	C. biomass
d) conserver	D. oil
e) solar energy	E. renewable
f) safety	F. active heating
g) aluminum	G. uranium
h) efficiency	H. goggles
i) solar collector	I. (output/input) × 100%
j) plants	J. recyclable metal

Contents

Chapter Nine

Buried Treasure

9.1 Are We Resourceful!

It's great when you can borrow the family car. You put on your jacket, grab the keys, hop in, check to see that there's gas in the tank, and away you go. Independence! Well, of a sort. Your car is mostly built from metals. Its fuel is made from crude oil. The parts not made from metals are probably some kind of plastic, perhaps one made from natural gas and salt. Even your jacket is probably a petroleum product (if it isn't cotton or wool). We depend on the Earth for all of these resources. They must be removed from the Earth and modified to meet our needs.

The general term for taking resources from the Earth is mining. Canada is fortunate to have rich deposits of such substances. Mining is vital to the country, providing products and jobs for many people. In a country as physically diverse as Canada, it isn't surprising that a variety of substances exist in different parts of the country, requiring various methods to obtain them.

Fig. 1 *An underground mine*

Fig. 2 *In Cape Breton, miners use great machines to dig coal from deep mines that reach far out under the ocean. In other parts of the country, coal is mined from open pits, such as you see in the photo. In the western mountains, huge coal mines operate in some regions, while minerals are extracted in others.*

337

Near Sudbury, minerals are extracted from the hard and ancient rocks of the Canadian Shield. In British Columbia, copper is mined from open pits.

Fig. 3 *Copper mining*

In Sarnia, salt is mined from under the same factory that uses it. Salt is a sedimentary deposit, protected by layers of rocks that have formed over it. Some salt is mined; some is recovered by pumping fresh water down into the salt layer and sucking the brine out.

Fig. 4 *Salt mining*

Across the Prairies, potash is mined. Oil is found underground near Calgary and Edmonton. In southern Alberta, oil is pumped from the Earth, while in the North, the tar sands supply heavy oil from which synthetic crude oil is made.

In the Arctic and on the East Coast, oil has been found under the oceans.

Oil, coal, salt, and minerals are all extensively mined in Canada. You could easily identify oil, coal, and salt, but you might not know exactly what a mineral is. A **mineral** is a substance that has all of the following properties:

- occurs naturally
- made up of substances that were never alive
- has the same chemical make-up wherever found
- has atoms arranged in a regular pattern to form crystals

In this chapter, you will focus on minerals.

FEEDBACK

1. Name three modern products that are made from natural resources.
2. Why is the mining industry vital to Canada?
3. Name five kinds of mining that can be found in Canada.

9.2 Buried Treasure

How do scientists locate the Earth's hidden riches, and how do they bring them to the surface? First, they have to find out where these resources are likely to be.

To do so, they make a best guess or hypothesis about where mineral resources might be. They consider the conditions under which the resources have been found in the past and they consider the properties of each resource. They use this knowledge to look for clues to the presence of the resource.

In this investigation, you will locate a metal using a method based on one of the properties of the mineral.

Find out

What property of a mineral is helpful to scientists trying to locate it?

You need

- sand table
- metre stick
- masking tape
- magnetic compass
- pieces of iron
- string
- scissors

Try this

1. Have someone secretly bury some pieces of iron under the sand on a sand table.

2. Across one side of the table, searchers attach small pieces of numbered masking tape, evenly spaced. On the adjacent side, they place lettered pieces of masking tape, evenly spaced.

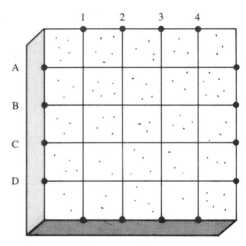

Fig. 5 *Setting up the sand table*

3. In your notebook, draw a diagram of the sand table. *Mark the numbers and letters to correspond to your table.*
4. The searchers determine the pattern they will move the compass along in an effort to find the iron.
5. Have a searcher slowly move the compass along the search pattern. *What do you notice about the compass at certain points? What does the behaviour of the compass indicate?*
6. *Mark the position of each "find" on your diagram.*

1. What property of the iron made it possible for it to be located in this way?
2. What's the advantage of making a diagram such as the one you made, rather than describing the location of your finds in a paragraph?
3. Ask the person who buried them if there are any pieces you didn't find. Is there any pattern to their location?
4. How might you have organized your search to find more?

Now you know

Some minerals can be located because one property they have is that they will deflect a compass needle. When scientists find such minerals, they use a technique similar to your use of a diagram to mark the location on a map. However, instead of letters and numbers, they use imaginary lines already in place on the Earth's surface—the parallels of latitude and the meridians of longitude. If scientists locate a possible find, they can easily locate it again if they wish to investigate it thoroughly. Scientists also use a systematic pattern in conducting a search, in order to cover as much of an area as possible.

Fig. 6 *After gold ore is obtained, it is analysed to find out how much gold is in it.*

Activity

9.3 Catch the Wave

You've probably had lots of experience with portable radios. You can go anywhere and still listen to your favourite station—except when something interferes with the reception. Can you obtain any useful information from that poor radio reception?

You need

- AM/FM radio

1. Tune in an AM station with a moderately strong signal.
2. Walk in a pattern around the classroom, noting the changes in the quality of reception. What happens when you bring the radio near a filing cabinet or another large metal object?
3. Now tune the radio to an FM station and retrace the pattern you followed in step 2. What do you notice?

Think about it

1. How does the radio reception change when you approach the filing cabinet?
2. How can the quality of reception for a radio signal be used to discover minerals?
3. Which form of radio transmission would be more sensitive to finding metal objects? Can you suggest why?

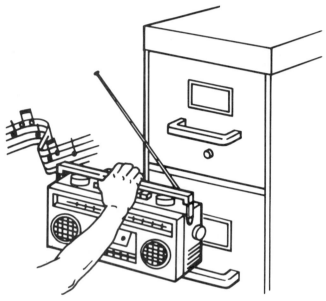

Fig. 7 *What happened when you brought the radio close to the filing cabinet?*

The method you have just used is similar to locating minerals by **electromagnetic surveying**.

Electromagnetic surveying began as a method of finding submarines in the ocean. Later, scientists converted the surveying instruments so that they could find bodies of minerals. A plane or helicopter tows an instrument called a receiving unit as it flies in a pattern. The plane sends out a radio signal which is detected by sensors in the receiving unit. If a change in the reception of the radio signal occurs as it bounces back from the Earth, geologists examine the area more closely.

In the activity, the radio station represented the plane and the radio represented the receiving unit.

9.4 Field Testing

Imagine yourself in a position to decide whether a company will invest in a mining operation. You give the go-ahead and the company spends millions of dollars digging a mine and building homes and stores for the workers it will need. When the mine opens, the mineral deposit turns out to be very small and is completely mined within a month. The mine closes down and so does the community. Many people are out of work, and you are the first to go!

Obviously, companies can't invest in an area where they can't expect a substantial return on their investment. It isn't enough to know that an area contains ore; they must also have a good idea of the amount and kinds of ore it contains.

If a person with X-ray vision existed, he or she would be very much sought-after by the mining industry. Since people with such abilities exist only in our imaginations, we have to rely on other methods to "see" underground. The different methods used to "see" under the surface of the Earth "see" different things. Methods are chosen because of what they can detect. Great amounts of data are gathered before a decision is made to develop a resource or look elsewhere. It helps to know that finding one substance usually means another one is close by, since the process in the Earth that made one mineral usually caused others to form.

9.5 Getting to the Core

In this activity, you will use one of the methods scientists use to "see" underground.

You need

- modelling clay in different colours
- plastic drinking straw
- knife

1. Carefully layer the different colours of clay on top of one another, until you have built up many layers.
2. Punch the sample down once so that the layers are disturbed.
3. Drill vertically through the modelling clay using a plastic straw. Cut the straw in half down its length.
4. Draw a diagram of the straw and its contents.

Think about it

1. a) Why do you think your teacher had you prepare layers of modelling clay instead of simply drilling into a block of one colour?
   b) What do the layers represent?

What you did with the drinking straw was to drill a **core**. Scientists use a similar method to drill into the Earth's crust. The drill used to obtain cores is hollow. As it bores into the Earth, a long cylinder of the rock that it travels through is left within the drill. This core is raised to the surface often and removed from the drill. The different layers of rock give clues to the presence of other types of rocks. If useful minerals are found, they can be examined chemically to determine how much of the resource is in the sample.

Fig. 8 *Core drilling equipment*

Drilling a core through modelling clay is very easy compared to drilling through many metres of hard rock. A drill that can cut through rock has to be made of very hard materials. Often, the tip of the drill is embedded with diamonds, the hardest natural substance known.

SUPERSLEUTH

The Earth continues to change, as it has for millions of years. What has caused folds in the rock structures of the Earth?

Fig. 9 *A drill tip*

9.6 Classification of Minerals

Minerals are found in rocks. All rocks are combinations of minerals. Minerals are made up of crystals. The type of mineral depends on two things: the chemical composition of the crystals and how the crystals are formed. Many different factors can cause the same chemical to produce different-looking crystals.

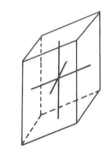

rhombohederal crystal

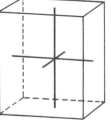

triclinic crystal

Fig. 10

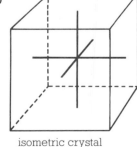

isometric crystal

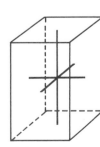

tetragonal crystal

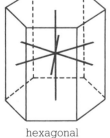

hexagonal crystal

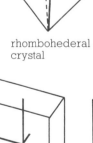

monoclinic crystal

orthorhombic crystal

Fig. 11 *Erupting volcano*

A. Classification by Formation

If a mineral has been formed by the cooling of molten rocks, the rate of cooling can affect the size of the crystals. When the rock cools rapidly, the crystals are usually very small. If the rocks cool slowly, the crystals have more time to form and are usually larger.

Fig. 12 *Volcanic rock*

Some minerals are found in **sedimentary rocks**. These rocks are formed by the action of water, a process called **sedimentation**. A fast-moving river can carry tiny pieces of rock. When the river slows down, the small pieces settle to the bottom and become cemented together under the pressure exerted by the water over many thousands of years. Waves at the edge of an ocean or huge lake, smashing into rocks for many years, break tiny bits of rock away from the shore and form them into sand. Over millions of years these bits of rock are welded together to make a rather soft, often crumbly stone. Again, the way the rock has formed affects the mineral crystals it contains.

Fig. 14 *Sandstone*

Fig. 13 *This column formation is characteristic of basalt.*

Fig. 15 *Conglomerate, a kind of sedimentary rock*

Fig. 16 *Quartz*

Fig. 17 *Asbestos*

B. Classification by Property

You have seen that rocks are formed in different ways and from different substances. This means that they have very different properties. In order to identify minerals, you must be able to recognize different properties of rocks. Some of the more common properties follow.

Fig. 18 *Granite*

- Magnetism
  Some minerals can be identified because they are magnetic.
- Hardness
  Minerals vary greatly in hardness. Hardness is measured by comparing a sample to a material known for its hardness, such as diamond or for its softness, such as talc.
- Streak (rubbing) colour
  When a sample of a mineral is rubbed against a harder rock, it leaves a mark, just like chalk on the classroom board. The colour of the streak is characteristic of the mineral.

- Density of the ore

  You can measure the density of a rock by finding the mass of the sample and then its volume by immersing it in water.

  The density of a sample can be compared to listed values for many different rocks to find its identity.

Fig. 19 *Limestone*

Fig. 20 *Finding the density of a rock*

- Chemical make-up

  Chemical tests are also used. A simple test for rocks that contain carbonates, such as calcite and dolomite, is to place a few drops of dilute acid on the rock. If the rock contains a carbonate, bubbles of carbon dioxide gas will be produced. Common rocks that give a positive test are chalk, limestone, and marble, all of which are forms of calcium carbonate.

  Each of the properties listed above can be used to help identify a rock. Usually more than one property is used to make an identification.

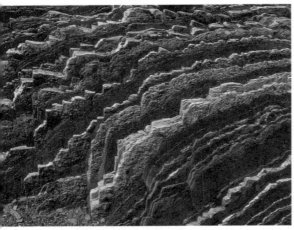

Fig. 21 *This formation results from tidal action back and forth over rocks.*

9.7 A Hole in the Ground

Many of Canada's exports involve the products of the mining industry, yet very few of us really know much about mines. The difference between one mine and another is the kind of hole used to get the resources out of the ground. For salt (sodium chloride) a small hole in the form of a pipe can be used to pump hot water down to the salt and then return it as a saturated salt solution. This kind of mining leaves few waste products and creates useful underground storage caverns. Similarly for crude oil and natural gas, the hole in the ground is a pipe. To get zinc, uranium, nickel, gold, and iron out of the ground a very different hole is needed. The hole must be big enough for transporting large quantities of the ore containing the minerals. The mountain of rock that is left over after the extraction of the mineral must also be considered as a part of the operation.

A great many decisions must be made before a mineral is extracted from a mine and changed into the products we want. One of the considerations is the kind of operation that will yield the greatest amount with the least effect on the environment. The decision to use a pipe, open pit, or deep shaft mine is complex and involves more than just money considerations. New mines must also be designed with people and the environment in mind. If changes are being planned to an older mine, the same considerations must now be applied. A great deal of exploration, planning, and communication must take place before digging begins.

If, after exploration and environmental surveys, the decision to proceed is made, a map is drawn of the best estimate of the underground ore body and its surroundings. Many cores are drilled to find out what is below the surface. From this information and the nature of the surrounding land, the hole in the ground is designed.

Many people think of a fantastic world of gleaming gold when they consider a mine. For those who are part of the team building the mine, the job is less fantastic and more like hard work.

Ore is blasted from the rock in very large rooms called **stopes** (100 m high, 22 m wide and from 3 m–20 m thick). This process involves highly skilled people drilling holes into the ore body in just the right pattern so that when explosives are placed in the holes, the ore will be easy to pick up and move to the crusher. The ore is crushed underground and sent to the surface for further refining. To most people the gold ore is indistinguishable from any other light grey rock.

On the surface, the ore is ground to a fine powder and then the gold is extracted into a solution by chemicals. Once in solution, the gold is removed by attaching it to the surface of activated carbon from where it is stripped and refined into bars of gold.

A gold mine, like other mines, requires many people with many different skills. Mechanics are required for the equipment that moves the ore underground and above ground. Just getting people down and the ore up is itself a big task.

Consider the main shaft at Noranda's Hemlo project. The shaft contains five separate compartments and is nearly 1.5 km deep. There are two lifts for ore, each of which can lift sixteen tonnes (**production skips**). To bring miners and the equipment up and down there is a lift which can carry forty-four people (**single deck cage**). There is also a compartment for pipes (**pipeway**), a staircase (**manway**) and a compartment for counterweights. Equipment which can't fit

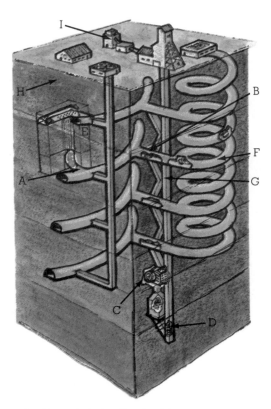

A	Scooptrain loading broken ore
B	Scooptrain dumping into ore pass
C	Jaw crusher in operation
D	Skip being filled at loading pocket
E	Stope
F	Ramp
G	Shaft
H	Ore body
I	Crushing and screening buildings

Fig. 22 *Cutaway of underground mine*

into these huge lifts must be brought down into the mine in parts and assembled below.

A mine is a huge hole in the ground. Somehow the mountains of waste it leaves must be handled so as to disrupt our environment the least. One obvious method to reduce the problem is to refill the great hole under the ground with the waste material when mining is completed. The immense amount of material which must be handled encourages decisions which are efficient and carefully thought out. Some of the waste can be used on the surface to build roads but only so many kilometres of roads are needed near a mine. The problem remains. We want the gold and the things it can buy. At the same time we want to guard our environment from destruction. The issue has no easy answer.

FEEDBACK

1. Why does salt mining do little harm to the environment?
2. Is gold mining energy efficient? (Hint: recall the production of a bag of potato chips from Chapter 8.)
3. How can large pieces of equipment be taken into a mine?
4. What problem can large mines cause in the environment? What kinds of solutions to these problems have been found?

Activity

9.7 Can You Concentrate?

When a mining company locates rock in which there are large bodies of ore, how are the minerals extracted from the rock?

Extraction of minerals from the rock in which they are found is different for each metal but some processes are widely used. In this activity, you will use a method that resembles a technique used in extracting minerals from rock.

You need

- contents of several pencil sharpeners
- 1000 mL beaker
- 500 mL water
- spoon

1. Add the pencil sharpener contents to 500 mL of water in the beaker.
2. Stir gently.
3. Allow the contents of the beaker to sit for a few moments and examine the mixture. What happens to the wood parts? the graphite dust?
4. Using a spoon, skim the wood from the surface. (Some graphite may still remain on the wood.)
5. Pour the water into the drain, saving the graphite.

Think about it

You used a physical property of the materials you were dealing with to separate them. Wood floats on water, so you were able to separate it from graphite, which doesn't float, by placing it in water. You were concentrating the minerals. Mining engineers also use techniques to concentrate the minerals. By so doing, they can save much time and money in transporting and refining the mineral from its ore.

Fig. 23

9.8 Refining Copper

You have seen how ore is detected; you have used a technique that shows how a mineral is removed from its ore. However, the process you used left many impurities in the mineral. Removing these impurities can be an expensive and complicated process, involving many different steps. How do you get rid of these impurities?

Find out

How can you refine an impure copper sample?

You need

- 1000 mL beaker
- 60 g sulfuric acid
- brass strip
- copper strip
- fine emery cloth
- 3 V battery or power supply
- 200 g copper sulfate
- connecting wire

SAFETY ALERT!

Wear safety goggles. Keep acid off your skin. Acid is corrosive.

Try this

1. Dissolve the copper sulfate in 500 mL water.
2. Add the sulfuric acid.

3. Add enough water to make the volume of the solution 1000 mL.
4. Clean both metal strips to remove grease and rub the brass with fine emery cloth.
5. Suspend the strips in the solution. Connect the brass strip to the negative terminal and the copper strip to the positive terminal of the battery or power supply.

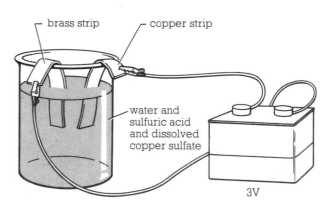

Fig. 24

6. *Describe what happens to the mixture over a period of about 20 min.*

What happened?

1. Did the metal strips change over a period of time? How? What was happening to them?
2. How did the liquid mixture appear after a period of time? Why?

You used electrical energy to remove impurities from the copper strip. This is one of the more common methods of purification. The electrical energy moves atom-sized particles of a metal through a solution, leaving the impurities behind.

Extracting metal from rock is no easy job. Great amounts of energy and expertise are required to concentrate the ore, and then to extract and refine the metal.

In a year, a mining company can take a mountain of rock and change it into:

- enough iron to cover a hockey rink to a depth of 7.5 m
- enough nickel to cover the same rink to a depth of 3.7 m
- pure copper piled to a height of 2.0 m
- a 6.0 mm pile of cobalt
- ten garbage cans of gold or silver.

Will This Be You?

Trucker

The freedom of the road . . . being . . . your own boss, . . . always on the move . . . does this sound like a great job?

A person who wishes to drive a truck or tractor trailer must obtain a special licence. Often the driver must attend a school to learn how to handle a heavy vehicle and oversize loads when driving in heavy traffic.

Driving programs include class time and time on the road with an instructor. The driver needs to know much more than how to start the engine. Tractor, trailers, and their connecting links need maintenance that a driver should understand. Some companies demand the driver complete emergency first-aid treatment courses so they can assist in case of an emergency.

Truck cabs are comfortable and designed to help the driver remain comfortable and alert for hours of safe driving. Often the cab has a radio for communication, a tape deck and stereo for entertainment, as well as a powerful air conditioner to keep the driver at peak performance. To start and drive is only part of the job. The driver must also know how to reduce the chance of the machine breaking down. If something stops running the way it is expected the driver must recognize the problem and know how to react.

Air brakes are very different from car brakes, especially in slippery conditions. Stopping an eighty-tonne vehicle gives much less room for error than does stopping a two-tonne van or a one-tonne car. Getting a rig going on a hill in a snowstorm likewise requires knowledge and practice.

If you want to be a trucker, you will have to learn how to keep your vehicle safe and how to protect yourself and others on the road. Having patience to get through traffic safely is similar to working through some kinds of school work. If you have the skills and the right attitude, the freedom of the open road could be for you. Will this be you?

Fig. 25 *Truckers operate vehicles of all sizes.*

Fig. 26 *A silver mine, 1899*

Fig. 27 *Gold washing, 1890*

9.9 **Metals in Modern Use**

Minerals have been mined in Canada for many, many years, and it's almost impossible to imagine life today without them.

Fig. 28 *Metals in modern buildings*

Fig. 29 *Copper quarry, 1860*

Fig. 31 *Iron mine, 1882*

Fig. 30 *Ontario's first mine, water colour by Susannah Moodie*

Fig. 32 *Panning for gold*

Fig. 33 *Gold bricks*

Iron is made into steel, which is needed for nails and trains and almost everything else you can travel on or use as a tool. Nickel is used to produce stainless steel for knives and boats. Zinc is used to cover (galvanize) iron objects so they won't rust. Silver is used for jewelry and specialty electronics. Lead is used to manufacture batteries for cars and motorcycles.

That's only the beginning of the list.

SUPERSLEUTH

Ask local business organizations to tell you what jobs in your community depend on the mining industry.

Fig. 34 *The Big Nickel, Sudbury*

Activity

9.10 Including the Kitchen Sink

1. Make a list of the metals used in this kitchen. Include those that you can see and those you know must be there that are out of view. Don't forget to include the kitchen sink!

Think about it

1. How was each of these metals obtained?

THIS CONCERNS YOU

Gold: Who Wants It?

Gold. The very sound of the word conjures up pictures of this precious gleaming metal. What makes gold so special?

It may surprise you to know that the product of the mining industry that we probably need least is gold. Iron, nickel, and aluminum have many practical uses. However, other than its monetary value, gold has few benefits. It's very soft, so it would be a poor choice for building a bridge or an airplane.

A lot of gold is obtained from underground mining, but some can be mined at the Earth's surface. **Placer mining** is a way of obtaining gold from gravel and sand deposits when there is plenty of water nearby. When this is done on a large scale, a form of placer mining called **hydraulicking** is used. Another method used when the gravel and sand are thick is **dredging**. Both of these kinds of mining destroy land and streams and have been forbidden in many countries.

Mining gold usually uses huge amounts of energy—it takes one tonne of ore to produce 30 g (a teaspoonful) of gold. It involves health and safety risks, and creates great environmental change.

The miners who dig out the ore descend to depths of five kilometres to drill, blast, crush, and transport ore. Even though employers attempt to make the mines as safe and comfortable as possible, working deep in the Earth always carries with it certain hazards. We've all heard stories of various kinds of mine disasters, resulting in injury and death to miners.

Why, then, when the risks seem so great and the benefits so few, do people want gold? There are several reasons. It's a beautiful metal, well suited for crafting jewellery. It is scarce, and people usually want what is hard to obtain. People have placed a high value on this soft, yellow metal. In recent times, gold has been bought and sold for as much as $840 for 30 g. It is so dependable that many countries use it as a form of international money. In the early 1900s, many based their entire monetary system on the value of gold—the **gold standard**.

The decision to mine any substance is based on comparing the expected benefits to the risks. We try to minimize the damage done to the environment by mining industries. We try to limit the health risks to those working in these industries. The benefits of the substances obtained are such that we are prepared to accept some risk. In the case of gold mining, perhaps we should be asking ourselves: who suffers the risks, and who reaps the benefits?

Think about it

1. Research the uses of gold. Make a poster to show some benefits of this metal.
2. Disposing of the mountains of rock and sand removed from a mine is a big issue. What methods could you suggest as a means of disposing of the part of the ore which is not gold?
3. Make up two teams of two people from your class to debate gold mining. Find out what is done to the environment by the various kinds of gold mining mentioned above. Use the information about the benefits of gold mining you found for question 1. Have your two teams debate the acceptability of gold mining in Canada.

Fig. 35 *Hardrock gold mines may extract only 30 g of gold from a tonne of ore. This photo shows the kind of impact some kinds of gold mining have on the environment.*

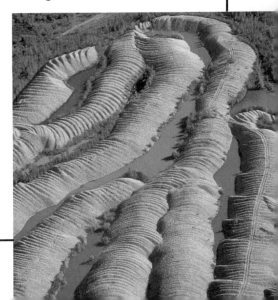

We seldom reflect on chemicals which make the things we use. Now and then curiosity may make us wonder where the metal in a ring or the salt on our food came from. In Buried Treasure you have learned a little about the resource industry which produces the metals and salts that we use.

Finding the resources buried beneath the surface of our planet is a difficult and expensive job most of the time. The areas most likely to contain an ore can be predicted from an understanding of rocks and their patterns. More precise locations can be found using the science and technology of radio wave interference. Even after these predictions, the Earth must still be drilled to determine if an ore is present and how much is available. Finally, before digging a hole or drilling into the ore, business people must decide if the mine will be profitable and how damage to the environment can be minimized. Government leaders must decide on our behalf if the damage to the environment is an acceptable cost for the benefits gained.

9.11 Chapter Summary

- Mining includes coal, gold, salt for our table, potash for fertilizer, iron, aluminum and many more common substances that we want from the earth.
- A mine can be an open pit, a pipe, or a large underground excavation.
- Minerals and salts are located by predictions based on information gathered by observations and the assistance of technology.
- The properties of a mineral which deflect radio waves or attract a magnet can be useful in locating minerals.
- Electromagnetic surveying can cover a large area.
- Drilling cores allows people to "see" under the ground.

- Minerals are classified by their properties and how they were formed.
- Crystal shape, hardness, streak, chemical tests, and density help to identify minerals.
- Concentrating the ore reduces the need to transport large quantities of waste material.
- Some metals, such as copper, can be refined using electricity.
- Although we benefit from the use of mined materials the environment near the mine and the refinery is stressed. Part of the decision to operate a mine involves balancing the benefits against the risks.

9.12 **Are You Ready to Go On?**

Do not write in the textbook.

1. Explain mining.

2. Name three different ways of mining.

3. What kind of substances are mined in the Canadian shield: ▓▓▓▓, the Prairies: ▓▓▓▓, the western mountains: ▓▓▓▓.

4. Crude oil and salt have a common method of mining. How are each of these substances brought to the surface?

5. Which of the following metals will deflect a magnetic compass needle: copper, iron, aluminum?

6. What effect do some minerals have on a radio wave?

7. Copy each statement into your notebook filling in each blank with the correct word.
   a) ▓▓▓▓ surveying locates minerals by using radio waves.
   b) A mineral is a substance that has the following properties: ▓▓▓▓, ▓▓▓▓, ▓▓▓▓.
   c) To survey a large area of land, a plane or helicopter tows a ▓▓▓▓ as it flies in a pattern.
   d) Electromagnetic waves include ▓▓▓▓ and ▓▓▓▓.

8. In your notebook, match the terms in column A with the descriptions in Column B.

Column A	Column B
small crystals	formed near water
sedimentary	rock cools slowly
large crystals	used to make steel
crystal shape	rock cools quickly
hardness	colour of rubbing
streak	as compared to diamond
iron	repeating regular shape

9. The A.D.J. Coal Company has just discovered a rich coal mine right beneath a small northern Ontario town. The coal must be mined using an open pit if it is to produce a profit. You are at a town meeting where a vote on the issue will be held. Pretend you are one of the following: a) banker; b) motel owner; c) doctor; d) student; e) construction worker.
   How would you like the council to vote on a motion to allow the mine? What would you say to convince them of the "right" decision? Present your argument to the class.

Contents

Chapter Ten

Far Out

10.1 **What's Up?**

Imagine that you were transported thousands of years back in time. With no televisions, movies, or games arcades, you might watch the stars for entertainment at night. As you and your friends sat outside in the dark, you could make up stories about patterns and shapes that you imagined among the stars. You might name each star group after a pet or a friend. You would be doing just what the ancient watchers-of-the-skies did. They named the patterns of stars. We call these patterns **constellations**.

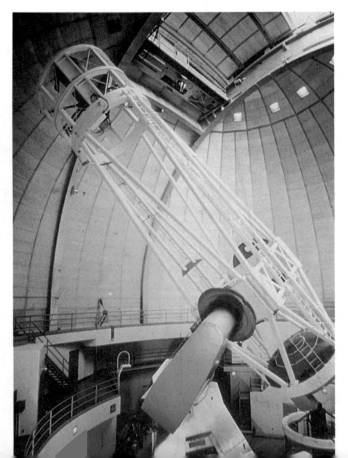

Fig. 1 *The constellation, Orion, is a familiar sight in our night sky.*

Fig. 2 *Sophisticated telescopes, such as the one shown here, have made it possible for us to observe the universe in incredible detail.*

Humans have always been interested in the mysteries that the sky contains. For many hundreds of years, only the unaided eye was available to make observations. Using the few facts they knew and lots of imagination, people created stories about what the heavens might really be like. These stories were passed from parents to children as legends, some of which remain with us today.

However, our understanding of the skies is now based on much more than legend. About four hundred years ago, the telescope was invented. Since then, more sophisticated telescopes and spectroscopes have made possible the observation of the universe in incredible detail. Space probes travel far into the solar system, passing close to distant planets and sending awe-inspiring photographs back to Earth. It seems that the more we learn about objects in the universe, the more curious we become. As soon as some questions are answered, more arise, such as: Where are we in the universe? How large is the universe? How old is Earth? Are we alone?

In this chapter you will find the answers to some of these questions. You will probably ask some questions of your own. More importantly, you will learn of the many kinds of activities in space science that may answer, during your lifetime, some of the BIG questions about our universe. Human curiosity keeps us asking questions and using science in an organized way to look for answers.

Fig. 3 *Perhaps someone you know will walk on Mars and bring you back a photo like this, instead of having it sent by machine.*

Activity

10.2 **What's My Sign?**

Perhaps you have been asked, "What's your sign? Some people believe that your zodiac sign can influence your life. The **zodiac** is a band of stars along the path of the Earth's orbit around the sun. There are many fascinating stories about the twelve star groups, the zodiac. Astrologers match them with human characteristics, predicting traits from a person's birthdate. In this activity you can be your own astrologer, and see if the stars and planets in the zodiac have affected you.

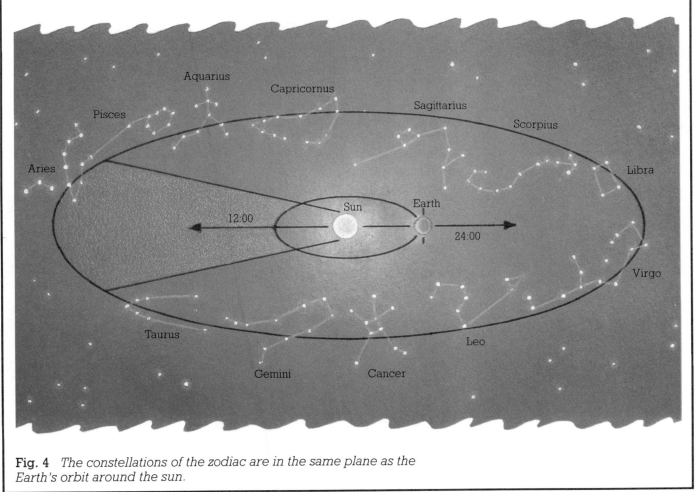

Fig. 4 *The constellations of the zodiac are in the same plane as the Earth's orbit around the sun.*

continued

- zodiac diagram
- ruler

1. Your birthdate determines your sign in the zodiac. Locate your birthdate on the Earth's path (the inside circle in figure 5).
2. Place the end of a ruler on your birthday and line the ruler up through the sun's centre out to the belt of the zodiac stars.

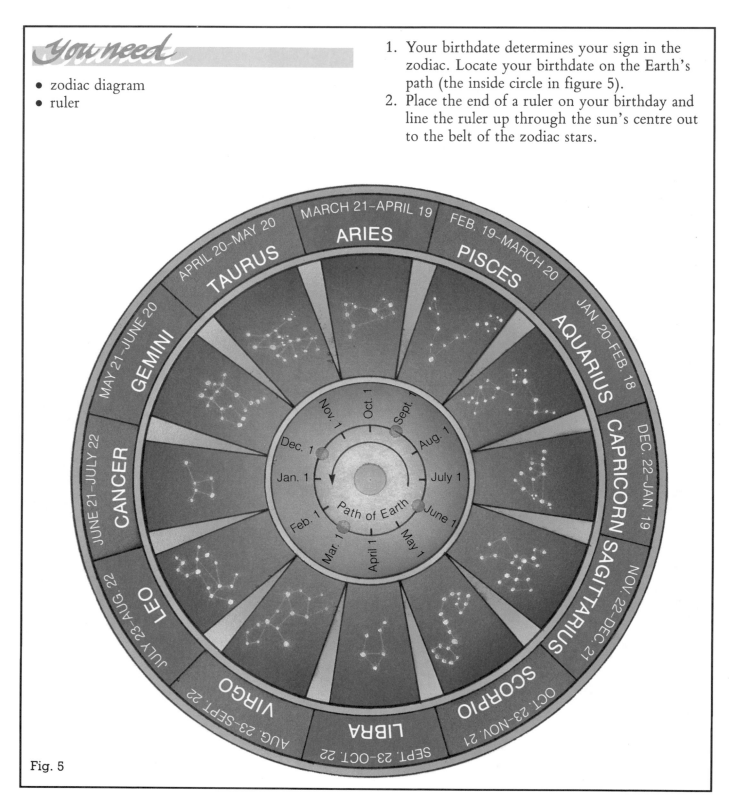

Fig. 5

3. Your sign is the one that is closest to the ruler's edge.
4. Look at the following list of characteristics. Choose five that you feel best describe you.

Determined	Versatile	Persistent
Able to lead	Modest	Fair-minded
Subtle	Friendly	Ambitious
Independent	Creative	Intense
Self-restrained	Egotistical	Calm
Restless	Possessive	Self-concerned
Diligent	Diplomatic	Optimistic
Cautious	Nonconforming	Changeable
Picky	Devious	Superficial
Self-motivated	Hesitant	Courageous
Enthusiastic	Practical	Original
Emotional	Impulsive	Unemotional
Talkative	Moody	Generous
Intellectual	Peace-loving	Aggressive
Quiet	Gentle	Outgoing

5. Now have a good friend choose five characteristics that he or she feels describe you best.
6. Did both you and your friend choose any traits that were the same?
7. Figure 6 shows some of the predicted character traits of people born under the twelve zodiac signs. The "ruling" planets include the sun, moon and eight planets. (Earth is not used.) Find your sign.

Fig. 6

CAPRICORN: Dec. 22—Jan. 19
Symbol: The Mountain Goat
Ruling planet: Saturn—planet of self-discipline, duty, and responsibility
Characteristics: Ambitious, cautious, practical, self-restrained

AQUARIUS: Jan. 20—Feb. 18
Symbol: The Water Carrier
Ruling planet: Uranus—planet of independence and unpredictability
Characteristics: Independent, nonconforming, original

PISCES: Feb. 19—March 20
Symbol: The Fishes
Ruling planet: Neptune—planet of confusion and imagination
Characteristics: Creative, changeable, emotional, devious

ARIES: March 21—April 19
Symbol: The Ram
Ruling planet: Mars—planet of energy and courage
Characteristics: Aggressive, courageous, self-motivating, impulsive

TAURUS: April 20—May 20
Symbol: The Bull
Ruling planet: Venus—planet of beauty, love, and peace
Characteristics: Determined, practical, unemotional, calm

GEMINI: May—June 20
Symbol: The Twins
Ruling planet: Mercury—planet of the intellect and motion
Characteristics: Versatile, restless, talkative, superficial

CANCER: June 21—July 22
Symbol: The Crab
Ruling planet: The moon—planet of emotions
Characteristics: Persistent, possessive, changeable, moody

LEO: July 23—Aug. 22
Symbol: The Lion
Ruling planet: The sun—planet of willpower and drive
Characteristics: Leadership ability, self-concerned, generous, egotistical

VIRGO: Aug. 23—Sept. 22
Symbol: The Virgin
Ruling planet: Mercury—planet of the intellect and motion
Characteristics: Modest, diligent, picky, intellectual snob

LIBRA: Sept. 23—Oct. 22
Symbol: The Scales
Ruling planet: Venus—planet of beauty, love, and peace
Characteristics: Fair-minded, diplomatic, hesitant, lover of peace

SCORPIO: Oct. 23—Nov. 21
Symbol: The Scorpion
Ruling planet: Pluto—planet of power and strength
Characteristics: Subtle, determined, possessive, intense

SAGITTARIUS: Nov. 22—Dec. 21
Symbol: The Archer
Ruling planet: Jupiter—planet of sociability, kindness, and generosity
Characteristics: Friendly, optimistic, enthusiastic, restless

continued

1. How many characteristics listed in steps 4 and 5 match characteristics predicted by your zodiac sign?

2. How many characteristics did NOT match the prediction? How accurate was this prediction?

3. Science is a means to repeat and try to explain certain events. People using the methods of science try to:
   - identify the causes of events
   - repeat these events under controlled conditions
   - predict what should happen.

   Using this definition of science, would you consider astrology to be a science? Explain your answer.

4. Astronomy is often confused with astrology.
   - Both are concerned with studies of heavenly bodies.
   - Both are concerned with pinpointing the locations of planets and stars.

   The early astrologers collected a lot of data, but personal viewpoints were added. Nostradamus predicted the world would end May 13, 1988 but we are still here.

   - Astrology is based on an ancient system that no longer reflects the reality of the sky.
   - Astronomy, however, is an exact science. It is based on observing, testing, and using only facts to explain what's happening in the skies.
   - Astrology does not meet the definition of true science. Observations are used, but the predictions are not based on known facts.
   - Astronomy does predict what will happen. Halley's comet was predicted to return 75 years after its last appearance, and it did. Why was it more likely that this prediction would come true than Nostradamus's prediction?

5. Horoscopes printed in the newspaper are really just for fun. Recently some newspapers have added a disclaimer with the horoscope which says they ''are intended only for their entertainment value.'' Even David Knight, manager of the Astrological Consulting service in Toronto said, ''Daily horoscopes are fun stuff with absolutely no bearing on true astrology.'' Why do you think newspapers have started printing a disclaimer with the daily horoscopes?

10.3 It's a Gas

The sun is a huge ball of hot gas. Its temperature is not the same everywhere, but its average surface temperature is about 6000°C. The mass of the sun is about equal to the mass of 333 000 Earths, and its gravity is enormous. This large force of gravity holds all the planets in their orbits around the sun.

SAFETY ALERT
You can be blinded permanently by staring at the sun. Never look directly at the sun through a telescope or with your naked eye. Two famous scientists, Newton and Galileo, both damaged their eyes by observing the sun.

The sun is really a giant nuclear reactor. A **nuclear reactor** is a device that produces vast amounts of energy, mainly in the form of heat, from a small amount of fuel. The heat and light energy that we receive on Earth comes from this reactor when hydrogen and helium atoms combine. Hydrogen makes up about 75% of the mass of the sun. Helium is about 25% of the sun's mass. All the other elements in the sun (fifteen in all) make up the rest. Scientists and engineers are trying to build a copy of the sun's reactor. This is very difficult because the temperature that is needed melts and vaporizes all matter. If they succeed in building this reactor, we will have almost unlimited energy. The fuel for the reactor will be hydrogen, obtained easily from water.

It's a Fact
The sun is actually a star. It is a yellow star of average size in relation to other stars but of immense size in comparison with our Earth.

It's a Fact
6000°C is about thirty times hotter than an oven you would use to cook a pizza.

It's a Fact
Some scientists believe that there may be a second star, called Nemesis, as part of our solar system. Right now it is far away, but every 63 million years it comes close and disrupts weather on Earth. This may have caused dinosaur extinctions.

It's a Fact
Helium was discovered on the sun before it was discovered here on Earth.

Fig. 7 *About 109 Earths could fit side by side across the diameter of the sun.*

Mercury Venus Earth Mars Jupiter Saturn Uranus Neptune Pluto

Fig. 8 *Galileo*

Experiments have been done on the space shuttle, in Skylab, and on some special satellites to study the properties of the sun. Some experiments measure the kinds and amounts of radiation given off by the sun. Others study the number and movement of sunspots, dark patches on the sun's surface caused by gas with a lower temperature. Scientists are trying to connect activities in the sun with the changes in climate and weather on Earth. We have learned a lot about the sun by studying its light, and carefully observing its sunspots and flares. The more we learn about our sun, the more we understand life on Earth.

FEEDBACK

1. What kind of star is our sun?
2. How does the sun produce heat and light?
3. What is the temperature of the sun?
4. Why do we study the sun?
5. Describe the composition (make-up) of the sun.

Investigation

10.4 Sunwatch

The hunters and farmers of olden days saw that the sun moved across the sky in a path that took one year to complete. In that one year, the seasons turned from cold to warm and back to cold. The days changed from short to long, and back to short. The sun moved from low on the horizon (the line where the ground meets the sky) at noon to high in the sky, and back to low again. By observing the motions of the sun, these ancient people learned a great deal. You can also learn by doing this investigation at home.

Find out

A. Does the sun set at the same time every day?
B. Does the sun set in the same place every day?
C. Does anything else about the sun change, such as colour, size, shape, or brightness?

You need

- compass
- paper (or Bristol board)
- pen and coloured pencils
- daily newspaper

1. Select a location where you can observe the sunset on the horizon *at least* once a week. Use the compass to find west. Face this direction.

2. *On a large sheet of paper, draw a picture of everything you see on the horizon from east to south to west, including buildings, trees, hills, and poles.* (You will use these landmarks to locate positions of the sun at certain times.)

3. Look in the daily newspaper to find the time of the sunset.

4. *Copy the chart below onto a piece of paper. Each time you observe the sunset, record the date and time of the sunset, the weather conditions, and the colour, shape, and brightness of the sun.*

5. About 15 min before sunset, go to the location that you picked. *Observe the sun, and complete the chart for week 1.*

SAFETY ALERT:
Never stare directly at the sun.

6. Note the location of the sun just as it touches the horizon. *Now draw the sun at this location on the drawing you made in step 2.* Try to show the size and shape. *Print the date above the sun.*

7. During one day for each of the next four weeks (at least), repeat steps 5 and 6. After five weeks, your drawing should look something like figure 10.

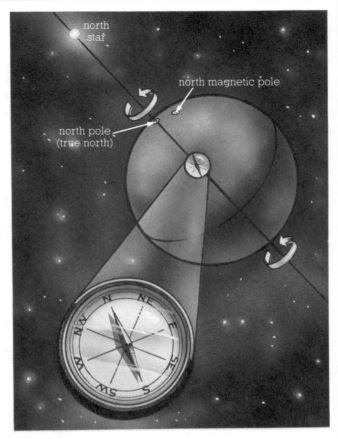

Fig. 9 *You can use a compass to find direction.*

1. Does the sun always set at the same time? If not, is it earlier or later each day?

2. What season of the year is it?

Week	Date	Time of sunset	Weather Conditions	Description		
				Colour	Shape	Brightness
1.						
2.						
3.						
4.						
5.						

DO NOT WRITE IN THE TEXTBOOK

continued

Fig. 10

NOV. 19 4:09 pm
NOV. 12 4:12 pm
NOV. 4 4:17 pm
OCT. 28 4:28 pm
OCT. 21 5:31 pm
OCT. 14 5:45 pm
OCT. 7 5:58 pm
SEPT. 30 6:08 pm
SEPT. 28 6:16 pm

3. Write a sentence that connects your answers to questions 1 and 2.
4. Does the sun always set in the same location on the horizon?
5. Does the colour of the sun seem to change? Explain.
6. Does the shape of the sun seem to change at sunset? Explain.

Now you know

The sun sets (and rises) at different times each day, depending on the season. For example, from the start of winter to the start of summer, the sun sets later each day. Summer officially begins June 21 each year. This is called the **summer solstice**. It is the longest day of the year, since the sun rises earliest and sets latest, so the Earth receives the most sunlight. On June 21 the sun rises and sets farthest north. It is also higher above the horizon than at any other time of the year. After June 21 the days get shorter until the **winter solstice** which occurs about December 22. In December the days are so short, you probably get up in the dark and may come home from school in the dark.

As sunset approaches, you can observe the sun changing from a bright yellow-white ball to a duller orange-red one. The sun may also appear to be a flattened shape at sunset. Both these effects occur because we are looking through more of the Earth's atmosphere at sunset.

Fig. 11 *The sun rises in the east and sets in the west. A sunset on Earth is one of the most beautiful natural occurrences.*

10.5 **Our Satellite: The Moon**

Our nearest neighbour in space is the moon which revolves around the Earth. An object in space that revolves around a larger object is a **satellite**. The moon averages 384 000 km away from Earth. Humans have always been very interested in the moon, and excited about the possibilities of exploring it. On July 20, 1969 dreams became reality when the two astronauts—Armstrong and Aldrin—stepped onto the moon's dusty, airless surface. They left their lunar lander, the Eagle, part of the Apollo 11 spacecraft, to walk on the moon one hundred and two hours and forty-five minutes after blasting off from Earth in a Saturn V rocket.

It's a Fact
The moon is the same age as the Earth, 4.6 million million years old. The rocks, mostly made of basalt, were formed by cooling lava. There is a thin layer of dust.

Do You Know?
What was the average speed in km/h, of these astronauts on their trip to the moon? How many days did the trip take?

373

Fig. 12 *An astronaut walks on the moon's surface.*

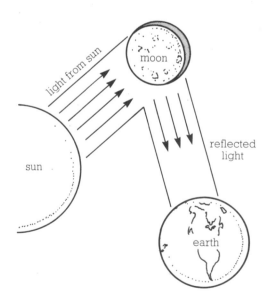

Fig. 13 *The moon does not produce its own light. It reflects sunlight to Earth. Light travels 300 000 km/s, and requires about 2-6 s to go from Earth to the moon and back.*

The astronauts on this, and five other Apollo spaceships, brought back samples of rocks from different areas on the moon. Scientists on Earth have studied these rocks to determine what the moon is made of and how old it is. Other experiments were set up and left operating on the moon. For example, a mirror (called a retroreflector) was placed on the moon during the Apollo 11 mission. A laser beam from the Earth can be bounced off this mirror and used to measure very precisely the distance from the Earth to the moon.

The same side of the moon always faces the Earth because it revolves around the Earth at the same rate that it rotates (spins around) on its axis. It takes the moon 27.33 days for one rotation and one revolution. Although we see the same side of the moon at all times, we see changing amounts of this side. These changing amounts are called the **phases of the moon**.

The moon is much smaller than Earth. The gravity on the moon is about one sixth of the gravity on the Earth. There is no air on the moon, so astronauts must wear pressurized suits to supply oxygen to breathe. A footprint in the moon's dust will remain there indefinitely because there is no air to produce a wind.

FEEDBACK

1. What is the Earth's closest neighbor in space?
2. What is the actual source of ''moonlight''?
3. How long does it take for the moon to revolve around the Earth? Why don't we see all sides of the moon as it spins?
4. You are the first student reporter to land on the moon. You have one minute on the national news to describe the moon and your feelings. Write a script for your news report.

It's a Fact
The back side of the moon was first observed when a Soviet unmanned spacecraft, Lunik 3, orbited the moon in 1959. It sent back photographs by radio signals.

Fig. 14 *To understand how the phases of the moon are seen, picture the moon as a ball and the sun as a candle. If you hold the ball as shown in the illustration, you will see how the "sun's" light enables you to see the moon's phases.*

Investigation

10.6 Phases of the Moon

You have already made some observations of the sun in investigation 10.4. This time you will be observing the moon. Unlike the sun, the moon has a shape that appears to change over time. In this investigation, you will find out when and how it changes as well as answering some other questions about the moon.

Find out

A. Can the moon be seen during the day?
B. In what direction does the moon rise and set?
C. How do the shape, colour, size and brightness of the moon change on any given night?

You need

- a compass
- a large piece of paper, Bristol board, or newsprint
- pen and coloured pencils
- binoculars or telescope

SAFETY ALERT:
Do not work alone in isolated areas at night. Be aware of obstacles and other dangers around you to avoid harming yourself in the dark.

Try this

1. Find a location where you can observe the moon at the same time AT LEAST five times during the next two weeks. Choose a spot on which to stand and face south.
2. *On a large sheet of paper, draw a picture of everything you see on the horizon from east to south to west, including buildings, trees, hills, and poles. (You will use these landmarks to locate positions of the moon at certain times.)*
3. *Mark compass points on the paper, showing east, south, and west.*
4. *Copy the chart on page 377 into your notes.*

Date	Time	Weather Conditions	Description			
			Size	Colour	Shape	Brightness
1.						
2.						
3.						
4.						
5.						

5. Choose a time after school to observe the moon. You must be at that location within 15 minutes of your chosen time on five occasions during a two-week period.

6. *At your viewing time and location draw the shape and location of the moon on your picture from step 2. Print the date above the moon.*

7. *Complete the chart for the first date. Mark any very bright stars on your drawing with the moon.*

8. Repeat steps 6 and 7 at least four more times during the next two weeks.

9. Use the binoculars or telescope to examine the surface of the moon. *Write a description of what you see.*

What happened?

1. From what direction does the moon rise? Where does it set?

2. Describe changes in the moon's shape, location, brightness, and colour during your viewing period.

3. Refer to figure 16, "Phases of the moon." What phase did you observe at the start? What phase did you see after two weeks?

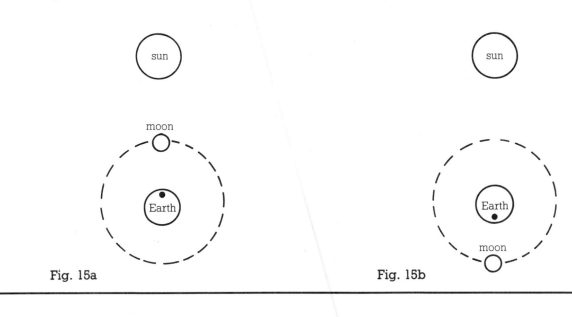

Fig. 15a   Fig. 15b

continued

4. Look at figure 15. You are the dot on the Earth. You are looking south at the moon.
   (a) In figure 15a, what time is it for the location of the sun that is shown? What does the moon look like? (Remember how you ''see'' the moon).
   (b) In figure 15b, what time is it? What does the moon look like at this time and position?
5. About how many days does the moon take to move from the position shown in a to the position in b?

Now you know

The moon, like the sun, rises in the east and sets in the western sky. Every day the moon rises about 50 minutes later than on the previous day.

Thus, at the same time one day, the moon appears further to the east than it did at that time on the previous day. During any two-week period, you can see two phases. A full moon is highest in the southern sky near midnight. About two weeks later, the new moon is highest in the southern sky around noon. In between are the quarter moons.

SUPERSLEUTH

Find out what you can about the moon's surface. Look at photographs and see if you can find the names of the features you described in step 9.

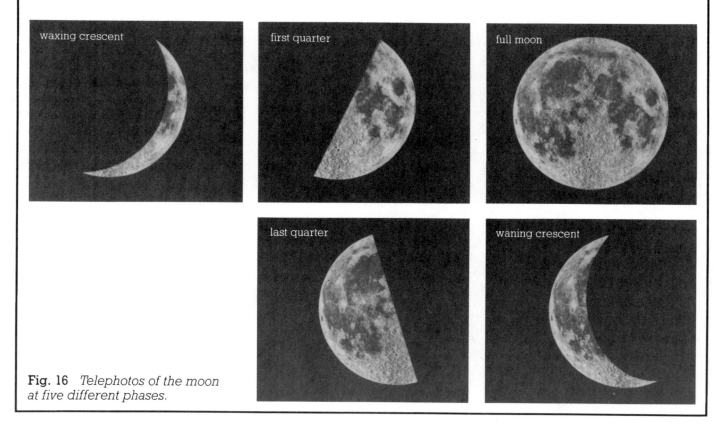

Fig. 16 *Telephotos of the moon at five different phases.*

waxing crescent

first quarter

full moon

last quarter

waning crescent

10.7 Finding Planets

Is it a plane? Is it a UFO? No, it's a planet! You may have noticed a very bright object in the sky and wondered what it was. If you see a bright, unblinking body in the sky near sunset, chances are you have seen a planet.

Some planets reflect so much sunlight that they can be seen before the stars come out. Venus, known as the "evening star," can often be seen before the sun sets. Mars, Jupiter, and Saturn are also very bright at times, depending on how close they are to Earth. Tiny Mercury is usually too close to the sun to be seen. The other planets are very hard to observe without a telescope or binoculars.

The inner planets — Mercury, Venus, Earth and Mars — orbit close to the sun. They are called the **Terrestrial planets** because they are most like Earth. The outer planets are called the **Jovian planets**. Most of them are giant balls of gas. Jupiter, Saturn, Uranus, Neptune, and Pluto are separated from the inner group by the asteroid belt.

Planets are seen in the sky because, like the moon, they reflect sunlight. Mars and Venus, our closest planets, are usually the brightest objects in the sky (not counting our moon). Mars has a reddish glow, since white sunlight is reflecting off its red sand.

You can easily distinguish a planet from a star by thinking about the children's rhyme:

> "Twinkle, twinkle little star,
> How I wonder what you are."

Stars twinkle but planets shine with a steady light, just like our moon. Also, planets seem to "wander" through the sky from day to day, whereas all the stars stay fixed in place, but seem to rotate together. Ancient Greek astronomers noticed this difference in motions. The name "planet" meant "wanderer" in Greek. The planets that could be seen with the naked eye were named after gods.

Fig. 17 *Mars, the "red planet"*

It's a Fact
The Greeks named planets that could be seen with the naked eye after Gods:

Jupiter (Jove) — King of the Roman gods
Mars — Roman god of war
Mercury — Messenger of the gods
Venus — Roman god of love and beauty
Saturn — Father of Jupiter, god of agriculture

Other than Earth, these five planets were the only ones known until 1781, when Uranus was accidentally discovered by William Herschel.

The planets, sun, and moon, all appear to move along the same path across the sky. This path is called the **ecliptic**. If you look close to the sun and moon's path you can see the visible planets in the sky. Not all planets are visible at all times—only those on the same side of the Earth as you.

FEEDBACK

1. What is the name of the path along which planets, the sun, and the moon travel?
2. What are the two kinds of planets?
3. When you see an object in the sky, how can you tell if it is a planet or a star?
4. What does the word "planet" mean?
5. Observation tables tell you the constellation where a planet will appear during each month. These tables also indicate whether it is better to view the planet in the morning or evening. Look at the sample astronomical observation table.

Planet	Month (1989)											
	Jan	Feb	Mar	Apr	May	Jun	Jul	Aug	Sep	Oct	Nov	Dec
Venus	Sc	Sa/Ca	Aq	Pi	Ar	Ta/Ge	Cn	Le	Vi	Li	Sc	Sa
Mars	Pi	Ar	Ar/Ta	Ta	Ge	Ge	Cn	Le	Le	Vi	Vi	Vi
Jupiter	Ta	Ta	Ta	Ta	Ta	Ta	Ta/Ge	Ge	Ge	Ge	Ge	Ge
Saturn	Sa	Sa	Sa	Sa	Sa	Sa	Sa	Sa	Sa	Sa	Sa	Sa

Abbreviations for the twelve constellations of the zodiac.

Aries (Ar)	Cancer (Cn)	Libra (Li)	Capricornus (Ca)
Taurus (Ta)	Leo (Le)	Scorpius (Sc)	Aquarius (Aq)
Gemini (Ge)	Virgo (Vi)	Sagittarius (Sa)	Pisces (Pi)

a) Which planets could be seen in January 1989?
b) Which planets could be seen tonight, (if it's clear)? In which constellation can each planet be seen? (Use an observation table for the current year).
c) If tonight is clear, go outside and find the constellation that contains the planet you are looking for. (Refer to section 10.12). Remember, the planet is NOT a star in the constellation. The planet will usually be much brighter than the stars, and will shine, rather than twinkle. It is best to use binoculars, and place them on a solid object like a railing or a rock. You might even see some of Jupiter's many moons, or Saturn's rings.

Activity

10.8 Getting to Know a Planet

Planets differ in many ways. The more scientists learn about them, the stranger some of them seem. In this activity you will learn about one planet (other than Earth).

You need

- astronomy books, magazines, videos, etc. from the school library or a public library

1. Your teacher will divide the class into small groups and assign you a planet to investigate.
2. Start this activity by deciding in your group what tasks have to be done and who is going to do them.
3. Your school librarian can give you information about your planet, or you could go to the public library.
4. At the end of the time period your group must have prepared:
   a) a brief (5–10 min) oral presentation describing your planet to the class. To make the presentation as interesting and informative as possible, consider using slides, large diagrams, a short video tape that you made, etc.
   b) a one-page fact sheet to share with your classmates. The fact sheet should include information such as: diameter of the planet, its distance from the sun, substances that make up the planet, the temperature ranges, surface features, atmosphere, size of gravity compared to Earth, etc. Also describe why your planet would or would not be a suitable place for human habitation.

Think about it

1. As other groups make their presentations, record the most interesting thing that you learn about each planet.
2. After the presentations, write three questions about each planet that you would like answered.
3. In general, what are some ways that scientists have learned about the planets?

Information Officer or Tour Guide

When does this tour leave? Where is the cafeteria? Is that a real lunar lander?

Would you like a job that could be different every day? If you enjoy meeting new people and working with the public, the job of information officer or tour guide could be for you?

Tour guides get asked many questions—quite often the same questions are asked many times a day by different people. You need a great deal of patience and a desire to be helpful to people. You would have to expect to work weekends and holidays because that is the time most people go on tours.

Tour guides often are required to handle ticket sales and ticket-taking at many events. Some tour guides drive special buses around large museums. Tour guides at the Kennedy Space Centre in Florida drive many thousands of people a day around the gigantic space centre. They point out interesting landmarks and tell stories.

Guides who work in science centres, or museums such as Science North in Sudbury would need a keen interest in science. A background of science courses in high school would be useful. An ability to learn the answers to questions people ask often would definitely be an advantage.

The job of information officer or tour guide would never be boring —there would always be new and interesting people to work with. To do this job, you would require a neat and clean appearance. It would be useful to be able to speak in public and to be able to handle crowds of people. You would have to be tolerant of all kinds of people, and enjoy being asked questions.

At least a high school education would be required to do this job. A special on-the-job training course would probably be required. Will this be you?

Fig. 18 *An information officer or tour guide might be responsible for giving informative talks and answering questions.*

10.9 Wish Upon a Star, a Comet

Did you ever wish on a falling star? "Falling stars" are actually not stars at all—they are meteors. **Meteors** are pieces of rock and metal that move quickly through space. If they enter the Earth's atmosphere, friction from air resistance heats the meteor so much that it turns white hot and vaporizes. The light that you see is produced during this vaporization. **Meteorites** are larger meteors that do not vaporize completely, and actually reach the Earth's surface. Occasionally, a meteorite may leave a large hole, called a **meteorite crater**, in the Earth's surface. Some are so huge, they can be seen from an airplane.

Fig. 19 *Meteor trails*

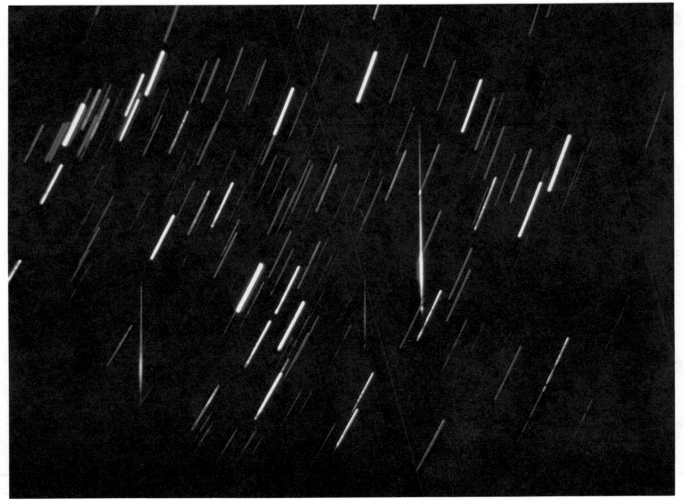

In 1986 a very bright comet went by Earth. In 1696 an English astronomer, named Edmund Halley, had predicted the return of this comet every 75 years. Halley's comet, like others, is a large ball of ice, dust, and frozen gases. A tail forms on the comet when the sun melts the frozen gases and ice. This tail always streams away from the sun. Some comets fall into the sun and disappear forever. Other comets go by the sun, further out to space—perhaps someday to return. Many meteors we observe are the result of Earth moving through debris from the tail of an ancient comet.

Thousands of small pieces of rock called **asteroids**, travel around the sun like tiny planets. These asteroids orbit between Mars and Jupiter like a "belt" around the sun. They may be the remains of a planet that broke up into chunks.

Fig. 20 *Halley's comet*

1. What is a "falling star"?
2. Are meteors and meteorites the same? Explain.
3. What is a comet?
4. How often does Halley's comet return?
5. What happens if a comet gets too close to the sun?
6. What are asteroids?

SUPERSLEUTH

The moon has no atmosphere. Would you see "falling stars" on the moon? Explain. What could meteorites do to the surface of the moon?

10.10 Our Home: the Solar System

Our solar system is an orderly group consisting of one star, nine planets, about 43 moons, thousands of tiny "planets" called asteroids and many millions of meteoroids and comets. The star, our sun, is at the centre of the solar system. It contains most of the matter in the solar system — about 99% of the total mass. Its great mass holds all these objects in their orbits. The solar system is part of the **Milky Way** which is a **galaxy** (family of stars). The Milky Way, in its turn, is part of the **universe** which consists of everything that exists anywhere in space and time. That's a pretty all-inclusive definition, but astronomers really don't know where (or if) the universe ends. They believe it is infinite. The human mind has great difficulty in grasping that concept — after a few moments' thought, you'll probably understand why.

FEEDBACK

1. What objects make up our solar system?
2. What is a galaxy?
3. What is the universe?

10.11 How Large Is the Solar System?

The solar system is large. Distances are beyond human experiences; thus, words alone can't give a sense of sizes. For example, our Earth is about 150 000 000 km from the sun, and our moon is 384 000 km from Earth. Pluto, the most distant planet, averages 5 900 000 000 km from the sun. The solar system even goes beyond Pluto, to include a huge region of dust and debris called the **Oort cloud**. Including this cloud, the size of the solar system is about 10 000 000 000 000 km across.

In this activity, building a scale model will help to give you a sense of the solar system's size. Scientists often use models to help them understand things that are too small, too large, or too complicated to observe easily.

Find out

How large, and how far apart, would the sun and planets be if the sun were at one end of a football field and Pluto were at the other end?

You need

- 100 m string
- metre stick or tape measure
- calculator
- About 20 balls of different sizes (ranging from a beach ball down to BB pellets)

Try this

1. *Make copies of the two charts that follow.*

Table 1 The Planets of the Solar System

Average distance from the sun for planet (km)		Scaled distance to planet if Pluto is 100 m from sun (m)
Mercury	58 000 000	
Venus	108 000 000	
Earth	150 000 000	
Mars	228 000 000	
Jupiter	780 000 000	
Saturn	1 430 000 000	
Uranus	2 870 000 000	
Neptune	4 500 000 000	
Pluto	5 900 000 000	100 m

Table 2

Diameter of a large ball that represents the sun = _____ cm.

Diameter of the sun = 1 392 000 km.

Planet	Diameter of planet (km)	Prediction of best ball to represent planet	Diameter of planet compared to sun	Diameter of ball representing planet (cm)	Kind of ball that represents planet
Mercury	4 880				
Venus	12 100				
Earth	12 800				
Mars	6 800				
Jupiter	142 800				
Saturn	120 000				
Uranus	51 200				
Neptune	48 600				
Pluto	2 600				

2. One person, representing the sun, should stand on one goal line of the football field (or at the end of a long hall). The second person, representing Pluto, stretches the 100 m of string out to the opposite end of the field or hall. Predict where the third person, representing Earth, should stand. *Record this prediction.*

3. Look at the sizes of the sun and planets in table 2. *In the table beside each planet, write a prediction for the kind of ball that could represent that planet, if the largest ball represents the sun.*

4. *Complete table 1 by calculating the scaled distance to each planet. To do this, divide the distance from the sun to the planet by the distance from the sun to Pluto, then multiply this*

continued

decimal by 100 m. Round off the answer to the nearest metre.

5. Complete table 2.
   a) First, measure the diameter, in centimetres of the largest ball. (It will be the sun in the scale model that you make.)
   b) Now divide the diameter of each planet by the diameter of the sun. *Round off the answer to two significant digits, and record it in the third column.*
   c) Now multiply each decimal in the third column by the diameter of the largest ball (the sun). *Record these answers in the fourth column.* They tell you the size in centimetres of the ball that will represent each planet.
   d) From the twenty balls, find the one that is closest in size to the scaled-down size of the planet. *In the last column, record the name of each kind of ball chosen.*

6. Using your calculations, place the balls at the correct scaled distances along the string to represent the sun and planets in our solar system.

7. The line below is 100 mm long, instead of the 100 m long string you used. *Make a 100 mm long line in your notebook.* Think of the distances in the second column of table 1 as being millimetres. *Mark the position of each planet, with an arrow, on your line. Label each arrow.*

8. Compare your scale model to others.

What happened?

1. How close (in metres) was the location of the Earth that you predicted to the scaled distance that you calculated?
2. For how many planets did you predict the right size of ball? For which planet were you most inaccurate?
3. What is the largest planet? About how many times larger than the Earth is it? About how many times farther from the sun is it than the Earth is from the sun?
4. What is the smallest planet? About how many times smaller than the Earth is it? About how many times farther from the sun is the Earth than this planet is from the sun?
5. Which two planets are closest together? Which two planets are farthest apart?

Now you know

A scale model of the solar system helps you to appreciate distances and sizes. From a scale model you could easily compare the sizes of the planets and their distances from the sun. Distances between planets are huge compared to the sizes of the planets, and there's nothing permanent to fill those areas. That is probably the reason we call the area out there ''space''!

Sun ● ————————————————————————— • Pluto

Fig. 21 *The satellites revolve around the planets; the planets revolve around the sun; the sun revolves within the Milky Way.*

10.12 Finding Your Way: the North Star, Big Dipper, and Little Dipper

Long before compasses, radio signals, radar, and satellites, travellers used stars to help find their direction. Stars stay in the same place relative to one another, and many of them make recognizable star patterns, called constellations. Because the Earth, with you on it, rotates on its axis once every 24 hours, the stars and constellations appear to rotate once every 24 hours also.

However one bright star, the North Star or Polaris, doesn't move. It is directly above the North Pole of the Earth. If the axis on which Earth spins were extended through the North Pole and many millions of kilometres straight through space, it would reach the North Star. If you want to find true north, just locate the North Star, point to it, lower your finger vertically till it points straight ahead: you are pointing north!

Fortunately, it is easy to find the North Star. All you have to do is locate a famous constellation, the Big Dipper. Look at figure 22. The dipper has a long, curved handle traced out by three stars, and a bowl formed by four bright stars. The two stars at one end of the bowl are the pointer stars. Draw a line from the pointer star on the bottom of the dipper through the second pointer star. Extend it straight; the first bright star the line passes through is the North Star, Polaris.

Once you learn to recognize the pattern of stars that make the Big Dipper you will never be lost. Or, at least, you will know how to find north! The Big Dipper, and all the other stars, seem to rotate throughout the night, and as the Earth revolves around the sun, they change with the time of year. So be prepared to see the Big Dipper upside down sometimes.

One constellation that is always upside down, compared to the Big Dipper, is the Little Dipper. Again, look at figure 22. The North Star is at the end of the Little Dipper's handle, and the rest of the dipper seems to be pouring something into the Big Dipper.

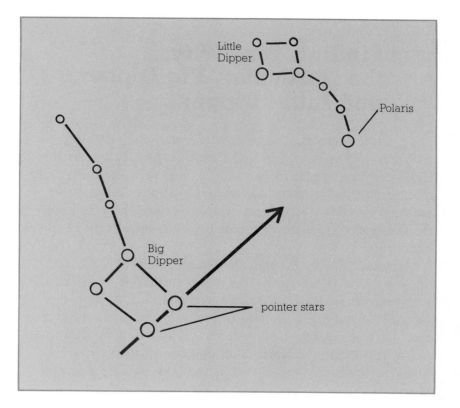

Fig. 22 *The Big Dipper, North Star, and Little Dipper are easy to find.*

390

THIS CONCERNS YOU

Going to Mars

How old will you be in 2010? This is the year that the USSR plans to land humans on Mars. Most astronauts are in their thirties and forties. By 2010 you would be exactly the right age. It would take six to seven months just to get to Mars. Taking the fastest route there and back would require 15 months. This means the astronauts will spend less than a month on the surface of Mars. This Mars mission will cost about $80,000,000,000—about $2.7 000 000 000 per day on Mars.

How do people plan for such a long space voyage? All the necessities would have to be taken along. One person requires 1.4 kg of food, 0.9 kg of oxygen and 2.3 kg of water everyday. (That doesn't include water for cleaning.) Fuel for the ship and supplies such as medicines, tools, and chemicals would have to go aboard. On a long mission, some astronauts would grow plants for food, since the spaceship would have room for only limited supplies. Plants would absorb carbon dioxide from people's breath and renew the ship's supply of oxygen. All liquids would have to be recycled, even

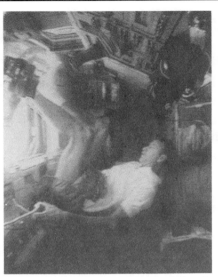

Fig. 23 *Astronauts are monitored on Earth during a voyage.*

wash water and urine. Possible problems and dangers would have to be anticipated. A plan of action would be needed for every possibility if the mission was to succeed.

Many scientists and other people as well think sending people into space is too expensive and too dangerous. Some people even believe money spent on spaceships of any kind is wasted. They feel that the money would be better spent on the poor and hungry. Governments have to decide how much money to spend on each item. Usually, they spend very little on scientific research and even less on space travel.

It is said that ten thousand people on Earth work to support every astronaut in space. The space industry creates a lot of work for many people who make clothing, food, medicine, and equipment for astronauts.

Why do countries spend money on space research? One reason is that people really want to know if there are other creatures in the universe. The study of space helps us undertand Earth. For example, we know that there is a hole in the ozone layer in the Earth because a satellite detected it.

Astronauts in space have seen Earth as a tiny blue marble floating in a black space, all alone in the dark. People realized that Earth was like a spaceship and everyone on the planet was in the ship. Space probes to other planets have shown there is no other place like Earth—other planets are too hot, or too cold, or people can't breathe their atmosphere. Earth is the only place that is just right for us—that we know of. If something happened to Earth, our spaceship, and we couldn't live here, where would we go?

1. a) How much will the Mars mission cost?
   b) Is space travel a worthwhile way to spend tax dollars?
2. What are some reasons you might want or not want to go to Mars?
3. Summarize for your classmates any newspaper articles you find about Mars.
4. Would Mars be a great place for humans to live? Why or why not?
5. Why is Mars called the "red planet"? (You may have to use your library to find out).

10.13 **Finding Constellations**

Now that you know how to find the North Star and the two dippers, you can use them to find other constellations. Cassiopeia is a pattern of five bright stars that make a "W" (or an "M"). Can you see Queen Cassiopeia seated on her throne in figure 24? A line drawn from the third star from the end of the handle of the Big Dipper and through Polaris will point to Cassiopeia. This constellation is about the same distance from the North Star as the Big Dipper.

In this activity you will learn how to locate some constellations in the night sky.

You need

- heavy paper
- large pin
- overhead projector
- star chart or astronomy book

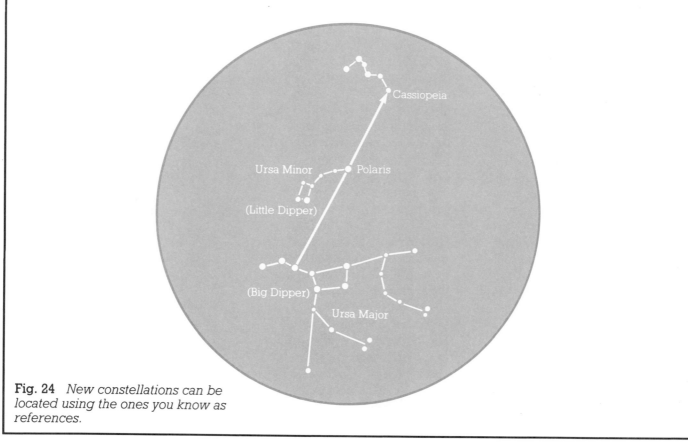

Fig. 24 *New constellations can be located using the ones you know as references.*

392

1. Locate some constellations on the star chart,
   or a star map for the current month. Your
   teacher will show you how.
2. Choose two constellations that are on the
   zodiac. For example, you could choose the
   zodiac sign that corresponds to the month
   you are now in. *For each, describe how the
   constellation can be located by using the North
   Star, the two dippers, or Cassiopeia as references.*
   Read your descriptions to a classmate to see if
   he or she can identify the constellation.
3. *Mark the locations of the stars that make up these
   four constellations on the heavy paper.* Use the
   pin to make a large hole where each star is
   located. Make larger holes for the brighter
   stars (as shown on the star chart). *Mark the
   names of the constellations on the paper, and the
   names of any bright star in the constellations.*
4. Place your constellation map on the overhead
   projector to see your star groups.
5. Take your own star map home and try to
   locate these constellations on a clear night.
   (Stand as far away from lights as possible).
   The description you wrote in step 2 will help.
6. Your teacher may want you to practise using
   the star chart to find certain constellations.

Think about it

1. Name the constellations that you can now
   find.
2. Choose two constellations that you think
   have interesting names. Find out the
   meanings of these names in the library.

10.14 Going for a Spin

Just being on the Earth is a moving experience. Every 365.25
days, the Earth **revolves** to complete its **orbit** around the sun,
producing our seasons.

Every 24 hours, the Earth **rotates** (spins) once on its axis.
You can easily see the effect of this rotation by watching how
shadows change in length and direction. As an object on the
Earth moves up over the horizon toward the sun, the object's
shadow is long. The shadow shortens as the object nears the
point where the sun is directly overhead. The object then
throws no shadow. As it moves toward the opposite horizon,
its shadow reappears and gradually lengthens as its angle from

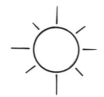

Fig. 26 *A sundial makes use of the Earth's rotation. As the Earth turns, the gnomon (marker) on the sundial throws a shadow which falls on a number representing the correct time.*

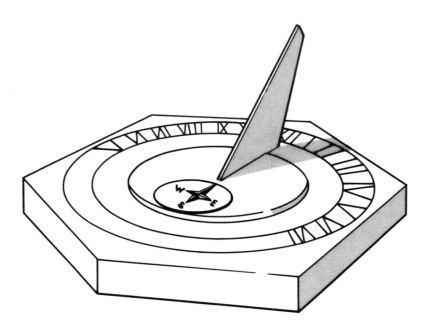

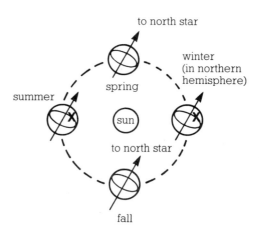

Fig. 25 *The Earth's axis always points in the same direction, and is tilted at 23.5° to the plane of the orbit. Without this tilt, there would be no seasons.*

the sun increases. This spinning, from west to east, makes the moon and sun seem to move across the sky, from east to west. Those who live near the Canadian border are rotating at a speed of 1250 km/h. Anyone living near the North Pole, would not be moving very fast at all.

FEEDBACK

1. Describe two ways that you are moving while standing still on Earth.
2. Look at figure 25. You are standing at the spot marked "X," in the northern hemisphere. Explain why it is hotter for you in summer than in winter. (Think of where the sun is in the sky at noon).

Fig. 27 *Some fascinating photographs of stars can be made by leaving the shutter of a camera open. With the camera fixed to the Earth, the stars leave curved trails on the exposed film as the Earth spins. This photo is a time exposure of the night sky in the northern hemisphere.*

Fig. 28 *Can you tell which vehicles were moving faster?*

3. It's a clear day, and you have nothing to do for 24 hours, so you lie outside and just look at the sky. Describe three different pieces of evidence of the Earth's spinning that you would observe.
4. Look at the star trails in figure 27. Which star is Polaris? Why is its "motion" different from that of other stars?
5. Some star trails are brighter than others in the photo. What does this tell you about the stars themselves?

SUPERSLEUTH

1. Look at figure 27. How many hours would be required for star trails to make one complete circle? Through how many degrees does the Earth turn in this time? How many hours are required for the Earth to rotate 90°?
2. Obtain a protractor. With the centre of the protractor on Polaris, measure the number of degrees from the start of a star trail to the end of the trail. Use what you learned by answering question 1 to calculate how long the camera shutter was open to make figure 27.

10.15 What's the latest?

Like all areas of science, astronomy is an area in which new discoveries are sometimes made, new theories are sometimes proposed, and people begin thinking of the science in a new way. Imagine how people's thinking changed when a Greek philosopher named Pythagoras suggested that the world was round and when many hundreds of years later, Copernicus said that the Earth revolved around the sun!

Today, you might expect that everything would have already been discovered, but that isn't so. With more and more powerful telescopes, astronomers sometimes discover new comets, even today. What else is new in astronomy? This activity will give you a chance to find out.

You need

- newspaper & magazine articles
- TV videos

1. In a small group, read some articles about current astronomy, until you find one that you think is especially interesting.
2. Discuss it among yourselves and talk with your teacher about any parts of it that are unclear to you.
3. Look for more information about the subject that has caught your interest. *Take notes on what you read.*
4. *Put your information together in a written report.* Add clear, visual materials that will help your classmates to understand your presentation.

You might want to organize it under headings such as: the current development; who is responsible; how he or she came to be involved in it; what led up to it; where it might lead; any controversy associated with it.

Think about it

1. In what area is astronomical knowledge growing: in learning about areas of space farther out from Earth, or in learning many more details about previously known aspects of the universe?
2. You may wish to explore some of these ideas further by joining, or starting, an astronomy club, and preparing brief presentations or news-sheets about newsworthy astronomical events.

Investigation

10.16 Colour my Flame!

Astronomers can find out a lot of things about stars, even though they have never been near one. Any matter will give off visible light if it is hot enough, and stars release an incredible amount of energy as light. The colour, brightness, and the organization of light from a star can tell scientists how hot the star is, what it is made of, how far away it is, and even how it will die.

White light can be broken up into a rainbow pattern of colours — a **spectrum** — when it is observed through a spectroscope. A spectrum (pl. spectra) with all the colours is called a **continuous spectrum**. Incandescent bulbs and our sun both produce continuous spectra.

What property of a substance causes the substance to burn with a particular colour?

You need

- safety goggles
- Bunsen burner
- concentrated solutions of 12 pure substances in labelled containers
- wires with small loop at end for each solution
- 2 wooden or cork handles for wire
- unknown substance in solution

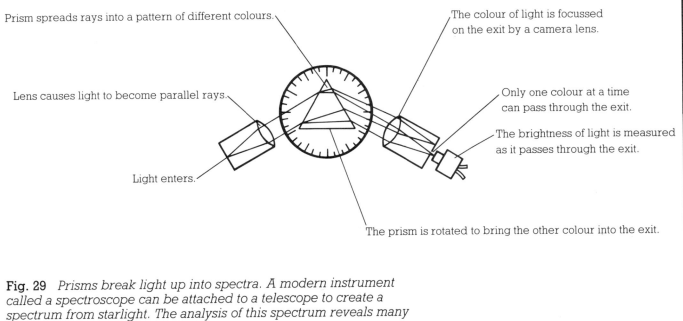

Prism spreads rays into a pattern of different colours.

Lens causes light to become parallel rays.

Light enters.

The colour of light is focussed on the exit by a camera lens.

Only one colour at a time can pass through the exit.

The brightness of light is measured as it passes through the exit.

The prism is rotated to bring the other colour into the exit.

Fig. 29 *Prisms break light up into spectra. A modern instrument called a spectroscope can be attached to a telescope to create a spectrum from starlight. The analysis of this spectrum reveals many details about the nature of a star.*

continued

1. *Copy the chart into your notebook.*

Substance number	Chemical name of substance	Colour of flame
1		
2		
3		
4		
5		
6		
7		
8		
9		
10		
11		
12		
unknown		

SAFETY ALERT:

Goggles must be worn. Do not touch or taste any of the solutions. Some of them may be poisonous.

2. Light the Bunsen burner (your teacher will tell you how). Adjust the air until the flame is very quiet and almost invisible. The hottest part of the flame is the top of the inner cone.
3. Choose one of the solutions. *Record the chemical name of the substance beside the correct number.* Dip the loop of the wire into the solution.
4. Hold the end of the wire that has the chemical on it in the hottest part of the flame. CAUTION: The wire will be hot!
5. *Record the colour of the flame.* Be as accurate as possible in describing the colour.
6. Repeat steps 3, 4, 5, for all the samples that are given. If you are unsure of a colour repeat the observations.
7. Repeat steps 3, 4, 5, for the solution with the unknown substance in it.

1. *Copy the chart below into your notebook and complete it.*
2. Some of the solutions produced a pale violet colour. List the names of the substances. What is the same in these names?
3. Reorganize the data from your observation table by grouping substances according to the ones that have the same flame colour. (Repeat observations for any samples you are unsure about.)
4. What is the connection between flame colour and chemical name?
5. Baking soda is the chemical sodium bicarbonate. What colour would the flame be if you strongly heated baking soda? How do you know?
6. Barium, lithium, potassium, sodium, strontium are some of 108 elements that are the basic building blocks of all matter. How could you tell if one of these substances was in the sun?

When a substance is strongly heated, it produces light of a certain colour. The colour of light is determined by the elements that make up the substance. Flame tests have been done on all the elements. Scientists know the kind of light that comes from each element. The light from a star tells us the kind of *elements* that are in that star. The light which comes from an element is a property of that element.

SUPERSLEUTH

Rolled up newspapers and pine cones were soaked in a chemical solution, then allowed to dry out before being burned in a fireplace. The papers and pine cones produced crimson red and emerald green-coloured flames. What elements were likely in the solution?

Colour of flame	Sample Numbers	Chemical Names of substances	What Each Name has in common

DO NOT WRITE IN THE TEXTBOOK

10.17 The Space Race

Humans have always wanted to fly like the birds. In very early days, some people tried jumping off cliffs, flapping home-made wings. They always landed where and when they didn't want to! Eventually, on December 17, 1903, the Wright brothers flew. Their plane, the Kitty Hawk, flew a very short distance (only 36.6 m), but this event marked the beginning of human flight. Inspired by the knowledge that flight was possible, many individuals and companies worked to improve airplane and engine design. Success followed success — transatlantic flight, planes flying at speeds that broke the sound barrier, huge cargo and passenger planes that flew long distances. In 1987 two Americans flew a plane called the Voyager around the Earth without refuelling.

Several decades ago, as flight near the surface of the Earth became more and more sophisticated, people began to consider the real possibility of space travel. Certainly, humans have always wondered about ''What's up there?'' and dreamed of sending people to the moon, planets, and stars. Many science fiction stories reflect this dream.

In 1957, the Russian government put the first satellite in space. This satellite was about the size of a beach ball, and it sent back a signal to Earth for 23 days. Sputnik 1 was its name, and all it sent back to Earth was a ''beep, beep'' signal. Still, it was the first real evidence that escape from Earth's surface was possible.

Everyone on Earth was very excited about Sputnik. Its launch signalled the beginning of the Space Age. Other countries in the world wanted to join this adventure in space, including the United States, which promised to put someone on the moon by the end of the 1960s. The race to conquer space had begun.

Fig. 30 *These people are taking a close look at a model of Sputnik I.*

FEEDBACK

1. What is the importance of the Kitty Hawk?
2. List some successes in airplane history.
3. What are some reasons that humans have wanted to conquer space?
4. What is the ''Space Race''? How did it begin?

SUPERSLEUTH

Make a poster for display in the classroom that shows some important event that involved planes or space vehicles.

Fig. 31 *Jet travel isn't for everyone. Some people still like to build their own personal flying machines.*

10.18 **Satellites**

Fig. 32 *This photo, taken from the moon, shows how spectacular the Earth looks from its natural satellite.*

There are two kinds of satellites:
- natural ones, such as our moon
- artificial ones, such as the Canadian ANIK satellites.

Moonrises on Jupiter or Saturn would be incredible, since each of these planets has more than fifteen natural satellites. As spacecrafts explore farther into the solar system, more and more natural satellites are being discovered.

Artificial satellites that orbit Earth do many important jobs. Communication satellites relay television programs and telephone calls between different locations on the Earth. A rocket taking off in Russia can be watched live on television in Canada, through a satellite relay. Space stations and satellites carry equipment to view the Earth from above the atmosphere to better predict the weather. Telescopes mounted on satellites look far into space without interference from Earth's air and clouds. Some satellites collect information about light reflecting off the Earth. Satellites can also help analyse chemicals in the Earth's atmosphere. Damage to the ozone layer surrounding the Earth is monitored from a satellite photograph. Some countries use satellites to spy on the weapons, armies, and secret bases of other countries. Space laws may have to be developed to control the use of certain satellites that may be able to destroy threatening satellites and rockets. At present, they are used in many peaceful ways to locate lost ships and planes, to examine the health of crops and forests, to find mineral deposits, and to send vital information around the world.

It's a Fact
Staying in space for long periods of time can cause serious changes in the human body. Scientists are learning how to stop these changes. They have been so successful that astronauts have been able to stay in space for longer and longer periods of time. Records are constantly being broken. A Soviet space flight launched in December 1987 was still in orbit twelve months later.

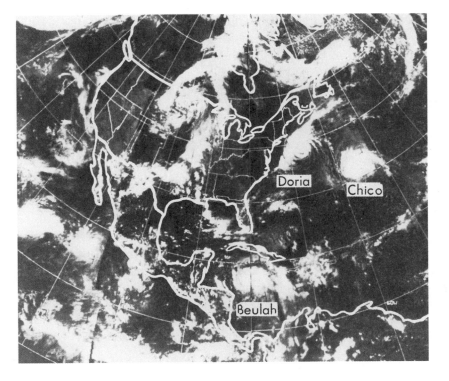

Fig. 33 *Satellite photos can show the development and progress of severe storms. This allows some warning to those who might be in the path of such a storm.*

1. What are the two main types of satellites?
2. What is an orbit?
3. List at least five uses for artificial satellites.

1. Make up a law that you think should exist to control the use of satellites.
2. Although scientists and engineers may create things like satellites, they don't control their use. Discuss.

10.19 Rocket Power

When you jump, why can't you stay up? You can't because gravity pulls you back down. If you jump harder and leave the ground faster, you rise higher into the air. If you could push hard enough so that you left the ground at 40 000 km/h, you would keep rising beyond the pull of Earth's gravity, far into space. This speed of 40 000 km/h is called **escape velocity**. The speed is the same for every object on Earth, unless it can continue ''pushing.'' Of course, a heavier object would require a harder push to make it leave the Earth. In each case, the push needed would have to be supplied by rocket power.

Rockets don't have to reach this high speed because they keep exerting a force, or ''pushing'' for a long period of time. It's like escaping the Earth by climbing a ladder instead of jumping. The force that pushes a rocket upward is called the **thrust**. In order to produce a large thrust, huge amounts of fuel and oxygen must be carried by rockets that lift large payloads (cargoes). The American space shuttle system carries about 100 tonnes of fuel and 600 tonnes of oxygen to lift a maximum payload of 100 tonnes.

As fuel is burned and oxygen is consumed, a rocket becomes lighter, and speeds up more from the same thrust.

When the fuel in one tank is gone, the whole section of the rocket that contains that tank is released to lighten the load. The empty fuel tank falls back to Earth, sometimes on a parachute, so it can be reused. Rockets that release sections as fuel is consumed are called **multi-stage rockets**. A multi-stage rocket, such as the Ariane shown in figure 35, is basically a system of three rockets that fire in sequence, eventually lifting a payload like a satellite to the desired distance from Earth.

FEEDBACK

1. What holds objects to the Earth? How fast would a rock have to be thrown to escape the Earth?
2. What is the purpose of any rocket? What is ''thrust''?
3. What percent of the total mass of the space shuttle is made up of fuel and oxygen?
4. Why does a rocket carry a large supply of oxygen?
5. Explain how a multi-stage rocket works.

Fig. 34 *NASA rocket ready for lift-off*

Fig. 35 *The three stages of a multi-stage rocket*

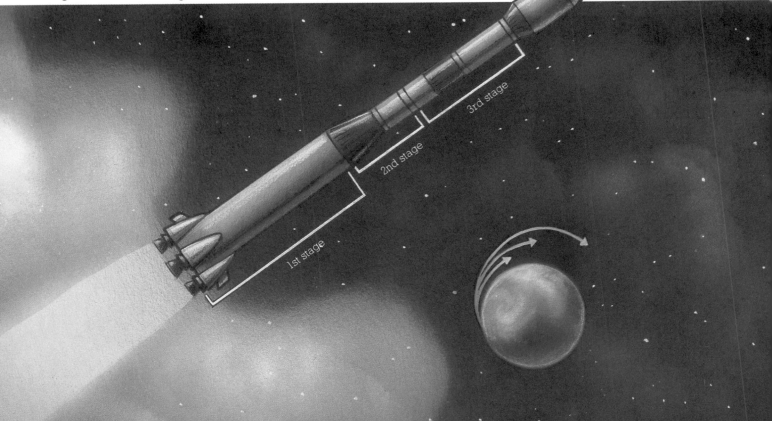

1st stage

2nd stage

3rd stage

10.20 Measuring Rocket Thrust

The amount of a rocket engine's thrust must be known so that distances, heights, and times can be calculated, and so that the rocket will go where it is supposed to. In this investigation, the thrust of a simple rocket engine — a balloon — is measured. You will also learn a basic principle of rocket engines: action–reaction.

Find out

A. How does a rocket engine make something move?
B. What is the maximum thrust from a balloon "engine"?

You need

- balloon
- straw
- 4 m of thread
- tape
- triple-beam balance
- small washers or paper clips
- twist tie or clamp to seal balloon

Try this

1. Insert the thread through the straw. Fasten one end of the thread to the ceiling, then fasten the other end vertically to the floor. The thread should be stretched tight.

2. Blow up the balloon, then clamp it closed. Tape the balloon to the straw so that the clamped end of the balloon is down. (See figure 36.)

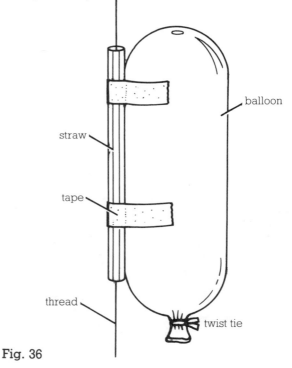

Fig. 36

3. Open the clamped end of the balloon as you release the balloon. In what direction does air from the balloon (engine) go? In what direction does the balloon move?

4. You are now going to load the engine until it will no longer "lift off." To do this, find the mass of a washer or paper clip. Blow up the balloon as before, then tape a washer or paper

clip to the bottom of the balloon. Release the balloon. Compare its motion now to its motion without a load.

5. Keep adding washers or paper clips until the balloon will no longer rise when released, but just slides down the string instead. Record the number of objects fastened to the balloon, and the total mass of this load.

What happened?

1. What action made the air from the balloon move downward? (Be as specific as possible.) What was the reaction of the balloon when it pushed the air down?
2. What makes a real rocket move? (Refer to step 1.)
3. What kinds of forces were acting on the balloon? How did these forces compare in step 5 when the rocket wouldn't rise?

Fig. 37

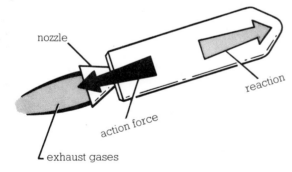

nozzle

reaction

action force

exhaust gases

The exhaust gases are the action force. The rocket moving the other way is the reaction force.

thrust

load

If load = thrust there is no liftoff.

4. What is the thrust of the balloon "engine" that you used? Compare your result to those of other groups.
5. What happened to the speed of the rocket as the load increased?

Now you know

The stretched, elastic rubber of a balloon forces air out the opening. This action force of the balloon pushing back on air created a reaction force of the air pushing forward on the balloon. This reaction force caused the balloon to rise against the force of gravity. In "real" rocket engines, fuel is burned in a combustion chamber and expands violently. The expanding gas escapes through a nozzle; the reaction force of the gas pushes the rocket forward. The harder the rocket pushes the gas back, the harder the gas pushes the rocket forward.

When the balloon engine was loaded down by enough mass, it couldn't lift up. At that time the thrust upwards just balanced the load pulling downward. When load equals thrust, a rocket cannot speed up to take off. The same "engines" all produced about the same thrust.

10.21 Canada in Space

Canada entered the space age by designing and building one of the first useful satellites. Alouette was built to study the ionosphere from the top.

Alouette was launched for Canada by the United States. It was designed to send back data for three years, but it worked so well, it wasn't turned off for ten years. Alouette sent back information about the ionosphere which helped Canada to develop one of the best communications systems in the world. Canada helped in putting the American astronauts on the moon too. Many Canadian engineers and scientists worked with the Americans on the Apollo moon missions. The legs of the lunar lander were designed by Canadian engineers. The Shuttle Remote Manipulator System or as it's better known, Canadarm, was also made by Canada. Every time the space shuttle repairs a satellite or builds a platform in space, the Canadarm is used. Every one of the shuttles has one of these extremely complicated robot arms.

Fig. 38 *Canada's Shuttle Remote Manipulator System (Canadarm)*

Canada's first communications satellite was called ANIK which means "little brother" in Inuit. This satellite was built in the United States with the help of Canadian engineers and scientists. The eleventh Canadian satellite was the first one to be made in Canada, mostly with Canadian parts. It was called the ANIK D. The ANIK D. and other satellites have been a communication medium, uniting Canadians in this century much as the railway did in the last century. We can phone anywhere in Canada as easily as we can phone across the street, thanks to satellites. Because of satellites, sports events can be seen on television as they are happening.

Canadians are continuing to design new kinds of space satellites. For example, PAXSAT (from "pax," the Latin word for peace) or peace satellite is a satellite that can act as a "watchdog," detecting another satellite's true purpose and sending the information back to Earth. This Canadian invention could help keep space free of weapons.

Fig. 39 *Plotting a satellite's orbit*

FEEDBACK

1. How did Canada enter the space age?
2. What are some of Canada's inventions which have helped explore space?
3. What is the Shuttle Remote Manipulator System? For what is it used?
4. What does the word "Anik" mean?
5. What is one role that Canada plays in the world? How does a satellite help?

10.22 Chapter Summary

- Astrology does not explain or predict events, so it is not considered a science.
- The sun is a yellow star made of hydrogen and helium gas.
- The sun rises in the east and sets in the west at different times each day, depending on the season.
- The moon rotates on its axis in the same time as it takes to orbit the Earth, so we always see the same side from Earth.
- The moon rises in the east and sets in the west. Different phases can be seen throughout its revolution around the Earth.
- Comets are large masses of rock, ice and gases.
- "Falling stars" are pieces of rock, called meteors, that burn up as they fall through the atmosphere of the Earth.
- The solar system consists of one sun, nine planets, about 43 moons, and smaller chunks of rocks called asteroids.
- A planet shines, but a star twinkles.

- The constellation, the Big Dipper, can be used to find the North Star, Polaris, and another constellation, Cassiopeia.
- The stars appear to revolve every 24 hours, but it's really the Earth that is revolving.
- The space age began in 1957 when the Russians launched Sputnik.
- Artificial satellites are used for important tasks such as communications, weather forecasting, and analysis of resources.
- Moons are natural satellites that orbit most of the planets.
- The force that moves a rocket forward or upwards is called the thrust. Thrust must be greater than the weight of the rocket for it to lift-off.
- Canada entered the space age with the launch of a very successful satellite called "Alouette."
- Mars may be the next destination for human exploration.

10.23 Are You Ready to Go On?

1. How is astrology different from astronomy?
2. What does an astronomer do?
3. Decide if each sentence below is true or false. If it is FALSE, rewrite the statement to make it true. If the statement is TRUE, copy it into your notebook.
   a) The sun rises in the west and sets in the east.
   b) The moon always shows the same face towards the Earth.
   c) There are four main phases for the moon.
   d) ''Falling stars'' are actually stars which crash into the Earth.
   e) A planet twinkles, but a star shines.
   f) The sun is composed of hydrogen gas and oxygen gas.
   g) The moon shines by light reflected off its surface.
   h) The two kinds of planets are called Terrestrial and Jovian.
   i) The Little Dipper empties into the Big Dipper.
   j) A constellation is a group of planets.
4. Why do the stars and constellations appear to rotate every 24 hours?
5. The group which consists of one sun, nine planets, several moons and many asteroids is called
   a) the Milky Way b) the solar system
   c) a galaxy   d) the universe.
6. Moons which orbit many of the planets are called
   a) chunks of rock b) artificial satellites
   c) natural satellites d) chunks of ice.
7. What are three uses for artificial satellites?
8. What are some reasons that people might want to go to Mars?
9. Why are multi-stage rockets used instead of single-stage rockets?
10. What are some benefits that have come from efforts to explore space?
11. The diagram shows the sky one dark night. Find the Big Dipper, North Star, Little Dipper, and Cassiopeia, then trace the stars of these constellations into your notebook.

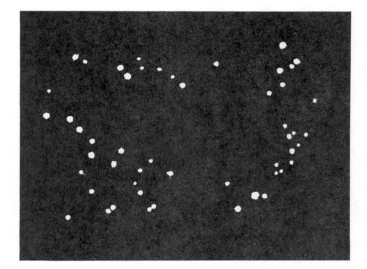

Index

4 5 4691-7